MODERN

EUROPEAN COINS

A GUIDE BOOK

of

MODERN EUROPEAN COINS

By
ROBERT P. HARRIS

Containing full mintage records and retail market valuations from mid-19th Century to date for the coins of Continental Europe and Colonies and the Republic of Ireland, and excluding Great Britain and the British Empire. For use as a companion volume to *A Catalog of Modern World Coins,* by R. S. Yeoman.

WHITMAN PUBLISHING COMPANY
RACINE, WISCONSIN

TABLE OF CONTENTS

Introduction.......................................5
Acknowledgements.................................7
Albania...9
Algeria..10
Angola...10
Austria..11
Azores...16
Belgian Congo....................................16
Belgium..19
Bohemia-Moravia..................................27
Bulgaria...27
Cameroons..30
Cape Verde Islands...............................30
Comoro Islands...................................31
Crete..31
Croatia..31
Curacao..32
Czechoslovakia...................................32
Danish West Indies...............................35
Danzig...36
Denmark..37
Eritrea..42
Estonia..43
Faroe Islands....................................44
Finland..44
France...49
French Cochin-China..............................61
French Equatorial Africa.........................61
French Indo-China................................62
French West Africa...............................66
German East Africa...............................66
German New Guinea................................68
Germany..68
Germany — States.................................91
Germany — Military Coinage.......................99
German Democratic Republic.......................99
Greece..100
Greenland.......................................102
Guadeloupe......................................102
Hungary...102
Iceland...107
Ireland...108
Italian Somaliland..............................110

TABLE OF CONTENTS— (Continued)

Italy.... 111
Kiao Chau...117
Latvia...117
Liechtenstein...118
Lithuania..119
Luxemburg..119
Macao..121
Madagascar...121
Martinique...122
Monaco...122
Montenegro...123
Mozambique...124
Netherlands..125
Netherlands Antilles...130
Netherlands East Indies......................................131
New Caledonia..133
Norway...134
Poland...140
Portugal...143
Portuguese Guinea..148
Portuguese India...149
Puerto Rico..151
Reunion..151
Romania..152
Russia...155
Saarland...169
St. Pierre and Miquelon......................................169
St. Thomas and Prince Islands................................170
San Marino...171
Serbia...172
Slovakia...173
Somalia..174
Spain..174
Spanish Philippines..178
Surinam..179
Sweden...179
Switzerland..188
Timor..194
Togo...195
Tonkin...195
Turkey...195
Vatican City...197
Yugoslavia...201

Introduction

This volume lists all modern regular and commemorative circulation coins of countries of Continental Europe and their colonies, and the Republic of Ireland. Coins that did not enter circulation such as patterns, proofs, local issues and the like are generally not listed in this book. Coins of all metals except gold and platinum are included. Coins of Great Britain and the British Empire are not included. For a detailed listing of coins of Great Britain proper, collectors are referred to *A Guide Book of English Coins* by K. E. Bressett.

SCOPE: Approximately a century, from mid-nineteenth century to date. Logical starting points for each country have been established. For some countries this was the start of the decimal system of coinage, such as Denmark in 1874; in others the actual creation of a unified nation such as Germany in 1873; and in others such as Russia the listing commences with the beginning of the reign of a new king (Alexander II in 1855).

VALUATIONS: Valuations of older coins are for coins in Fine condition, i.e., coins with lettering, dates and major design features clearly outlined. Valuations on recent issues are for coins in new or nearly new condition. The prices in this book are only estimates. Valuations quoted are helpful figures for collectors to use in exchanging coins with each other. Coins may actually sell for more or for less than the prices listed herein. Older coins in superior condition may in some instances sell for considerably more than quoted valuations.

QUANTITIES MINTED: Collectors must take into consideration that quantities listed in this book are not always reliable. In some instances fiscal year mintage totals (1 July to 30 June) are used, and in other instances dies of the previous year or years were used. The author has made every effort to reconcile the above to make the figures as true as possible. In considering value of a coin the quantity available is one of the more important factors. Consideration must also be given to various conditions which bear on the number of a given coin that reached circulation and continued in circulation for a number of years. Commencing with the early part of the twentieth century, monetary systems of most of the major European countries underwent a gradual decline because of inflation extending over a period of many years. As an example, the One Franc silver coin of France dated 1900 had a face value of about 20¢ U. S. at the time it was issued, while an aluminum One Franc French coin of 1959 had a face value of about ¼¢ U. S. This change in value and metal content caused large-scale melting down and recall of gold and silver coins.

Coins suffer heavy casualties during wars. Coins of silver and other metals were confiscated and melted down by the millions by invading armies. Changes in coinage laws caused coins to be retired from circulation. As an example of this, Belgium, in compliance with terms of a European monetary alliance, recalled many of her silver coins in 1867 because of a change of silver content required by the new law. Of the 2 Franc Belgian silver coin minted from 1834 to 1844 to the amount of 2,255,557 pieces, 89.33% (2,014,925 pieces) were retired from circulation; this left 240,632 pieces (10.67%) to attempt survival to the present date.

Mention must be made of the practice in Russia of restriking coins from official dies at a later date. For this reason caution must be exercised in paying high prices for early coins of low mintage. An example is the 3 kopeck

CIIB 1867. Official mint records indicate that only 54 pieces were minted in 1867; however, unknown quantities of this coin were minted at some later date but prior to 1890 and from the original die.

Although the author made considerable effort to substantiate the existence of all dates of coins listed, it is possible in a few instances that coins are listed and valued which in fact do not exist. Such listings might occur from mintage statistics in which the dates appearing on the coins are different from the actual years in which the coins were struck. Any possible corrections are welcome.

DESCRIPTION: When description of a specific date is omitted, it may be assumed to be the same type, size, metal, etc., as the last previously described. For example, Finland 50 pennia 1940 is copper-nickel and is 18.5mm in diameter, while the 1941 coin is copper, new design, but same diameter 18.5mm. Normally, coins have the name of the country inscribed thereon in the native language. Occasionally coins do not show the name of the country; such instances are recorded in the text. Thus, all modern Danish coins are inscribed DANMARK except for the types noted.

Metal description may not be accurate from a metallurgical standpoint, but is intended primarily as an identification aid. It will be found that copper and bronze are used interchangeably to describe older coins of a brown color. Brass coins are of a yellow color, while copper-nickel coins are generally of a white or off-white color.

A Catalog of Modern World Coins, by R. S. Yeoman, was employed extensively in preparing this work, and its numbering system — the "Y" numbers — have been used throughout the text and listings. The greater portion of the coins listed herein are illustrated in *A Catalog of Modern World Coins.*

Acknowledgements

The author wishes to thank the following who helped by contributing factual data and obtaining references. Some of these friends gave valuable advice, criticism and suggestions.

P. K. Anderson	G. B. Kelemen
Thomas G. Beatty	Alex Koritz
Lawrence Block	Frank Lapa
Kenneth E. Bressett	R. Lapassade
F. X. Calico	Dr. V. A. Mandrussow
Dr. Paolo Cartoni	Gary K. Olsen
Thomas F. Coen	Dr. Antonio de Andrade Rebelo
Dr. John S. Davenport	Jerome K. Remick
Greg Erickson	Hans M. F. Schulman
John Gartner	Neil Shafer
Dr. K. M. Gaver	John Skotnicki
Willy Herssens	R. S. Yeoman
Kurt Jaeger	American Numismatic Association
Robert W. Julian	American Numismatic Society
William C. Johnson	Smithsonian Institution

I wish to express my thanks to the officials of the mints and national banks of the following countries, without whose assistance this volume would not have been possible:

Austria	Italy
Belgium	Netherlands
Bulgaria	Norway
Czechoslovakia	Portugal
Denmark	Sweden
Finland	Switzerland
France	Turkey
Germany	United States
Great Britain	Yugoslavia
Greece	

The following published mint reports were of major importance in the preparation of this volume:

Annual Reports of the Deputy Master of the Royal Mint (London) 1870-1962

Annual Reports of the U. S. Mint (Washington) 1875-1962

Rapport au Ministre des Finances (Paris) Operations de 1896 a 1956

Because of the large amount of material involved in this work, errors and omissions are inevitable. The author would be pleased to hear from anyone with new information. New data will appear in a subsequent edition of this volume. Please write directly to the author at Box 1147, Oceanside, California 92057.

Robert P. Harris

ALBANIA

(Shqipni, Shqiperi)

In southeastern Europe between Greece and Yugoslavia, bordering on the Adriatic Sea.

100 Qinder Leku = 1 Lek
100 Qinder Ari = 1 Frank = 5 Lek

	Mintage	Value
5 QINDER LEKU		
Y1 (bronze) 18mm		
1926..............512,250		$1.00
1 QINDER ARI		
Y3 (bronze) 18mm		
1935...........2,000,000		1.00
10 QINDER LEKU		
Y2 (bronze) 21.5mm		
1926..............511,250		2.50
2 QINDER ARI		
Y4 (bronze) 21.5mm		
1935...........1,500,000		1.50
¼ LEKU		
Y5 (nickel) 21.5mm		
1926..............505,960		1.50
1927..............755,738		1.50
½ LEKU (nickel) 24mm		
Y6 eagle		
1926...........1,001,813		2.00
Y7 arms		
1930..............500,000		2.00
1931..............500,000		2.00
1 LEK		
Y8 (nickel) 26.5mm		
1926...........1,004,139		2.00
1927..............506,329		2.50
1930...........1,250,000		2.00
1931...........1,000,000		2.00
1 FRANK (silver) 23mm		
Y9 ship		
1927..............100,000		5.00
1928...............60,000		6.00
Y12 arms		
1935..............700,000		5.00
1937..............600,000		5.00
Y18 commemorative		
1937...............50,000		10.00
2 FRANK (silver) 28mm		
Y10		
1926...............50,000		8.50

	Mintage	Value
1928...............60,000		$8.50
Y13 arms		
1935..............150,000		7.50
Y19 commemorative		
1937...............25,000		16.00
5 FRANK		
Y11 (silver) 32mm		
1925...............59,950		137.50
1927...............40,000		137.50
Italian Occupation		
0.05 LEK		
Y27 (aluminum-bronze) 19mm		
1940...........1,400,000		.75
1941..............200,000		7.50
0.10 LEK		
Y28 (aluminum-bronze) 22mm		
1940..............800,000		1.00
1941..............250,000		7.50
0.20 LEK		
Y29 (acmonital) 21mm		
1939..............900,000		.75
1940..............700,000		1.00
1941...........1,400,000		1.25
0.50 LEK		
Y30 (acmonital) 23mm		
1939..............100,000		1.00
1940..............500,000		1.25
1941..............900,000		2.00
1 LEK		
Y31 (acmonital) 26mm		
1939...........2,100,000		1.25
2 LEK		
Y32 (acmonital) 28mm		
1939...........1,300,000		2.00
5 LEK		
Y33 (silver) 23mm		
1939...........1,350,000		7.50
10 LEK		
Y34 (silver) 27mm		
1939..............175,000		15.00

	Mintage	Value			Mintage	Value

Republic 1946

2 LEK

½ LEKU

Y35 (zinc) 18.5mm
1947 . . . .　$ .40

Y37 (zinc) 22mm
1947 . . . .　$ .65

1 LEK

5 LEK

Y36 (zinc) 19.5mm
1947 . . . .　.50

Y38 (zinc) 26mm
1947 . . . .　1.00

ALGERIA
(Algerie)

A former overseas territory of France in North Africa. Gained independence in 1962.

20 FRANCS

Y1 (copper-nickel) 23mm
1949 . . . . 17,731,200　.50
1950 . . . . 7,268,200　.50
1951 . . . . 556,400　1.00
1956 . . . . 7,500,000　.50

50 FRANCS

Y2 (copper-nickel) 26.5mm
1949 . . . . 1,329,500　1.50

1950 . . . . 16,670,500　1.00

100 FRANCS

Y3 (copper-nickel) 31mm
1950 . . . . 10,083,000　1.50
1951 . . . . 12,105,600　1.50
1952 . . . . 8,516,800　1.50
1953 . . . . 3,483,200　1.75

ANGOLA

A Portuguese province on the west coast of Africa.

100 Centavos = 1 Escudo

1 CENTAVO

Y12 (bronze) 19mm
1921 . . . . 1,360,300　2.00

2 CENTAVOS

Y13 (bronze) 22mm
1921 . . . . 530,300　1.50

5 CENTAVOS

Y14 (bronze) 25mm
1921 . . . . 720,000　1.25
1922 . . . . 5,680,300　.75
1923 . . . . 5,840,000　.75

Y18 (nickel-bronze) 15mm
1927 . . . . 2,002,100　.50

10 CENTAVOS

Y15 (copper-nickel) 19mm
1921 . . . . 160,000　2.00
1922 . . . . 340,000　1.25
1923 . . . . 2,960,000　.50

Y19 new design, 20mm
1927 . . . . 2,002,600　.90
1928 . . . . 1,000,000　.90

Y22 (bronze) 17.5mm
1948 . . . . 10,000,000　.25
1949 . . . . 10,000,000　.25

20 CENTAVOS

Y16 (copper-nickel) 23mm
1921 . . . . 2,115,000　.75
1922 . . . . 1,730,300　.75

Y20 (nickel-bronze) 24mm
1927 . . . . 2,001,495　1.00
1928 . . . . 500,000　1.50

Y23 (bronze) 20.5mm
1948 . . . . 7,850,000　.25
1949 . . . . 2,150,000　.30

Y23a (bronze) 18mm
1962 . . . . 2,500,000　.20

	Mintage	Value
50 CENTAVOS		
Y17 (nickel) 31mm		
1922	6,000,000	$2.00
1923	4,780,000	2.00
Y21 (nickel-bronze) 23mm		
1927	1,608,013	2.50
1928	1,600,000	2.50
Y24 new design		
1948	8,006,000	.40
1950	4,484,000	.50
Y25 (bronze) 20mm		
1953	16,731,300	.20
1955	1,126,430	.40
1957	8,873,233	.25
1958	17,525,083	.20
1961	8,750,150	.25

	Mintage	Value
1 ESCUDO		
Y26 (bronze) 26mm		
1953	2,013,150	$ .35
1956	3,988,850	.35
2.50 ESCUDOS		
Y27 (copper-nickel) 20mm		
1953	6,008,000	.50
1956	9,999,850	.50
10 ESCUDOS		
Y28 (silver) 24mm		
1952	2,023,450	1.25
1955	1,976,550	1.25
20 ESCUDOS		
Y29 (silver) 30mm		
1952	1,003,150	2.50
1955	996,850	2.50

AUSTRIA
(Oesterreich)

A republic in central Europe. All coins inscribed OESTERREICH, AUSTR, AUSTRIAE, or similar except for Y26-30. Until 1868 coins were for Austro-Hungarian Empire. From 1868 separate coins were issued for Hungary. Mint mark A was used at Vienna. From 1873 Austrian coins bore no mint mark.

100 Kreuzer = 1 Florin (1868-1891)
100 Heller = 1 Krone (Corona) (1892-1916)
100 Groschen = 1 Schilling (1925 to date)

		Value
5/10 KREUZER		
Franz Joseph 1 (1848-1916)		
Y6 (copper) 17mm		
1877		.25
1881	4,200,000	.25
1885	2,000,000	.25
1891	2,000,000	.25
1 KREUZER		
Y7 (copper) 19.5mm		
1878		.25
1879		.25
1881	37,900,000	.25
1885	29,000,000	.25
1891	23,849,000	.25
10 KREUZER		
Y11 (billon) 18mm		
1868	11,681,680	.30
1869	29,628,270	.30

		Value
1870	34,878,309	.30
1871	1,700,680	.60
1872	6,600,461	.35
20 KREUZER		
Y12 (billon) 21mm		
1868	29,621,005	.35
1869	31,042,165	.35
1870	29,821,875	.35
1872	575,635	1.00
¼ FLORIN		
Y14 (silver) 22.5mm		
1868A		2.50
1869A		2.50
1870A	7,956	10.00
1871A		2.50
1872	104,364	1.50
1873	48,016	2.00
1874		2.00
1875	20,008	2.50

	Mintage	Value
1 FLORIN		
Y15 (silver) 29mm		
1868A...................		$2.00
1869A...................		2.00
1870A...................		2.00
1871A...................		2.00
1872A...................		4.00
1872 older face,		
no mmk .. ab 3,000,000		1.50
1873............7,879,761		1.50
1874............2,479,005		2.00
1875............5,053,287		1.50
1876............7,282,710		1.50
1877...........13,963,072		1.25
1878...........18,963,072		1.25
1879...........37,485,342		1.25
1880............6,504,624		1.50
1881............6,127,731		1.50
1882............5,476,005		1.50
1883............6,035,954		1.50
1884............4,303,125		1.50
1885............3,394,538		1.50
1886............6,709,534		1.50
1887............5,692,232		1.50
1888............6,572,045		1.50
1889............5,052,537		1.50
1890............4,163,886		1.50
1891............4,234,950		1.50
1892............2,503,593		2.00
Y17 commem. Pribram Mine		
1875..............10,000		35.00
2 FLORINS		
Y16 (silver) 35mm		
1868A...................		5.00
1869A...................		5.00
1870A...................		5.00
1871A...................		5.00
1872A...................		5.00
1872 older face,		
no mmk.....ab 45,000		5.00
1873..............98,739		5.00
1874..............79,056		5.00
1875.............105,948		5.00
1876..............91,854		5.00
1877.............105,057		5.00
1878.............147,258		5.00
1879.............275,724		5.00
1880..............82,701		5.00
1881.............104,004		5.00
1882.............120,771		5.00
1883..............69,579		5.00
1884..............87,296		5.00
1885..............78,101		5.00

	Mintage	Value
1886...............92,988		$5.00
1887..............117,499		5.00
1888...............73,450		5.00
1889..............146,943		5.00
1890..............103,680		5.00
1891..............117,351		5.00
1892...............31,707		5.00
Y19 Silver Wedding		
1879..............275,319		7.50
Y20 Kuttenberg Mine		
1887.................400		100.00
Kronen Standard (1892-1918)		
1 HELLER		
Franz Joseph I		
Y26 (copper) 17mm		
1892..............very few		10.00
1893...........29,022,000		.25
1894...........30,120,000		.25
1895...........49,515,000		.25
1896...........15,600,000		.25
1897...........12,465,000		.25
1898............6,780,000		.40
1899............1,901,000		1.00
1900...........26,981,000		.20
1901...........52,096,000		.20
1902...........20,553,000		.20
1903...........13,779,000		.20
1909...........12,668,000		.20
1910...........21,941,000		.20
1911...........18,387,000		.20
1912...........27,053,000		.20
1913............8,782,000		.20
1914............9,906,000		.20
1915............5,673,000		.20
1916.............ab. 390		15.00
Y27 reverse changed		
1916...........12,484,000		1.00
2 HELLER		
Franz Joseph I		
Y28 (copper) 19mm		
1892.............260,000		2.50
1893...........41,507,000		.25
1894...........78,036,000		.25
1895...........25,610,000		.25
1896...........43,080,000		.25
1897...........98,055,000		.25
1898...........10,720,000		.25
1899...........42,734,000		.25
1900............7,942,000		.30
1901...........12,157,000		.20

	Mintage	Value
1902	18,760,000	$ .20
1903	26,983,000	.20
1904	12,863,000	.20
1905	6,679,000	.30
1906	20,104,000	.20
1907	23,804,000	.20
1908	21,984,000	.20
1909	25,975,000	.20
1910	28,406,000	.20
1911	50,007,058	.20
1912	74,234,000	.20
1913	27,432,000	.20
1914	60,674,000	.20
1915	7,871,000	.25

Y33 (iron) 17mm

	Mintage	Value
1916	61,909,000	.25

Karl (1916-1918)

Y53 same design

	Mintage	Value
1917	81,186,000	.25
1918	66,353,000	.25

10 HELLER

Franz Joseph I

Y29 (nickel) 19mm

	Mintage	Value
1892	very few	7.50
1893	43,524,000	.25
1894	45,558,000	.25
1895	79,918,000	.25
1907	8,662,000	.30
1908	7,772,000	.30
1909	20,462,000	.20
1910	10,164,000	.25
1911	3,634,000	.50

Y31 (copper-nickel-zinc)

	Mintage	Value
1915	18,366,000	.25
1916	27,487,000	.25

Y32 reverse changed

	Mintage	Value
1916	14,804,000	.35

20 HELLER

Franz Joseph I

Y30 (nickel) 21mm

	Mintage	Value
1892	1,500,000	1.00
1893	41,457,000	.25
1894	50,116,000	.25
1895	32,927,000	.25
1907	7,650,000	.30
1908	7,469,000	.30
1909	7,592,000	.30
1911	19,560,000	.20
1914	2,342,000	.40

Y34 (iron)

	Mintage	Value
1916	130,770,000	$ .25

Karl

Y54 same design

	Mintage	Value
1917	127,420,000	.25
1918	100,202,000	.25

1 KRONE
(silver) 23mm

Franz Joseph I

Y35 Laureate head

	Mintage	Value
1892	235,000	5.00
1893	50,124,000	1.00
1894	28,002,500	1.00
1895	15,115,000	1.00
1896	3,068,000	1.25
1897	2,142,000	1.25
1898	5,855,000	1.25
1899	11,820,000	1.00
1900	3,068,000	1.25
1901	10,387,000	1.00
1902	2,947,000	1.25
1903	2,198,000	1.25
1904	993,000	1.50
1905	505,000	1.75
1906	164,500	4.00
1907	244,500	2.50

Y36 Jubilee

	Mintage	Value
1908	4,784,992	1.50

Y37 Plain head

	Mintage	Value
1912	8,457,000	.90
1913	9,345,000	.90
1914	37,897,000	.75
1915	23,000,134	.75
1916	12,415,404	.75

2 KRONEN

Franz Joseph I

Y38 (silver) 28mm

	Mintage	Value
1912	10,244,500	1.50
1913	7,256,002	1.50

5 KRONEN
(silver) 35mm

Franz Joseph I

Y39 Laureate head

	Mintage	Value
1900	8,961,416	4.50
1907	1,539,200	5.00

Y40 Jubilee

	Mintage	Value
1908	3,941,600	7.50

Y41 Plain head

	Mintage	Value
1909	1,708,800	5.00

	Mintage	Value
Y-A41 ST. SCHWARTZ		
under head		
1909............1,775,787		$5.00

Republic — 1923 to Present

100 KRONEN

Inflationary Coinage 1923-1924

Y56 (bronze) 17mm

	Mintage	Value
1923............6,403,680		.50
1924............42,898,820		.40

200 KRONEN

Y57 (bronze) 19mm

	Mintage	Value
1924............57,160,000		.75

1000 KRONEN

Y58 (copper-nickel) 21.5mm

	Mintage	Value
1924............72,353,000		.75

1 GROSCHEN

Coinage Reform of
December 20, 1924

Y60 (bronze) 17mm

	Mintage	Value
1925............30,465,000		.20
1926............15,487,000		.20
1927.............9,318,000		.25
1928............17,189,000		.20
1929............11,400,000		.20
1930.............8,893,000		.25
1931..............971,000		1.00
1932.............3,041,000		.40
1933.............3,940,000		.40
1934.............4,232,000		.40
1935.............3,741,000		.40
1936.............6,027,000		.30
1937.............5,830,000		.30
1938.............1,652,000		.50

2 GROSCHEN

Y61 (bronze) 19mm

	Mintage	Value
1925............29,892,000		.20
1926............17,782,000		.20
1927.............7,757,000		.25
1928............19,478,000		.20
1929............16,184,000		.20
1930.............5,708,000		.30
1934..............812,000		1.00
1935.............3,148,000		.40
1936.............4,412,000		.30
1937.............3,791,000		.30
1938..............864,000		1.00

5 GROSCHEN

Y62 (copper-nickel) 17mm

	Mintage	Value
1931............16,631,000		.25

	Mintage	Value
1932.............4,701,000		$ .30
1934.............3,210,000		.30
1936.............1,240,000		.50
1937.............1,548,000		.50
1938..............876,000		.75

10 GROSCHEN

Y63 (copper-nickel) 22mm

	Mintage	Value
1925............66,199,000		.25
1928............11,468,000		.30
1929............12,020,000		.30

½ SCHILLING

Y67 (silver) 18mm

	Mintage	Value
1925............18,370,000		.50
1926............12,370,000		.50

50 GROSCHEN

Y64 (copper-nickel) 24mm

	Mintage	Value
1934.............8,224,822		5.00

Y65 new design

	Mintage	Value
1935............11,435,000		.60
1936.............1,000,000		2.00

1 SCHILLING

Y59 (silver) 26mm

	Mintage	Value
1924............11,086,000		1.25

Y68 25mm

	Mintage	Value
1925............38,209,000		1.25
1926............20,157,000		1.00
1932..............700,000		3.00

Y66 new design (copper-nickel)

	Mintage	Value
1934............30,641,000		.60
1935............11,987,000		.75

2 SCHILLING
COMMEMORATIVES
(silver) 30mm

Y69 Schubert

	Mintage	Value
1928.............6,900,000		2.00

Y70 Dr. Billroth

	Mintage	Value
1929.............2,000,000		2.50

Y71 Vogelweide

	Mintage	Value
1930..............500,000		3.00

Y72 Mozart

	Mintage	Value
1931..............500,000		3.00

Y73 Haydn

	Mintage	Value
1932..............300,000		3.50

Y74 Dr. Seipel

	Mintage	Value
1933..............400,000		3.00

Y75 Dollfuss

	Mintage	Value
1934.............1,500,000		3.00

Y76 Lueger

	Mintage	Value
1935..............500,000		3.00

	Mintage	Value
Y77 Prince Eugene		
1936	500,000	$3.00
Y78 Karlskirche		
1937	500,000	3.00

5 SCHILLING (silver) 31mm
Y79 Madonna

1934	3,066,000	4.50
1935	5,377,000	4.00
1936	1,557,000	5.00

WORLD WAR II

Coins of Germany from 1938 to 1944 with B mint mark were minted at Vienna. (See Germany).

Republic —
New Coinage Commencing 1946

1 GROSCHEN
Y86 (zinc) 17mm

1947	23,519,000	.15

2 GROSCHEN
Y89 (aluminum) 18mm

1950	21,652,000	.10
1951	7,377,000	.10
1952	37,851,000	.10
1954	20,081,000	.10
1957	21,370,000	.10
1962	5,430,000	.10

5 GROSCHEN
Y87 (zinc) 19mm

1948	17,269,000	.10
1950	19,426,431	.10
1951	12,454,569	.10
1953	84,931,000	.10
1955	17,077,000	.10
1957	20,778,000	.10
1961	3,429,000	.10
1962	5,999,000	.10

10 GROSCHEN
Y88 (zinc) 21mm

1947	6,844,580	.10
1948	66,205,000	.10
1949	51,202,000	.10

Y90 (aluminum) 20mm

1951	9,573,000	.10
1952	45,911,400	.10
1953	39,002,200	.10
1955	27,525,800	.10
1957	33,509,000	.10
1959	80,719,000	.10
1961	11,183,000	.10
1962	24,635,000	.10

	Mintage	Value
20 GROSCHEN		
Y95 (aluminum-bronze) 22mm		
1950	1,619,000	$ .15
1951	7,781,000	.15
1954	5,343,000	.15

50 GROSCHEN
Y91 (aluminum) 22mm

1946	13,058,000	.15
1947	26,990,000	.15
1952	7,455,000	.15
1955	10,525,000	.15

Y103 (aluminum-bronze) 20mm

1959	14,122,000	.15
1960	22,404,000	.15
1961	19,891,000	.15
1962	10,008,000	.15

1 SCHILLING
Y92 (aluminum) 25mm

1946	27,336,000	.35
1947	35,838,000	.35
1952	23,331,000	.35
1957	28,649,000	.35

Y104 (aluminum-bronze) 22.5mm

1959	46,726,000	.20
1960	46,111,000	.20
1961	51,115,000	.20
1962	9,303,000	.20

2 SCHILLING
Y93 (aluminum) 28.5mm

1946	10,082,000	.50
1947	20,140,000	.50
1952	148,500	1.50

5 SCHILLING
Y94 (aluminum) 31mm

1952	29,872,600	.85
1957	240,200	1.50

Y106 (silver) 23.5mm

1960	12,618,000	.60
1961	17,902,000	.60
1962	6,771,000	.60

10 SCHILLING
Y99 (silver) 27mm

1957	15,635,500	1.00
1958	27,280,000	1.00
1959	2,216,500	1.00

25 SCHILLING
(silver) 31mm

Y96 Bundestheater

1955	1,500,000	6.00

	Mintage	Value		Mintage	Value
Y97 Mozart			**Y107** Burgenland		
1956............5,000,000		$5.00	1961............1,400,000		$3.00
Y98 Mariazell			**Y108** Bruckner		
1957............5,000,000		4.50	1962............2,000,000		3.00
Y100 Von Welsbach					
1958............5,000,000		4.00	**50 SCHILLING**		
Y102 Archduke Johann			(silver) 33mm		
1959............2,024,410		4.50	**Y101** Andreas Hofer		
Y105 Carinthia			1959............2,994,000		6.00
1960............1,563,200		3.50			

AZORES

A group of islands in the North Atlantic Ocean, part of the Republic of Portugal. Coinage obsolete: coins of Portugal circulating. Coins are not inscribed "Azores."

5 REIS			1866............inc. above	12.50
Louis I (1861-1889)				
Y1 (copper) 25mm			*Carlos I*	
1865...............90,000	2.50		**Y5**	
1866...............60,000	3.50			
1880..............400,000	1.00		1901..............600,000	3.00
Carlos I (1889-1908)				
Y4			**20 REIS**	
1901..............800,000	2.00		*Louis I*	
			Y3 (copper) 35mm	
10 REIS				
Louis I			1865..............177,500	2.00
Y2 (copper) 30mm			1866..............272,500	2.00
1865..............525,000	1.25			

BELGIAN CONGO
(Belgisch Congo, Congo Belge)

Formerly a free state in central Africa ruled by King Leopold II of Belgium. In 1908 became a Belgian colony and in 1960 became an independent nation. Coins with **H** mint mark were minted at Birmingham, England (Heaton).

100 Centimes = 1 Franc

1 CENTIME			2 CENTIMES	
Leopold II (1865-1909)			*Leopold II*	
Y1 (copper) 18mm			**Y2** (copper) 23mm	
1887...........inc. w/1888	3.00		1887...........inc. w/1888	4.00
1888..............175,000	1.00		1888..............125,000	.75
Albert I (1909-1934)			*Albert I*	
Y15			**Y16**	
1910............2,000,000	.50		1910............1,500,000	.50
1919..............500,000	.75		1919..............500,000	.75

5 CENTIMES

Leopold II

Y3 (copper) 30mm

	Mintage	Value
1887	inc. w/1888	$5.00
1888	175,000	1.00
1894	148,274	1.00

Y9 (copper-nickel) holed 19mm

	Mintage	Value
1906	100,000	1.00
1908	175,000	.75

Y12

	Mintage	Value
1909	1,800,000	1.00

Albert I

Y17

	Mintage	Value
1910	6,000,000	.40
1911	5,000,000	.40
1917H	1,000,000	1.00
1918H	2,000,000	1.00
1919	6,850,000	.40
1920	2,740,000	.50
1921	17,260,000	.30
1921H	3,000,000	.50
1925	11,000,000	.30
1926	5,765,000	.40
1927	2,000,000	.50
1928	1,500,000	.60

10 CENTIMES

Leopold II

Y4 (copper) 35mm

	Mintage	Value
1887	inc. w/1888	6.00
1888	40,000	1.50
1889	100,000	1.25
1894	148,870	1.25

Y10 (copper-nickel) holed 22mm

	Mintage	Value
1906	100,000	1.50
1908	800,000	1.00

Y13

	Mintage	Value
1909	1,500,000	1.50

Albert I

Y18

	Mintage	Value
1910	5,000,000	.50
1911	5,000,000	.50
1917H	500,000	1.25
1919	3,425,000	.60
1919H	1,000,000	.75
1920	1,506,000	.90
1921	13,542,000	.50
1921H	3,000,000	$ .60
1922	14,952,000	.50
1924	3,600,000	.60
1925	4,800,000	.60
1927	2,024,000	.75
1928	5,600,000	.50

20 CENTIMES

Leopold II

Y11 (copper-nickel) 25mm

	Mintage	Value
1906	100,000	2.00
1908	400,000	1.25

Y14

	Mintage	Value
1909	300,000	2.00

Albert I

Y19

	Mintage	Value
1910	1,000,000	.60
1911	1,250,000	.60

50 CENTIMES

Leopold II

Y5 (silver) 18mm

	Mintage	Value
1887	20,000	3.00
1891	60,000	2.50
1894	40,000	2.50
1896	200,000	2.00

Albert I

Y20 (copper-nickel) 24mm

	Mintage	Value
1921 Belgique	4,000,000	1.50
1921 Belgie	4,000,000	1.50
1922 Belgique	5,796,000	1.25
1922 Belgie	5,796,000	1.25
1923 Belgique	7,204,000	1.25
1923 Belgie	7,204,000	1.25
1924 Belgique	4,048,000	1.50
1924 Belgie	4,048,000	1.50
1925 Belgique	13,352,000	1.00
1925 Belgie	13,352,000	1.00
1926 Belgique	20,600,000	1.00
1926 Belgie	20,600,000	1.00
1927 Belgique	7,400,000	1.25
1927 Belgie	7,400,000	1.25
1928 Belgie	7,484,000	1.25
1929 Belgique	3,810,000	1.50
1929 Belgie	3,810,000	1.50

	Mintage	Value
1 FRANC		

Leopold II

Y6 (silver) 23mm

	Mintage	Value
1887	20,000	$6.00
1891	70,000	3.50
1894	70,000	3.50
1896	156,000	3.00

Albert I

Y21 (copper-nickel) 28mm

	Mintage	Value
1920 Belgique	2,337,500	1.50
1920 Belgie	2,337,500	1.50
1921 Belgique	1,762,500	1.50
1921 Belgie	1,762,500	1.50
1922 Belgique	10,000,000	1.50
1923 Belgique	6,181,192	1.50
1923 Belgie	6,181,192	1.50
1924 Belgique	5,318,808	1.50
1924 Belgie	5,318,809	1.50
1925 Belgique	10,000,000	1.50
1925 Belgie	10,000,000	1.50
1926 Belgique	14,750,000	1.50
1926 Belgie	14,750,000	1.50
1927 Belgique	15,250,000	1.50
1928 Belgie	9,250,000	1.50
1929 Belgique	5,006,250	1.50
1929 Belgie	5,006,250	1.50
1930 Belgique	5,000,000	1.50

Leopold III (*1934-1950*)

Y22 (brass) 19mm

	Mintage	Value
1944	25,000,000	.50
1946	15,000,000	.50
1949	15,000,000	.50

	Mintage	Value
2 FRANCS		

Leopold II

Y7 (silver) 27mm

	Mintage	Value
1887	15,000	10.00
1891	25,000	7.50
1894	80,000	6.00
1896	100,000	5.00

Leopold III (*brass*)

Y24 hexagonal, 25mm

	Mintage	Value
1943	25,000,000	3.50

	Mintage	Value
Y23 round, 22mm		
1946	25,000,000	$ .85
1947	19,122,439	.85

5 FRANCS

Leopold II

Y8 (silver) 37mm

	Mintage	Value
1887	8,000	40.00
1891	30,000	35.00
1894	50,000	35.00
1896	110,000	30.00

Leopold III

Y26 (nickel-bronze) 34mm

	Mintage	Value
1936	2,600,000	3.00
1937	11,402,000	3.00

Y25 (brass) 27mm

	Mintage	Value
1947	10,000,000	2.50

50 FRANCS

Leopold III

Y27 (silver) 30mm

	Mintage	Value
1944	1,000,000	15.00

BELGIAN CONGO AND RUANDI-URUNDI

50 CENTIMES

Baudouin I (1951 to date)

Y29 (aluminum) 18mm

	Mintage	Value
1954	4,700,000	.25
1955	20,300,000	.20

1 FRANC

Baudouin I

Y30 (aluminum) 21.5mm

	Mintage	Value
1957	10,000,000	.35
1958	20,000,000	.35
1959	20,000,000	.35
1960	20,000,000	.35

5 FRANCS

Baudouin I

Y28 (brass) 28mm

	Mintage	Value
1952	10,000,000	1.00

Y31 (aluminum)

	Mintage	Value
1956	10,000,000	.65
1958	26,110,000	.65
1959	3,980,000	.65

(Belgique, Belgie)

In western Europe, bordering on the North Sea. From 1886 coins are inscribed in French (Fr): BELGIQUE; Flemish (Fl); BELGIE; or both. From 1938 coins may have name of country in both French and Flemish. (Fr) indicates BELGIQUE-BELGIE, and (Fl) indicates BELGIE-BELGIQUE. Zinc coins 1915-1918 and 1941-1947 were types used during German occupation. Those coins dated 1832 to 1860 with quantity listed as unknown are probably patterns. "B" numbers refer to listings in "A Catalog of Modern World Coins," *5th edition.*

100 Centimes = 1 Franc

	Mintage	Value
1 CENTIME		
Leopold I (1831-1865)		
B1 (copper) 17mm		
1832	unknown	$8.00
1833	5,007,323	1.00
1835	4,367,249	1.00
1836	4,255,720	1.00
1841	unknown	8.00
1844	1,821,947	1.50
1845	8,324,286	1.00
1846	8,240,951	1.00
1847	5,138,259	1.00
1848	383,031	3.00
1849	1,218,482	1.00
1850	2,308,509	1.00
1856	2,428,036	1.00
1857	948,175	1.50
1858	916,441	1.50
1859	982,251	1.50
1860	1,580,603	1.00
1861	1,696,346	1.00
1862	11,906,967	.60
Leopold II (1865-1909)		
Y1 16.5mm		
1869	5,064,341	.50
1870	3,930,000	.50
1873	2,036,317	.50
1874	3,906,728	.50
1875	2,970,461	.50
1876	2,965,939	.50
1882	5,000,000	.35
1887 (Fl)	5,000,000	.30
1894 (Fl)	5,000,000	.30
1899 (Fr)	2,500,000	.40
1899 (Fl)	2,500,000	.40
1901 (Fr)	3,742,800	.30
1901 (Fl)	3,738,457	.30
1902 (Fr)	2,847,349	.40
1902 (Fl)	2,482,438	.40
1907 (Fr)	3,966,780	.30
1907 (Fl)	3,965,780	.30

	Mintage	Value
Albert I (1909-1934)		
Y22		
1912 (Fr)	2,540,495	$ .40
1912 (Fl)	2,542,156	.40
1914 (Fr)	869,587	1.00
2 CENTIMES		
Leopold I		
B2 (copper) 22mm		
1833	16,747,919	1.00
1834	3,267,853	2.00
1835	26,774,007	1.00
1836	27,083,610	1.00
1841	2,226,437	2.00
1842	2,822,614	2.00
1844	1,801,739	2.00
1845	8,324,003	1.00
1846	8,088,029	1.00
1847	3,431,601	1.50
1848	419,939	2.50
1849	3,690,261	1.00
1850	403,578	2.00
1851	2,406,903	1.00
1852	731,092	1.50
1853	465,830	2.00
1855	171,199	4.00
1856	6,255,114	.75
1857	4,611,945	1.00
1858	3,177,248	1.00
1859	4,074,187	1.00
1860	3,070,182	1.00
1861	2,923,603	1.00
1862	6,589,058	.60
1863	18,621,228	.50
1864	16,839,612	.50
1865	2,447,297	1.00
Leopold II		
Y2 21.5mm		
1869	2,971,930	.75
1870	5,653,780	.30
1871	inc. above	1.00
1873	7,490,637	.30

	Mintage	Value
1874	7,875,928	$ .30
1875	7,931,768	.30
1876	10,471,512	.25
1902 (Fr)	2,489,877	.50
1902 (Fl)	2,488,114	.50
1905 (Fr)	4,981,359	.30
1905 (Fl)	4,986,481	.30
1909 (Fr)	4,983,236	.30
1909 (Fl)	565,062	1.00

Albert I

Y23

	Mintage	Value
1910 (Fl)	1,248,248	.30
1911 (Fr)	644,657	.50
1911 (Fl)	6,441,007	.25
1912 (Fr)	4,927,694	.25
1912 (Fl)	16,013,410	.25
1914 (Fr)	490,543	.60
1919 (Fr)	5,000,000	.25
1919 (Fl)	4,997,921	.25

5 CENTIMES

Leopold I

B3 (copper) 28mm

	Mintage	Value
1832	unknown	10.00
1833	4,436,798	2.00
1834	2,514,616	2.00
1835	unknown	10.00
1837	12,037,595	1.00
1838	unknown	10.00
1841	2,508,518	2.00
1842	5,536,540	1.00
1847	1,130,524	2.00
1848	1,845,154	2.00
1849	1,447,142	2.00
1850	2,689,025	2.00
1851	2,381,059	2.00
1852	1,942,901	2.00
1853	704,853	2.50
1855	264,870	3.50
1856	5,655,880	.75
1857	2,299,303	1.00
1858	2,711,519	1.00
1859	2,591,287	1.00
1860	198,997	5.00

B6 25th Anniversary

	Mintage	Value
1856 (Fr)	ab. 215,000	2.00
1856 (Fl)	ab. 3,000	12.50

B20 (copper-nickel) 19mm

	Mintage	Value
1861	8,259,264	.30
1862	14,149,380	.30
1863	16,055,072	.30
1864	2,512,574	.60

Leopold II

Y3

	Mintage	Value
1894 (Fr)	3,110,953	$ .30
1894 (Fl)	1,658,000	.30
1895 (Fr)	3,693,250	.30
1895 (Fl)	4,957,405	.30
1898 (Fr)	1,004,083	.40
1898 (Fl)	985,000	.50
1900 (Fr)	1,666,128	.30
1900 (Fl)	1,669,735	.30
1901 (Fr)	2,494,063	.30
1901 (Fl)	2,491,287	.30

Y12 holed

	Mintage	Value
1901 (Fr)	202,100	1.00
1902 (Fr)	1,416,017	.20
1902 (Fl)	1,485,467	.20
1903 (Fr)	863,878	.30
1903 (Fl)	1,001,932	.20
1904 (Fr)	5,813,932	.20
1904 (Fl)	5,811,667	.20
1905 (Fr)	9,575,374	.20
1905 (Fl)	7,002,418	.20
1906 (Fr)	8,463,239	.20
1906 (Fl)	11,015,564	.20
1907 (Fr)	993,028	.30
1907 (Fl)	997,965	.30

Albert I

Y24

	Mintage	Value
1910 (Fr)	8,011,286	.20
1910 (Fl)	8,032,999	.20
1913 (Fr)	5,005,423	.20
1914 (Fr)	1,004,034	.25
1914 (Fl)	6,039,540	.20

German Occupation

Y38 (zinc)

	Mintage	Value
1915	10,199,240	.15
1916	45,464,000	.15

Y24 regular

	Mintage	Value
1920 (Fr)	10,040,000	.10
1920 (Fl)	10,030,000	.10
1921 (Fl)	4,200,000	.10
1922 (Fr)	12,640,000	.10
1922 (Fl)	13,180,000	.10
1923 (Fr)	9,000,000	.10
1923 (Fl)	3,530,000	.10
1924 (Fl)	5,260,000	.10
1925 (Fr)	15,860,000	.10
1925 (Fl)	13,000,000	.10
1926 (Fr)	7,000,000	.10
1927 (Fr)	2,000,000	.15
1927 (Fl)	6,938,000	.10

	Mintage	Value
1928 (Fr)	12,506,500	$ .10
1928 (Fl)	6,252,000	.10
Y24a		
1930 (Fl)	3,000,000	.30
1931 (Fl)	6,000,000	.20
1932 (Fr)	6,950,000	.20

Leopold III (1934-1950)
Y42

	Mintage	Value
1938 (Fr)	4,970,000	.15
1939 (Fl)	3,000,000	.15
1940 (Fl)	1,970,000	.25

German Occupation
Y51 (zinc)

	Mintage	Value
1941 (Fr)	10,000,000	.15
1941 (Fl)	4,000,000	.15
1942 (Fl)	18,430,000	.15
1943 (Fr)	7,606,000	.15

10 CENTIMES
Leopold I

B4 (copper) 32mm

	Mintage	Value
1832	993,308	4.00
1833	993,651	4.00
1847	134,696	6.00
1848	776,706	4.00
1849	inc. above	8.00
1855	190,766	4.00
1856	inc. above	5.00

B5 Marriage, Duke of Brabant

	Mintage	Value
1853	104,050	2.50

B21 (nickel) 21mm

	Mintage	Value
1861	9,080,145	.30
1862	15,129,027	.30
1863	14,481,659	.30
1864	3,202,342	1.00

Leopold II
Y4 22mm

	Mintage	Value
1894 (Fr)	18,886,000	.25
1894 (Fl)	9,209,110	.25
1895 (Fr)	736,208	.75
1895 (Fl)	3,529,192	.25
1898 (Fr)	3,499,000	.25
1898 (Fl)	3,499,634	.25
1901 (Fr)	556,414	1.00
1901 (Fl)	556,414	1.00

Y13 holed

	Mintage	Value
1901 (Fr)	582,377	.75
1902 (Fr)	5,865,609	.20
1902 (Fl)	1,560,041	.25
1903 (Fr)	763,387	.50

	Mintage	Value
1903 (Fl)	5,658,303	$ .25
1904 (Fr)	16,354,035	.20
1904 (Fl)	16,833,912	.20
1905 (Fr)	14,392,432	.20
1905 (Fl)	13,758,239	.20
1906 (Fr)	1,482,882	.40
1906 (Fl)	2,016,857	.40

German Occupation
Y39 (zinc)

	Mintage	Value
1915	9,681,224	.25
1916	37,382,011	.15
1917	1,447,300	.50

Albert I
Y25

	Mintage	Value
1920 (Fr)	6,520,000	.15
1920 (Fl)	5,050,000	.15
1921 (Fr)	7,215,000	.15
1921 (Fl)	7,580,000	.15
1922 (Fl)	6,250,000	.15
1923 (Fr)	20,625,000	.10
1924 (Fl)	5,825,000	.15
1925 (Fl)	8,160,000	.15
1926 (Fr)	6,916,000	.15
1926 (Fl)	6,250,000	.15
1927 (Fr)	8,125,000	.15
1927 (Fl)	10,625,000	.10
1928 (Fr)	6,895,000	.15
1928 (Fl)	6,750,000	.15
1929 (Fr)	12,260,000	.10
1929 (Fl)	4,668,000	.20

Y25a

	Mintage	Value
1930 (Fr)	2,000,000	.40
1930 (Fl)	1,581,000	.40
1931 (Fr)	6,270,000	.20
1931 (Fl)	5,000,000	.20
1932 (Fr)	1,270,000	1.00

Leopold III
Y43

	Mintage	Value
1938 (Fr)	6,000,000	.15
1939 (Fr)	7,000,000	.15
1939 (Fl)	8,425,000	.15

German Occupation
Y52 (zinc)

	Mintage	Value
1941 (Fr)	10,000,000	.20
1941 (Fl)	7,000,000	.20
1942 (Fr)	17,000,000	.20
1942 (Fl)	21,000,000	.20
1943 (Fr)	22,500,000	.20
1943 (Fl)	22,000,000	.20
1944 (Fl)	28,140,000	.20
1945 (Fl)	8,000,000	.25
1946 (Fl)	5,370,000	1.00

20 CENTIMES

Leopold I

B12a (silver) 15mm

	Mintage	Value
1852	300,640	$ 4.00
1853	1,965,054	1.50
1858	865,252	4.00

B22 (nickel) 25mm

	Mintage	Value
1860	unknown	8.00
1861	1,803,670	1.00

Baudouin I (1951 to date)

Y62 (bronze) 17mm

	Mintage	Value
1953 (Fr)	14,150,000	.10
1954 (Fl)	50,130,000	.10
1957 (Fr)	13,300,000	.10
1958 (Fr)	8,700,000	.10
1959 (Fr)	19,670,000	.10
1960 (Fl)	7,530,000	.10
1962 (Fr)	410,000	.20

¼ FRANC

Leopold I

B7 (silver) 15mm

	Mintage	Value
1834	762,188	4.00
1835	640,019	4.00
1843	8,000	15.00
1844	966,000	3.00

B12 new design, 13mm

	Mintage	Value
1849	unknown	20.00
1850	100,836	7.50

25 CENTIMES

Leopold II

Y14 (nickel) holed 26mm

	Mintage	Value
1908 (Fr)	4,006,878	.25
1908 (Fl)	4,011,357	.25
1909 (Fr)	1,998,086	.40

Albert I

Y26

	Mintage	Value
1910 (Fl)	2,006,473	.35
1913 (Fr)	2,010,554	.35
1913 (Fl)	2,010,342	.35

German Occupation

Y40 (zinc)

	Mintage	Value
1915	8,079,538	.30
1916	10,671,132	.30
1917	3,554,868	.40
1918	5,489,200	.35

Y26 regular

	Mintage	Value
1920 (Fr) as 1913	2,844,000	.35
1921 (Fr)	7,464,000	.20
1921 (Fl)	11,173,208	.20

	Mintage	Value
1922 (Fr)	7,600,000	$ .20
1922 (Fl)	14,200,000	.20
1923 (Fr)	11,356,000	.20
1926 (Fr)	1,300,000	.50
1926 (Fl)	6,400,000	.20
1927 (Fr)	8,800,000	.20
1927 (Fl)	3,799,000	.25
1928 (Fr)	4,351,000	.25
1928 (Fl)	9,200,000	.20
1929 (Fr)	9,600,000	.20
1929 (Fl)	8,980,000	.20

Leopold III

Y44

	Mintage	Value
1938 (Fr)	7,200,000	.25
1938 (Fl)	14,932,000	.25
1939 (Fr)	7,732,000	.25

German Occupation

Y53 (zinc)

	Mintage	Value
1942 (Fr)	14,400,000	.25
1942 (Fl)	14,400,000	.25
1943 (Fr)	21,600,000	.25
1943 (Fl)	21,600,000	.25
1944 (Fl)	25,960,000	.25
1945 (Fl)	9,844,000	.25
1946 (Fl)	8,200,000	.25

½ FRANC

Leopold I

B8 (silver) 18mm

	Mintage	Value
1833	58,350	10.00
1834	1,578,047	3.00
1835	805,042	4.00
1838	550,367	6.00
1840	347,370	6.00
1841	unknown	40.00
1843	364,000	6.00
1844	1,584,000	3.00

B13 new design

	Mintage	Value
1849	unknown	30.00
1850	209,571	10.00

50 CENTIMES

Leopold II

Y5 (silver) 18mm

	Mintage	Value
1866	6,806,000	1.00
1867	1,014,000	1.50
1868	1,075,864	1.50
1881	200,000	6.00
1886 (Fr)	1,250,000	1.50
1886 (Fl)	3,750,000	1.00
1898 (Fr)	499,000	2.00
1898 (Fl)	501,000	2.00

	Mintage	Value
1899 (Fr)............500,000		$2.00
1899 (Fl)............500,000		2.00

Y15 new design

	Mintage	Value
1901 (Fr)..........3,000,000		.75
1901 (Fl)..........3,000,000		.75

Y16 new design

	Mintage	Value
1907 (Fr)............545,000		1.00
1907 (Fl)............545,000		1.00
1909 (Fr)..........2,510,000		.75
1909 (Fl)..........2,510,000		.75

Albert I

Y33

	Mintage	Value
1910 (Fr)..........1,900,000		.50
1910 (Fl)..........1,900,000		.50
1911 (Fr)..........2,063,000		.50
1911 (Fl)..........2,063,000		.50
1912 (Fr)..........1,000,000		.50
1912 (Fl)..........1,000,000		.50
1914 (Fr)............240,000		1.25

German Occupation

Y41 (zinc)

	Mintage	Value
1918.............7,394,400		1.00

Y27 regular (nickel)

	Mintage	Value
1922 (Fr)..........6,180,000		.15
1923 (Fr)..........8,820,000		.15
1923 (Fl).........15,000,000		.15
1927 (Fr)..........1,750,000		.25
1928 (Fr)..........3,000,000		.20
1928 (Fl).........10,000,000		.15
1929 (Fr)..........1,000,000		.30
1930 (Fr)..........1,000,000		.30
1930 (Fl)..........2,252,000		.25
1932 (Fr)..........2,530,000		.25
1932 (Fl)..........2,000,000		.25
1933 (Fr)..........2,861,000		.25
1933 (Fl)..........3,189,000		.20
1934 (Fr)............935,482		.30
1934 (Fl)............935,482		.30

Baudouin I

Y63 (bronze) 19mm

	Mintage	Value
1952 (Fr)..........3,520,000		.15
1952 (Fl)..........5,830,000		.10
1953 (Fr).........22,620,000		.10
1953 (Fl).........22,930,000		.10
1954 (Fl).........15,730,000		.10
1955 (Fr).........29,160,000		.10
1956 (Fl)..........5,640,000		.10
1957 (Fl).........13,800,000		.10
1958 (Fr)..........9,750,000		.10
1958 (Fl).........19,480,000		.10

	Mintage	Value
1959 (Fr).......17,350,000		$ .10
1962 (Fr)........6,160,000		.10
1962 (Fl)........4,150,000		.10

1 FRANC

Leopold I

B9 (silver) 23mm

	Mintage	Value
1833...............60,836		10.00
1834..............481,551		6.00
1835..............830,698		5.00
1838..............525,362		6.00
1840..............261,041		7.50
1841.............unknown		40.00
1843.............unknown		40.00
1844............2,196,400		3.00

B14 new design

	Mintage	Value
1849...............46,662		20.00
1850..............162,016		10.00

Leopold II

Y6

	Mintage	Value
1866............3,041,000		2.00
1867............6,652,000		1.00
1868............675,000		4.00
1869............1,393,608		2.00
1881 119,484		7.00
1886 (Fr)........1,250,000		1.00
1886 (Fl)........1,026,000		1.00
1887 (Fl)........2,724,000		.75

Y9 50-Year Jubilee

	Mintage	Value
1880..............545,222		5.00

Y17 new design

	Mintage	Value
1904 (Fr)...........803,000		1.25
1904 (Fl)...........803,000		1.25
1909 (Fr)..........2,250,000		1.00
1909 (Fl)..........2,250,000		1.00

Albert I

Y34

	Mintage	Value
1910 (Fr).........2,190,000		1.25
1910 (Fl).........2,750,000		1.25
1911 (Fr).........2,810,000		1.25
1911 (Fl).........2,250,000		1.25
1912 (Fr).........3,250,000		1.25
1912 (Fl).........3,250,000		1.25
1913 (Fr).........3,000,000		1.25
1913 (Fl).........3,000,000		1.25
1914 (Fr).........11,221,581		1.25
1914 (Fl).........11,221,581		1.25

Y28 new design (nickel)

	Mintage	Value
1922 (Fr).........14,000,000		.25
1922 (Fl).........19,000,000		.25
1923 (Fr).........22,500,000		.25

	Mintage	Value
1923 (Fl)	17,500,000	$ .25
1928 (Fr)	5,000,000	.30
1928 (Fl)	4,975,000	.30
1929 (Fr)	7,415,000	.25
1929 (Fl)	10,365,000	.25
1930 (Fr)	2,500,000	.40
1933 (Fr)	1,998,000	.50
1933 (Fl)	inc. above	4.00
1934 (Fr)	10,262,500	.25
1934 (Fl)	8,025,000	.25
1935 (Fl)	2,237,500	.40

Leopold III
Y45 21.5mm

	Mintage	Value
1939 (Fr)	46,865,000	.25
1939 (Fl)	36,000,000	.25
1940 (Fl)	10,865,000	.25

German Occupation
Y54 (zinc)

	Mintage	Value
1941 (Fr)	16,000,000	.25
1942 (Fr)	25,000,000	.25
1942 (Fl)	42,000,000	.25
1943 (Fr)	28,000,000	.25
1943 (Fl)	28,000,000	.25
1944 (Fl)	24,190,000	.25
1945 (Fl)	15,930,000	.25
1946 (Fl)	36,000,000	.25
1947 (Fl)	3,000,000	.30

Postwar
Y57 (copper-nickel) 21mm

	Mintage	Value
1950 (Fr)	13,630,000	.15
1950 (Fl)	10,000,000	.15

Baudouin I
Y57 identical to 1950 type

	Mintage	Value
1951 (Fr)	51,025,000	.15
1951 (Fl)	53,750,000	.15
1952 (Fr)	53,205,000	.15
1952 (Fl)	49,145,000	.15
1953 (Fl)	9,915,000	.15
1954 (Fr)	4,980,000	.20
1954 (Fl)	4,940,000	.20
1955 (Fr)	10,000,000	.15
1955 (Fl)	3,960,000	.20
1956 (Fr)	10,000,000	.15
1956 (Fl)	10,053,000	.15
1957 (Fl)	18,315,000	.15
1958 (Fr)	31,750,000	.15
1958 (Fl)	17,365,000	.15
1959 (Fr)	9,000,000	.15
1959 (Fl)	5,830,000	.15
1960 (Fr)	10,000,000	.15
1960 (Fl)	5,555,000	.15

	Mintage	Value
1961 (Fr)	5,030,000	$ .15
1961 (Fl)	9,350,000	.15
1962 (Fr)	12,250,000	.15
1962 (Fl)	10,720,000	.15

2 FRANCS

Leopold I
B10 (silver) 27mm

	Mintage	Value
1834	276,356	15.00
1835	225,055	20.00
1838	300,305	30.00
1840	236,341	20.00
1841	unknown	75.00
1843	734,500	12.00
1844	483,000	12.00

B15 new design

	Mintage	Value
1849	unknown	75.00

B19 Commemorative:
25th Anniversary

	Mintage	Value
1856 ANNIVERSAIRE, etc	11,545	10.00
1856 VERJAEDAG, etc	1,898	70.00

Leopold II
Y7 regular

	Mintage	Value
1866	1,942,000	3.00
1867	3,789,000	2.00
1868	2,164,230	3.00
1887	150,000	10.00

Y10 50-Year Jubilee

	Mintage	Value
1880	117,647	4.00

Y18 new design

	Mintage	Value
1904 (Fr)	400,000	2.50
1904 (Fl)	400,000	2.50
1909 (Fr)	1,087,500	1.75
1909 (Fl)	1,087,500	1.75

Albert I
Y35

	Mintage	Value
1910 (Fr)	800,000	2.00
1911 (Fr)	1,000,000	2.00
1911 (Fl)	1,775,000	2.00
1912 (Fr)	375,000	2.00
1912 (Fl)	375,000	2.00

Y29 (nickel)

	Mintage	Value
1923 (Fr)	7,500,000	.35
1923 (Fl)	6,500,000	.35
1924 (Fl)	1,000,000	.75
1930 (Fr)	1,250,000	.75
1930 (Fl)	1,252,000	.75

	Mintage	Value
Allied Issue		
Y56 (zinc-coated steel)		
1944 (Philadelphia)		
	25,000,000	$ .35

2½ FRANCS

Leopold I

B16 (silver) 30mm

	Mintage	Value
1848	559,415	3.50
1849	2,002,847	3.00
1850	159,152	15.00

5 FRANCS

Leopold I

B11 (silver) 37mm

	Mintage	Value
1832	37,352	20.00
1833	1,125,666	7.50
1834	349,976	10.00
1835	369,768	10.00
1838	5,203	75.00
1840	unknown	100.00
1841	unknown	100.00
1844	80,200	18.00
1847	699,601	5.00
1848	2,516,283	5.00
1849	6,922,095	5.00

B17 new design

	Mintage	Value
1849	inc. above	3.00
1850	5,265,296	3.00
1851	3,707,922	3.00
1852	4,604,676	3.00
1853	2,426,598	3.00
1858	18,102	20.00
1865	907,360	5.00

B18 Marriage

	Mintage	Value
1853	31,739	10.00

Leopold II

Y8

	Mintage	Value
1865	inc. w/1867	7.00
1866	inc. w/1867	8.00
1867	3,693,144	3.00
1868	6,750,564	3.00
1869	12,657,542	3.00
1870	10,486,075	3.00
1871	4,783,434	3.00
1872	2,045,000	3.00
1873	22,340,959	2.50
1874	2,400,000	3.00
1875	2,980,941	3.00
1876	2,159,885	3.00

	Mintage	Value
Y11 50-Year Jubilee		
1880	6,714	$35.00

Albert I

Y30 (nickel) 31mm

	Mintage	Value
1930 (Fr)	1,600,000	1.00
1930 (Fl)	5,086,000	.75
1931 (Fr)	9,032,000	.75
1931 (Fl)	5,336,000	.75
1932 (Fr)	3,600,000	.90
1932 (Fl)	3,683,000	.90
1933 (Fr)	1,386,500	1.00
1933 (Fl)	2,513,500	1.00
1934 (Fr)	1,000,000	1.00

Leopold III

Y47

	Mintage	Value
1936 (Fr)	650,000	1.00
1936 (Fl)	2,497,500	.75
1937 (Fr)	1,847,500	.75

Y46 25mm

	Mintage	Value
1938 (Fr)	11,419,000	.50
1938 (Fl)	3,200,000	1.50
1939 (Fl)	8,219,000	.50

German Occupation

Y55 (zinc)

	Mintage	Value
1941 (Fr)	15,200,000	.25
1941 (Fl)	27,544,000	.25
1943 (Fr)	16,236,000	.25
1944 (Fr)	1,868,000	.50
1945 (Fr)	3,200,000	.40
1945 (Fl)	7,200,000	.25
1946 (Fr)	4,452,000	.30
1947 (Fr)	3,100,000	.40
1947 (Fl)	36,000	2.50

Postwar

Y58 (copper-nickel) 24mm

	Mintage	Value
1948 (Fr)	5,304,000	.40
1948 (Fl)	4,800,000	.40
1949 (Fr)	38,752,000	.40
1949 (Fl)	31,500,000	.40
1950 (Fr)	23,948,000	.40
1950 (Fl)	34,728,000	.40

Baudouin I

Y58 same design

	Mintage	Value
1958 (Fr)	5,304,000	.40
1958 (Fl)	2,672,000	.40
1960 (Fl)	5,896,000	.40
1961 (Fr)	6,000,000	.40
1961 (Fl)	4,120,000	.40
1962 (Fr)	6,565,000	.40
1962 (Fl)	7,624,000	.40

	Mintage	Value
10 FRANCS		
Albert I		
Y31 (nickel) 34mm		
1930 (Fr)........2,699,000		$4.00
1930 (Fl)........3,000,000		4.00
20 FRANCS		
Albert I		
Y32 (nickel) 37mm		
1931 (Fr)........3,957,000		5.00
1931 (Fl)........2,600,000		5.00
1932 (Fr)........5,472,000		5.00
1932 (Fl)........6,950,000		5.00
Y36 new design (silver) 28mm		
1933 (Fr)..........200,000		3.50
1933 (Fl)..........200,000		3.50
1934 (Fr).......12,300,000		2.50
1934 (Fl).......12,300,000		2.50
Leopold III		
Y49		
1934.............1,250,000		2.00
1935............10,760,475		2.00
Y59 27mm		
1949 (Fr)........4,600,000		1.50
1949 (Fl)........5,545,000		1.50
1950 (Fr).......12,957,000		1.50
Baudouin I		
Y59 same design		
1951 (Fl)........7,885,000		1.50
1953 (Fr)........3,952,500		1.50
1953 (Fl)........6,625,000		1.50
1954 (Fr)........4,835,000		1.50
1954 (Fl)........5,322,500		1.50
1955 (Fr)........1,730,000		1.50
1955 (Fl)........3,760,000		1.50
50 FRANCS		
Leopold III		
Y48 (silver) 35mm		
1935 Brussels Fair (Fr)		
.............140,436		12.50

	Mintage	Value
1935 same (Fl)......140,436		$12.50
Y50 regular, 33mm		
1939 (Fr).........1,000,000		4.00
1939 (Fl).........1,000,000		4.00
1940 (Fr)..........631,135		4.00
1940 (Fl)..........631,135		4.00
Postwar		
Y60 30mm		
1948 (Fr)........2,000,000		2.50
1948 (Fl)........3,000,000		2.50
1949 (Fr)........4,354,000		2.50
1950 (Fl)........4,110,000		2.50
Baudouin I		
Y60 same design		
1951 (Fr)........2,904,000		2.50
1951 (Fl)........1,698,000		2.50
1954 (Fr)........3,232,000		2.50
1954 (Fl)........2,978,000		2.50
Y64 Brussels Fair		
1958 (Fr)..........476,000		2.50
1958 (Fl)..........382,000		2.50
Y65 Marriage commem.		
1960..............500,000		2.50
100 FRANCS		
Leopold III		
Y61 (silver) 33mm		
1948 (Fr)........1,000,000		5.00
1948 (Fl)........1,000,000		5.00
1949 (Fr)..........106,000		5.00
1949 (Fl)........2,271,000		5.00
1950 (Fr)........2,807,000		5.00
1951 (Fl)........4,691,000		5.00
Baudouin I		
Y61 same design		
1954 (Fr)........2,517,000		5.00

(Bohmen Und Mahren — Cechy A Morava)

Part of Czechoslovakia. A German Protectorate during World War II. Coinage obsolete.

100 Haleru = 1 Koruna

	Mintage	Value		Mintage	Value
10 HALERU			**50 HALERU**		
Y-B29 (zinc) 17mm			**Y-B31** (zinc) 22mm		
1940		$ .20	1940		$ .50
1941		.20	1941		.50
1942		.20	1942		.50
1943		.20	1943		1.25
1944		.20	1944		.50
20 HALERU					
Y-B30 (zinc) 20mm			**1 KORUNA**		
1940		.30	**Y-B32** (zinc) 23mm		
1941		.30	1941		.60
1942		.30	1942		.60
1943		.30	1943		.60
1944		.30	1944		.60

BULGARIA
(Blgariya)

One of the Balkan countries facing the Black Sea, south of Romania.

100 Stotinki = 1 Lev

	Mintage	Value		Mintage	Value
1 STOTINKA			**2½ STOTINKI**		
Ferdinand I (1887-1918)			*Ferdinand I*		
Y16 (bronze) 15mm			**Y8** (copper-nickel) 15mm		
1901	20,000,000	.50	1888	12,000,000	.30
1912	20,000,000	.50			
People's Republic (1946 to date)			**3 STOTINKI**		
Y46 (brass) 15mm			*People's Republic*		
1951		.15	**Y47** (brass) 20mm		
Y53 new design (bronze)			1951		.20
1962		.10			
2 STOTINKI			**5 STOTINKI**		
Alexander I (1879-1886)			*Alexander I*		
Y1 (copper) 20mm			**Y2** (copper) 25mm		
1881	4,996,345	.40	1881	10,000,000	.40
Ferdinand I			*Ferdinand I*		
Y17 (bronze)			**Y9** (copper-nickel) 17mm		
1901	40,000,000	.30	1888	14,000,000	.30
1912	40,000,000	.30	**Y18** design changed		
People's Republic			1906	14,000,000	.25
Y54 (bronze) 18mm			1912	14,000,000	.25
1962		.15	1913	20,850,035	.25

	Mintage	Value
Y18a (zinc)		
1917 53,200,000		$ .50
People's Republic		
Y48 (brass) 22mm		
1951		.25
Y55 new design (bronze)		
1962		.20

10 STOTINKI

Alexander I

Y3 (copper) 30mm
1881 15,000,000   .75

Ferdinand I

	Mintage	Value
Y10 (copper-nickel) 19mm		
1888 10,000,000		.40
Y19 design changed		
1906 13,000,000		.30
1912 13,000,000		.30
1913 20,000,035		.30
Y19a (zinc)		
1917 59,100,000		.75

People's Republic

	Value
Y49 (copper-nickel) 17mm	
1951	.40
Y56 new design	
1962	.30

20 STOTINKI

Ferdinand I

	Mintage	Value
Y11 (copper-nickel) 21mm		
1888 5,000,000		.50
Y20 design changed		
1906 10,000,000		.40
1912 10,000,000		.40
1913 5,000,035		.40
Y20a (zinc)		
1917 40,000,000		1.00

People's Republic

	Value
Y49a (copper-nickel) 20mm	
1954	.50
Y57 new design, 21mm	
1962	.40

25 STOTINKI

People's Republic

Y50 (copper-nickel) 22mm
1951 75

50 STOTINKI

Alexander I

	Mintage	Value
Y4 (silver) 18mm		
1883 3,000,000		$1.00

Ferdinand I

	Mintage	Value
Y12 head left		
1891 2,000,046		.60
Y24 head right		
1910 400,016		1.00
Y27 head left		
1912 5,000,088		.75
1913 2,282,061		.80

Boris III (1918-1943)

Y41 (aluminum-bronze)
1937 30,000,000   .20

People's Republic

	Value
Y51 (copper-nickel) 23mm	
1959	1.00
Y58 new design	
1962	.75

1 LEV

Alexander I

	Mintage	Value
Y5 (silver) 23mm		
1882 4,500,015		1.50

Ferdinand I

	Mintage	Value
Y13 head left		
1891 4,000,150		1.25
1894 1,000,039		1.50
Y25 head right		
1910 3,000,125		1.50
Y28 head left		
1912 5,500,148		1.50
1913 2,282,068		1.50

Boris III

	Mintage	Value
Y32 (aluminum)		
1923 40,000,000		1.25
Y34 (copper-nickel) 20mm		
1925 70,018,105		.30
Y34a (iron)		
1941 10,000,000		.35

People's Republic

	Value
Y52 (copper-nickel) 25mm	
1960	1.25
Y59 new design	
1962	1.25

	Mintage	Value
2 LEVA		
Alexander I		
Y6 (silver) 27mm		
1882............2,000,000		$3.00
Ferdinand I		
Y14 head left		
1891............1,500,157		2.00
1894............1,000,081		2.00
Y26 head right		
1910..............400,005		2.50
Y29 head left		
1912............1,500,032		2.50
1913............1,141,033		2.50
Boris III		
Y33 (aluminum)		
1923............20,000,000		2.00
Y35 (copper-nickel) 23mm		
1925............40,015,375		.40
Y35a (iron)		
1941............15,000,000		.50
Simeon II (1943-1946)		
1943.....................		.50
5 LEVA		
Alexander I		
Y7 (silver) 37mm		
1884.............512,473		15.00
1885............1,426,000		15.00
Ferdinand I		
Y15		
1892............1,000,108		12.50
Y15a legend differs		
1894............1,800,192		12.50
Boris III		
Y36 (copper-nickel) 26mm		
1930............20,001,050		1.00
Y36a (iron)		
1941............15,000,000		1.00

	Mintage	Value
Simeon II		
Y36b (nickel-clad steel)		
1943.....................		$1.00
10 LEVA		
Boris III		
Y37 (copper-nickel) 30mm		
1930...........15,001,040		1.50
Y37a (iron)		
1941............2,200,000		1.50
Simeon II		
Y37b (nickel-clad steel)		
1943.....................		1.50
20 LEVA		
Boris III		
Y38 (silver) 21mm		
1930...........10,008,491		1.50
Y42 (copper-nickel)		
1940.....................		1.00
50 LEVA		
Boris III		
Y39 (silver) 27mm		
1930............9,028,500		3.00
Y44 new design		
1934............3,000,000		4.00
Y43 (copper-nickel)		
1940............4,000,000		1.50
Simeon II		
Y43a (nickel-clad steel)		
1943.....................		2.00
100 LEVA		
Boris III		
Y40 (silver) 34mm		
1930............1,556,323		10.00
Y45 design changed		
1934............2,500,000		8.00
1937............2,200,000		8.00

CAMEROONS
(Cameroun)

In West Africa. Was part of French Equatorial Africa. Attained sovereignty in 1960.

100 Centimes = 1 Franc

	Mintage	Value
50 CENTIMES		
Y1 (aluminum-bronze) 17.5mm		
1924............4,000,000	$1.50
1925............2,500,000	2.00
1926............4,999,981	1.50
1927............2,800,049	2.00
Wartime "Free France"		
Y4 (bronze) 20mm		
1943............4,000,000	2.50
Y6 same w/LIBRE		
1943............4,000,000	2.50
1 FRANC		
Y2 (aluminum-bronze) 22mm		
1924............3,000,000	2.00
1925............1,721,922	3.00
1926............6,784,206	2.00
1927............5,143,872	2.00
Wartime "Free France"		
Y5 (bronze) 25mm		
1943............3,000,000	2.50
Y7 same w/LIBRE		
1943............3,000,000	2.50

	Mintage	Value
Postwar Issue		
Y8 (aluminum) 23mm		
1948............8,000,000	$ .50
2 FRANCS		
Y3 (aluminum-bronze) 27mm		
1924............500,000	3.00
1925............100,000	4.50
Postwar Issue		
Y9 (aluminum)		
1948............5,000,000	.75
Integrated Coinage, French Equatorial Africa - Cameroons		
5 FRANCS		
Y10 (aluminum-bronze) 19mm		
1958............30,000,000	.40
10 FRANCS		
Y11 (aluminum-bronze) 23mm		
1958............25,000,000	.60
25 FRANCS		
Y12 (aluminum-bronze) 27mm		
1958............12,000,000	1.00

CAPE VERDE ISLANDS
(Cabo Verde)

A group of islands lying 600 miles west of Africa. An overseas province of Portugal.

100 Centavos = 1 Escudo

	Value
5 CENTAVOS	
Y1 (bronze) 19mm	
1930............1,000,000	.75
10 CENTAVOS	
Y2 (bronze) 22.5mm	
1930............1,500,000	1.00
20 CENTAVOS	
Y3 (bronze) 25mm	
1930............1,500,000	1.25
50 CENTAVOS	
Y4 (nickel-bronze) 23mm	
1930............1,000,000	1.50
Y6 new design	
1949............1,000,000	.75

	Value
1 ESCUDO	
Y5 (nickel-bronze) 27mm	
1930............50,000	2.00
Y7 new design	
1949............500,000	1.00
Y8 (bronze) 26mm	
1953............250,000	1.00
2½ ESCUDOS	
Y9 (nickel-bronze) 20mm	
1953............500,000	1.25
10 ESCUDOS	
Y10 (silver) 24mm	
1953............400,000	2.00

\ French protectorate in the Indian Ocean. Coinage obsolete.

100 Centimes = 1 Franc

	Mintage	Value		Mintage	Value
5 CENTIMES			**5 FRANCS**		
Y1 (bronze) 24mm			**Y3** (silver) 37mm		
890.............300,200		$8.00	1890.............2,050		$400.00
10 CENTIMES					
Y2 (bronze) 30mm					
1890.............150,200		12.50			

CRETE

(KPHTIKH)

Island in the Mediterranean, formerly self-governing, now a part of Greece. Coinage obsolete. Currency of Greece now circulating.

100 Lepta = 1 Drachma

1 LEPTON			**20 LEPTA**	
Y1 (bronze) 15mm			**Y5** (copper-nickel) 21mm	
1900.............289,283	7.50		1900............1,250,000	3.50
1901...........1,710,717	3.00		**50 LEPTA**	
2 LEPTA			**Y6** (silver) 18mm	
Y2 (bronze) 20mm			1901.............600,000	4.00
1900.............793,079	5.00		**1 DRACHMA**	
1901.............706,922	5.00		**Y7** (silver) 23mm	
5 LEPTA			1901.............500,000	5.00
Y3 (copper-nickel) 17mm			**2 DRACHMAI**	
1900...........4,000,000	3.00		**Y8** (silver) 27mm	
10 LEPTA			1901.............175,000	6.50
Y4 (copper-nickel) 19mm			**5 DRACHMAI**	
1900...........2,000,000	3.00		**Y9** (silver) 37mm	
			1901.............150,000	15.00

CROATIA

(Nezavisna Drzava Hrvatska)

Part of Yugoslavia. Formed into a state by Germany during World War II. Coinage obsolete.

2 KUNE
Y1 (zinc) 20mm
1941....................   6.50

Islands in the West Indies, north of Venezuela, part of the Kingdom of the Netherlands. Wartime coins with D mint mark were minted in Denver, and those with P were minted in Philadelphia. 1941-44 coins have mint mark as letter and palm tree.

100 Cents = 1 Guilder

	Mintage	Value
1 CENT		
(bronze) 17mm		
1942P type of Netherlands Y36 for Curacao and Surinam	2,500,000	$ .30
Y3 Curacao		
1944D	3,000,000	.20
1947	1,500,000	.20
2½ CENTS		
Y4 (bronze) 22mm		
1944D	1,000,000	.20
1947	500,000	.25
1948	1,500,000	.20
5 CENTS		
(German Silver)		
diamond-shaped 16.5mm		
1943 type of Netherlands Y34a for Curacao and Surinam	8,595,000	.20
Y9 Curacao (copper-nickel)		
1948	1,000,000	.20
10 CENTS		
(silver) 13mm		
1941P type of Netherlands Y43 for Curacao and Surinam	800,000	.40
1943P similar	4,500,000	.25

	Mintage	Value
1/10th GUILDER		
Y1 (silver) 13mm		
1901	300,000	$1.00
Y5 new design		
1944D	1,500,000	.25
1947	1,000,000	.25
Y8		
1948	1,000,000	.25
25 CENTS		
(silver) 17mm		
1941P type of Netherlands Y44 for Curacao and Surinam	800,000	.50
1943P similar	2,500,000	.50
¼ GUILDER		
Y2 (silver) 17mm		
1900	480,000	1.25
Y6 new design		
1944D	1,500,000	.50
1947	1,000,000	.50
1 GUILDER		
Y7 (silver) 26.5mm		
1944D	500,000	1.00
2½ GULDEN		
Y10 (silver) 37mm		
1944D	200,000	8.00

CZECHOSLOVAKIA
(Ceskoslovenska)

A republic in Central Europe. In 1939 a German Protectorate was established over Bohemia-Moravia and Slovakia. The republic was reestablished in 1945.

100 Haleru = 1 Koruna

2 HALERU		
Y1 (zinc) 17mm		
1923	4,230,121	1.00
1924	15,769,880	1.00
1925	2,000,000	1.00

5 HALERU		
Y2 (bronze) 16mm		
1923	40,000,000	.15
1925	12,000,000	.20
1926	1,084,000	.75

	Mintage	Value
1927	8,916,000	$ .25
1928	5,320,000	.25
1929	12,680,000	.20
1930	5,000,000	.25
1931	7,448,000	.25
1932	3,556,000	.35
1938		.25

10 HALERU
Y3 (bronze) 17mm

	Mintage	Value
1922		.20
1923	21,340,095	.15
1924	6,087,500	.25
1925	23,912,500	.15
1926	11,979,905	.20
1927	10,680,000	.20
1928	14,290,000	.20
1929	5,710,000	.25
1930	6,980,000	.25
1931	6,740,000	.25
1932	11,280,000	.20
1933	4,190,000	.30
1934	13,200,000	.20
1935	3,420,000	.45
1936	8,560,000	.25
1937		.25
1938		.25

20 HALERU
Y4 (copper-nickel) 20mm

	Mintage	Value
1921	40,000,000	.15
1923	459,240	.75
1924	22,212,048	.20
1925	3,837,952	.50
1926	14,360,760	.20
1927	10,840,000	.20
1928	14,935,000	.20
1929	4,225,000	.35
1931	5,000,000	.30
1933		.25
1937		.25
1938		.25

25 HALERU
Y5 (copper-nickel) 21mm

	Mintage	Value
1933	22,711,000	.40

50 HALERU
Y6 (copper-nickel) 22mm

	Mintage	Value
1921	3,000,000	.35
1922		.35
1924	10,000,000	.25
1925	2,000,000	.40
1926	999,860	.60

	Mintage	Value
1927	2,000,000	$ .40
1931	5,000,000	.30

1 KORUNA
Y7 (copper-nickel) 25mm

	Mintage	Value
1922		.35
1923	15,402,848	.35
1924	23,406,864	.35
1925	6,190,288	.50
1929	5,000,000	.50
1930	5,000,000	.50
1937		.50
1938		.50

5 KORUN
Y8 (copper-nickel) 30mm

	Mintage	Value
1925	16,505,589	1.75
1926	8,569,411	1.75
1927	4,925,000	1.75

Y9 (silver) 27mm

	Mintage	Value
1928	1,710,000	1.50
1929	12,861,000	1.25
1930	10,429,000	1.25
1931	2,000,000	1.25
1932	1,000,000	1.75

Y10 (nickel)

	Value
1937	1.50
1938	1.50

10 KORUN
(silver) 30mm

Y11 10th Anniversary

	Mintage	Value
1928	1,000,000	4.00

Y12 regular

	Mintage	Value
1930	4,948,500	3.00
1931	6,689,000	3.00
1932	11,372,500	3.00
1933	990,000	4.00

20 KORUN
Y13 (silver) 34mm

	Mintage	Value
1933	2,280,000	5.00
1934	3,280,000	4.50

Y14 President Masaryk

	Mintage	Value
1937	1,000,000	6.00

German Occupation
(World War II) 1939-1945

See: BOHEMIA— MORAVIA and
SLOVAKIA.

Republic Restored 1945

20 HALERU
Y33 (bronze) 18mm

	Mintage	Value
1948	24,340,000	.15

	Mintage	Value
Y34 (aluminum) 16mm		
1951		$ .10

50 HALERU
Y35 (bronze) 20mm

	Mintage	Value
1947	50,000,000	.25
1948	20,000,000	.25
1949		.25
1950		.25

Y36 (aluminum) 18mm

1951		.20
1952		.20

1 KORUNA
Y37 (copper-nickel) 21mm

	Mintage	Value
1946		.35
1947	12,650,000	.35

Y38 (aluminum)

1950		.20
1951		.20
1952		.20

2 KORUNY
Y39 (copper-nickel) 23mm

	Mintage	Value
1947	20,000,000	.50
1948	20,000,000	.50

5 KORUN
Y-A39 (aluminum) 24mm

1952		40.00

This coin was not released to circulation.

50 KORUN
(silver) 28mm

Y40 Banska Bystrica

1947	1,000,000	2.50

Y41 3rd Anniversary

1948	1,000,000	3.00

Y45 Stalin

1949		4.00

100 KORUN
(silver) 31mm

Y42 Charles University

1948	1,000,000	7.50

Y43 1918-1948

1948	1,000,000	7.50

Y44 Mining Privileges

1949		7.50

Y46 Stalin

1949		7.50

	Mintage	Value
Y47 Gottwald		
1951		$6.00

Monetary Reform of June 1, 1953

1 HALER
Y48 (aluminum) 16mm

1953		.15
1954		.15
1955		.15
1956		.15
1957		.15
1958		.15
1959		.15
1960		.15

Y62 new design

1962		.15

3 HALERE
Y49 (aluminum) 18mm

1953		.15
1954		.15
1958		.15

Y63 new design

1963		.15

5 HALERU
Y50 (aluminum) 20mm

1953		.20
1954		.20
1955		.20

Y64 new design

1962		.20

10 HALERU
Y51 (aluminum) 22mm

1953		.25
1954		.25
1956		.25
1958		.25

Y65 new design

1961		.25
1962		.25

25 HALERU
Y52 (aluminum) 24mm

1953		.35
1954		.35

Y66 new design

1962		.35

50 HALERU
Y67 (bronze) 21.5mm

1963		.45

	Mintage	Value
1 KORUNA		
Y61 (aluminum-bronze) 23mm		
1957....................		$ .60
1958....................		.60
1959....................		.60
1960....................		.60
Y68 new design		
1961....................		.60
1962....................		.60
1963....................		.60
10 KORUN		
(silver) 30mm		
Y53 10th Anniv. Slovak Uprising		
1954....................		7.50
Y55 10th Anniv.		
Liberation from Nazis		
1955....................		8.50
Y59 Willenberg		
1957....................		6.00

	Mintage	Value
Y60 Komensky		
1957....................		$6.00
25 KORUN		
(silver) 34mm		
Y54 10th Anniv. Slovak Uprising		
1954....................		10.00
Y56 10th Anniv.		
Liberation from Nazis		
1955....................		8.50
50 KORUN		
(silver) 37mm		
Y57 10th Anniv.		
Liberation from Nazis		
1955....................		15.00
100 KORUN		
(silver) 40mm		
Y58 10th Anniv.		
Liberation from Nazis		
1955....................		20.00

DANISH WEST INDIES
(Dansk Vestindisk Mønt, Dansk Vestindien)

A former Danish colony consisting of a group of islands lying southeast of Puerto Rico in the Caribbean. Became the U. S. Virgin Islands in 1917. Coinage obsolete; U. S. currency now circulating.

20 Cents = 1 Franc

	Mintage	Value
½ CENT		
Christian IX (1863-1906)		
Y5 (bronze) 19mm		
1905 (2½ bit).......	199,776	$2.50
1 CENT		
(bronze) 21mm		
Frederik VII (1848-1863)		
1859..............	216,300	3.50
1860..............	250,000	3.00
Christian IX		
Y1 20mm		
1868....................		3.00
1878....................		7.50
1879....................		12.50
1883....................		5.00
Y6 23mm		
1905 (5 bit).......	500,659	2.50
Christian X (1912-1947)		
Y16		
1913 (5 bit).......	200,115	3.00

	Mintage	Value
2 CENTS		
Christian IX		
Y7 (bronze) 27mm		
1905 (10 bit).......	150,138	3.00
3 CENTS		
(silver) 12mm		
Frederik VII		
1859..............	290,085	3.50
5 CENTS		
(silver) 16mm		
Frederik VII		
1859....................		2.50
Christian IX		
Y2		
1878....................		7.50
1879....................		7.50
Y8 (nickel) 21mm		
1905 (25 bit).......	199,161	2.50

	Mintage	Value
10 CENTS		
(silver) 21mm		
Frederik VII		
1859......................		$3.50
1862......................		4.00
Christian IX		
Y3 20mm		
1878......................		3.00
1879......................		10.00
Y9 18mm		
1905 (50 bit).......175,030		2.00
20 CENTS		
(silver) 26mm		
Frederik VII		
1859......................		6.00
1862......................		6.00

	Mintage	Value
Christian IX		
Y4		
1878......................		$9.00
1879......................		10.00
Y10 23mm		
1905 (1 Franc)......150,035		7.50
Frederik VIII (1906-1912)		
Y14		
1907 (1 Franc)......101,050		7.50
40 CENTS		
(silver) 27mm		
Christian IX		
Y11		
1905 (2 Francs)......37,530		10.00
Frederik VIII		
Y15		
1907 (2 Francs)......25,049		17.50

DANZIG

A port on the Baltic Sea. Was a free territory from 1920 to 1939; annexed by Germany in 1939. Became a province of Poland in 1945. Coinage obsolete.

100 Pfennig = 1 Gulden

1 PFENNIG		
Y1 (bronze) 17mm		
1923............4,000,000		$1.50
1926............1,500,000		2.00
1929............1,000,000		2.50
1930............2,000,000		2.00
1937............3,000,000		1.50
2 PFENNIG		
Y2 (bronze) 19.5mm		
1923............1,000,000		2.00
1926............1,750,000		2.00
1937.............500,000		3.00
5 PFENNIG		
Y5 (copper-nickel) 17.5mm		
1923....:......3,000,000		1.75
1928............1,000,000		2.00
Y3 (aluminum-bronze)		
1932............4,000,000		1.75
10 PFENNIG		
Y-A1 (zinc) 21.5mm		
1920 10 on shield..1,000,000		4.50
Y6 (copper-nickel)		
1923............5,000,000		1.75

Y4 (aluminum-bronze) 21mm		
1932............5,000,000		1.75
½ GULDEN		
Y11 (silver) 19.5mm		
1923............1,000,000		2.50
1927.............400,000		3.00
Y7 (nickel) 19mm		
1932............1,400,000		2.50
1 GULDEN		
Y12 (silver) 23mm		
1923............3,500,000		4.50
Y8 (nickel)		
1932............2,500,000		3.00
2 GULDEN		
Y13 (silver) 26.5mm		
1923............1,250,000		7.50
Y15 26mm		
1932............1,250,000		10.00
5 GULDEN		
Y14 (silver) 35mm		
1923.............700,000		30.00
1927.............160,000		35.00

	Mintage	Value
Y16 church, 30mm		
1932..............430,000		$20.00
Y17 grain elevator		
1932..............430,000		22.50
Y9 (nickel) 29mm		
1935..............800,000		15.00

	Mintage	Value
10 GULDEN		
Y10 (nickel) 34mm		
1935..............380,000		$35.00

The 10 Pfennig 1920 with large numeral on reverse is a pattern.

DENMARK
(Danmark)

In northern Europe separating the North and Baltic Seas. All coins inscribed DANMARK except for Y8-10 and Y28-32. All Danish coins after 1863 were minted at Copenhagen; mint mark is small heart. Initials on coins are those of Mintmasters and Designers. These are not listed except where there are two different sets of initials for a given year (1927). For regular types dated 1941 without mint mark and designer's initials, see Faroe Islands.

100 Øre = 1 Krone

1 ØRE
Christian IX (1863-1906)

Y8 (bronze) 15.5mm

1874.............5,539,736		.30
1875.............2,360,728		.30
1876.............1,482,820		.30
1878.............1,016,300		.35
1879.............1,491,291		.30
1880.............1,988,664		.30
1881..............260,000		1.25
1882.............1,781,773		.30
1883.............1,781,800		.30
1886..............996,800		.40
1887.............3,000,000		.30
1888.............1,504,700		.30
1889.............2,999,200		.30
1891.............4,448,000		.25
1892..............494,200		.50
1894.............4,982,461		.25
1897.............2,987,547		.30
1899.............5,012,114		.25
1902.............3,007,487		.25
1904.............4,962,475		.25

Frederik VIII (1906-1912)

Y20

1907.............5,974,924		.25
1909.............2,985,207		.25
1910.............2,994,318		.25
1912.............3,006,055		.25

Christian X (1912-1947)

Y28

1913.............5,011,462		.25
1915.............4,939,663		.25
1916.............2,438,676		.25
1917.............2,527,672		.25
1919.............6,343,298		.20
1920............inc. above		.20
1921.............3,731,402		.20
1922.............1,130,000		.25
1923.............5,035,433		.20

Y28a (iron)

1918.............5,726,212		.25
1919.............4,017,295		.25

Y46 new design

1926............11,009,373		.15
1927 HCN.......inc. above		.25
1927 N.........inc. above		.25
1928............16,780,445		.15
1929.............4,638,947		.20
1930.............9,311,581		.20
1932.............5,088,595		.20
1933.............1,152,802		.25
1934.............3,681,832		.20
1935.............5,085,633		.20
1936.............5,444,916		.20
1937.............6,070,367		.20
1938.............4,826,107		.20
1939.............5,661,869		.20
1940.............1,964,799		.25

Y51 (zinc)

1941............21,570,250		.15
1942.............6,996,900		.15
1943............15,082,150		.15
1944............11,981,400		.15
1945..............915,650		.50
1946..............100,000		1.00

Mintage	Value

Frederik IX (1947 to date)
Y56

1948	300,000	$ .75
1949	1,271,268	.25
1950	9,340,407	.10
1951	3,237,880	.10
1952	6,139,129	.10
1953	11,993,826	.10
1954	11,439,517	.10
1955	14,155,391	.10
1956	17,412,889	.10
1957	21,928,345	.10
1958	15,985,215	.10
1959	18,317,651	.10
1960	18,625,962	.10
1961	20,984,182	.10
1962	19,993,724	.10

2 ØRE

Christian IX

Y9 (bronze) 20.5mm

1874	7,690,298	.30
1875	2,816,858	.30
1876	231,062	1.25
1880	1,012,274	.35
1881	1,483,580	.35
1883	1,375,000	.35
1886	1,492,750	.40
1887	inc. above	.40
1889	1,992,900	.35
1891	1,902,500	.35
1892	572,600	.60
1894	2,485,772	.30
1897	2,478,800	.30
1899	2,503,737	.30
1902	3,501,629	.25
1906	1,903,713	.25

Frederik VIII
Y21

1907	3,495,877	.25
1909	2,484,672	.25
1912	2,479,863	.25

Christian X
Y29

1913	372,500	.75
1914	2,126,486	.25
1915	2,485,269	.25
1916	1,382,530	.25
1917	1,117,049	.25
1919	882,500	.35
1920	6,760,976	.20
1921	2,545,226	.20
1923	3,057,500	.20

Mintage	Value

Y29a (iron)

1918	2,936,900	$ .30
1919	1,944,010	.30

Y47 new design

1926	10,554,187	.15
1927 HCN	inc. above	.25
1927 N	inc. above	.25
1928	9,505,581	.15
1929	2,966,417	.15
1930	4,734,252	.15
1931	3,409,260	.15
1932	1,726,183	.15
1934	495,470	.45
1935	1,651,206	.15
1936	1,896,882	.15
1937	3,722,607	.15
1938	1,866,108	.15
1939	5,661,869	.10
1940	1,581,971	.15

Y52 (aluminum)

1941	26,204,566	.20

Y52a (zinc)

1942	12,934,335	.15
1943	9,603,387	.15
1944	6,069,400	.15
1945	328,550	.75
1947	588,590	.50

Frederik IX
Y57

1948	1,498,052	.20
1949	1,350,758	.20
1950	4,289,953	.10
1951	3,703,526	.10
1952	3,872,493	.10
1953	8,112,206	.10
1954	6,327,285	.10
1955	7,179,021	.10
1956	8,954,102	.10
1957	12,361,706	.10
1958	13,098,950	.10
1959	9,523,693	.10
1960	11,447,635	.10
1961	18,451,730	.10
1962	12,979,982	.10

5 ØRE

Christian IX

Y10 (bronze) 27mm

1874	2,762,383	.35
1875	207,242	1.00
1882	321,026	.75

	Mintage	Value
1884	321,020	$ .75
1890	172,000	1.00
1891	614,960	.35
1894	594,620	.35
1898	396,668	.35
1899	601,215	.30
1902	600,798	.30
1904	396,925	.30
1906	600,392	.30

Frederik VIII

Y22

	Mintage	Value
1907	1,399,381	.30
1908	1,198,394	.30
1912	999,180	.35

Christian X

Y30

	Mintage	Value
1913	216,000	.75
1914	784,591	.40
1916	989,803	.35
1917	1,015,235	.30
1919	993,738	.30
1920	2,618,486	.25
1921	3,248,213	.25
1923	369,030	.50

Y30a (iron)

	Mintage	Value
1918	1,732,536	.40
1919	1,035,294	.40

Y48 new design

	Mintage	Value
1927 HCN	4,564,310	.25
1927 N	inc. above	.25
1928	6,703,911	.20
1929	1,115,564	.20
1930	2,152,948	.20
1932	1,010,509	.20
1934	524,435	.40
1935	976,058	.25
1936	978,133	.25
1937	902,967	.25
1938	1,387,124	.25
1939	1,402,172	.25
1940	2,734,566	.15

Y53 (aluminum)

	Mintage	Value
1941	16,984,314	.50

Y53a (zinc)

	Mintage	Value
1942	2,963,470	.25
1943	4,522,394	.20
1944	3,744,040	.25
1945	863,920	.35

Frederik IX

Y58

	Mintage	Value
1950	504,015	$ .40
1951	1,764,014	.20
1952	2,507,694	.15
1953	5,806,234	.15
1954	3,786,443	.15
1955	2,306,732	.15
1956	5,134,619	.15
1957	7,582,262	.15
1958	8,057,640	.15
1959	9,006,192	.15
1960	7,945,564	.15
1961	10,242,929	.15
1962	10,480,137	.15

10 ØRE

Christian IX

Y11 (silver) 14.5mm

	Mintage	Value
1874	8,874,694	.40
1875	1,386,584	.50
1882	1,056,790	.50
1884	inc. above	.50
1886	508,360	.60
1888	306,430	.75
1889	1,030,110	.40
1891	1,507,100	.40
1894	1,521,471	.40
1897	737,567	.50
1899	2,049,737	.30
1903	3,006,578	.30
1904	744,000	.50
1905	2,276,001	.25

Frederik VIII

Y23

	Mintage	Value
1907	3,067,727	.25
1910	2,529,658	.25
1911	578,535	.50
1912	1,950,741	.30

Christian X

Y36

	Mintage	Value
1914	3,043,439	.30
1915	2,007,710	.30
1916	2,679,529	.30
1917	4,014,185	.25
1918	5,041,795	.25
1919	10,183,853	.25

Y31 (copper-nickel)

	Mintage	Value
1920	6,400,030	.20
1921	11,897,746	.20
1922	3,065,444	.20
1923	430,000	.50

Mintage	Value
Y49 17.5mm	
1924 10,018,103	$ .20
1925 12,142,000	.20
1926 6,482,809	.20
1929 5,036,793	.20
1931 3,054,428	.20
1933 769,649	.30
1934 2,517,170	.20
1935 2,072,750	.20
1936 2,680,438	.20
1937 3,638,659	.20
1938 1,137,202	.25
1939 2,973,373	.20
1940 2,998,129	.20
1941 748,078	.30
Y49a (zinc)	
1941 7,705,708	.20
1942 8,676,082	.20
1943 2,180,862	.20
1944 7,994,050	.20
1945 1,280,400	.25
Y49 (nickel)	
1946 459,551	.50
1947 1,532,232	.25
Frederik IX	
Y59	
1948 3,896,232	.15
1949 6,867,649	.15
1950 7,733,169	.15
1951 7,934,199	.15
1952 7,164,306	.15
1953 10,284,202	.15
1954 17,180,209	.15
1955 23,079,694	.15
1956 9,696,911	.15
1957 12,225,963	.15
1958 14,969,814	.15
1959 289,399	.50
1960 3,613,315	.15
Y69 design changed	
1960 . . . . .inc. above	.10
1961 18,621,051	.10
1962 17,170,797	.10
25 ØRE	
Christian IX	
Y12 (silver) 16.5mm	
1874 8,138,500	.35
1891 1,214,360	.35
1894 1,202,236	.35
1900 1,205,784	.35

Mintage	Value
1904 1,209,571	$ .35
1905 2,434,042	.30
Frederik VIII	
Y24	
1907 2,008,569	.35
1911 2,015,363	.35
Christian X	
Y37	
1913 2,015,624	.30
1914 346,741	.75
1915 2,862,084	.30
1916 938,194	.30
1917 1,353,947	.30
1918 2,090,174	.30
1919 9,295,049	.25
Y32 (copper-nickel)	
1920 7,736,030	.25
1921 12,267,589	.25
1922 5,792,728	.25
Y50 new design, 22.5mm	
1924 8,256,830	.25
1925 3,319,812	.25
1926 2,660,762	.25
1929 2,225,514	.25
1930 2,079,356	.25
1932 846,311	.35
1933 479,065	.50
1934 1,148,411	.25
1935 1,202,492	.25
1936 1,610,374	.25
1937 1,796,372	.25
1938 1,098,327	.25
1939 1,971,662	.25
1940 1,356,212	.25
Y50a (zinc)	
1941 15,331,978	.30
1942 997,425	.45
1943 5,784,445	.35
1944 10,664,950	.35
1945 4,542,660	.35
Y50 (nickel)	
1946 2,323,291	.25
1947 2,388,466	.25
Frederik IX	
Y60	
1948 417,882	.50
1949 8,296,538	.25
1950 16,696,475	.25
1951 7,443,007	.25
1952 2,035,744	.25

	Mintage	Value
1953	6,220,901	$ .25
1954	12,443,768	.25
1955	7,146,772	.25
1956	9,222,592	.25
1957	7,963,259	.25
1958	5,545,271	.25
1959	1,266,370	.25
1960	3,494,597	.25

Y70 design changed

	Mintage	Value
1961	15,916,388	.20
1962	16,074,601	.20

½ KRONE

Christian X
Y33 (aluminum-bronze) 20mm

	Mintage	Value
1924	2,150,000	.75
1925	3,432,030	.75
1926	715,706	1.00
1939	225,831	2.50
1940	1,870,604	.75

1 KRONE

Christian IX
Y13 (silver) 25mm

	Mintage	Value
1875	4,039,532	1.00
1876	1,283,995	1.00
1892	701,115	1.25
1898	200,746	2.00

Christian X
Y38

	Mintage	Value
1915	1,409,735	1.25
1916	991,985	1.50

Y34 (aluminum-bronze) 25.5mm

	Mintage	Value
1924	5,225,010	.50
1925	inc. above	.50
1926	4,794,522	.50
1929	390,220	.75
1930	651,478	.60
1931	540,035	.60
1934	688,398	.60
1935	345,642	.75
1936	557,836	.60
1938	406,792	.75
1939	1,517,111	.50
1940	1,436,103	.50
1941	661,185	.60

Y54 new design

	Mintage	Value
1942	3,952,175	.75
1943	798,074	1.00
1944	1,760,428	.75
1945	2,581,410	.75
1946	4,321,308	.75
1947	4,897,218	.75

Frederik IX
Y61

	Mintage	Value
1947	inc. above	$ .50
1948	4,373,604	.40
1949	1,285,103	.40
1952	940,132	.45
1953	1,757,339	.40
1954	584,026	.60
1955	619,367	.50
1956	2,489,947	.40
1957	7,167,715	.40
1958	5,344,789	.40
1959	1,196,919	.40

2 KRONER

Christian IX
Y14 (silver) 31mm

	Mintage	Value
1875	3,395,330	2.50
1876	1,480,942	2.50
1897	150,635	3.50
1899	152,267	3.50

Y15 25th Anniversary

	Mintage	Value
1888	101,253	5.00

Y16 Golden Wedding

	Mintage	Value
1892	101,322	5.00

Y17 40-Year Reign

	Mintage	Value
1903	103,392	5.00

Frederik VIII
Y25 commemorative

	Mintage	Value
1906	150,775	5.00

Christian X
Y40 Succession

	Mintage	Value
1912	101,917	5.00

Y39 regular

	Mintage	Value
1915	302,396	3.00
1916	757,933	3.00

Y41 Silver Wedding

	Mintage	Value
1923	203,357	5.00

Y35 (aluminum-bronze) 32mm

	Mintage	Value
1924	27,000	5.00
1925	3,528,500	1.00
1926	1,955,843	1.00
1936	400,444	1.00
1938	190,657	1.50
1939	722,927	1.00
1940	742,704	1.00
1941	128,904	1.50

Y42 (silver)

	Mintage	Value
1930 60th Birthday	302,640	5.00

	Mintage	Value
Y43		
1937 25 Years....... 208,699		$5.00
Y55		
1945 75th Birthday.. 156,642		5.00
Frederik IX		
Y62 (aluminum-bronze)		
1947............... 502,561		.75
1948............. 1,284,777		.75
1949............... 493,501		.90
1951............. 1,049,806		.75
1952............. 1,802,820		.75
1953............... 961,166		.75
1954............... 577,703		.75
1955............... 542,096		.75
1956............. 1,100,509		.75
1957............. 2,257,725		.75

	Mintage	Value
1958............. 3,053,134		$ .75
1959............... 491,710		.75
Y63 (silver)		
1953 Greenland Fund		
.... 151,170		4.00
Y64		
1958 Margarethe.... 301,426		4.00
5 KRONER		
Frederik IX		
Y72 (copper-nickel) 33mm		
1960 regular....... 4,324,285		2.00
1961............. 10,136,068		2.00
1962............. 2,074,303		2.00
Y65 (silver)		
1960 Silver Wedding. 409,838		5.00

ERITREA
(Colonia Eritrea)

A former Italian colony in Africa bordering on the Red Sea. In 1952 became federated with Ethiopia. Coinage obsolete.

100 Centesimi = 1 Lira
5 Lire = 1 Tallero

50 CENTESIMI
Y1 (silver) 17mm

	Mintage	Value
1890............. 1,799,164		10.00

1 LIRA
Y2 (silver) 23mm

	Mintage	Value
1890............... 598,702		17.50
1891............. 2,401,298		15.00
1896............. 1,500,000		25.00

2 LIRE
Y3 (silver) 26mm

	Mintage	Value
1890............. 1,000,000		25.00

	Mintage	Value
1896............... 750,000		25.00

5 LIRE
Y4 (silver) 39mm

	Mintage	Value
1891............... 70,399		100.00
1896............... 200,000		100.00

1 TALLERO
Y5 (silver) 40mm

	Mintage	Value
1918............... 510,000		10.00

(Eesti)

In northern Europe, bordering on the Baltic Sea and the Gulf of Finland. Formerly a part of Russia, Estonia became a free country in 1918, but was reabsorbed by the U.S.S.R. in 1940. Coinage obsolete.

100 Mark = 1 Kroon (1923-27)
100 Senti = 1 Kroon (1928-40)

	Mintage	Value
1 MARK		
Y4 (copper-nickel) 18mm		
1922............5,024,809		$ 2.00
Y4a (nickel-bronze)		
1924............1,984,760		2.00
Y8 design changed		
1926............3,979,330		2.50
3 MARKA		
Y5 (coperp-nickel) 20mm		
1922............2,089,028		2.50
Y5a (nickel-bronze)		
1925............1,134,000		2.50
Y9 design changed		
1926..............902,860		3.50
5 MARKA		
Y6 (copper-nickel) 23mm		
1922............3,982,980		3.00
Y6a		
1924............1,335,000		3.50
10 MARKA		
Y7 (nickel-bronze) 26mm		
1925............2,200,000		5.00
Y-A10 design changed		
1926............2,789,400		30.00
25 MARKA		
Y-B10 (nickel-bronze) 27.5mm		
1926............1,000,000		

This coin was never put into circulation because of change of currency. All were supposedly melted; however, a few entered circulation accidently.

New Currency
1 SENT

	Mintage	Value
Y1 (bronze) 16mm		
1929............22,052,300		2.50

	Mintage	Value
Y1a		
1939............5,000,000		$10.00
2 SENTI		
Y2 (bronze) 19.5mm		
1934............5,837,550		2.50
5 SENTI		
Y3 (bronze) 23mm		
1931............11,000,000		2.50
10 SENTI		
Y11 (nickel-bronze) 18mm		
1931............4,089,000		2.00
20 SENTI		
Y12 (nickel-bronze) 21mm		
1935............4,250,000		2.25
25 SENTI		
Y13 (nickel-bronze) 27.5mm		
1928............2,025,000		3.50
50 SENTI		
Y14 (nickel-bronze) 27.5mm		
1936............1,256,000		4.50
1 KROON		
Y18 (silver) 25mm		
1933 commem.......350,000		25.00
Y15 (aluminum-bronze)		
1934 regular.......3,304,000		12.50
2 KROONI		
Y16 (silver) 30mm		
1930............1,276,455		15.00
Y17 Univ. of Tartu		
1932...............100,000		30.00

A Danish possession in the North Atlantic Ocean. Danish coins are used. During World War II regular Danish coins dated 1941 without designers' initials and mint marks were minted in London for use in the Faroe Islands.

100 Øre = 1 Krone

	Mintage	Value
1 ØRE		
Y1 (bronze) 15.5mm		
1941...............100,000		$2.50
2 ØRE		
Y2 (bronze) 20.5mm		
1941...............100,000		2.50
5 ØRE		
Y3 (bronze) 27mm		
1941...............100,000		2.50

	Mintage	Value
10 ØRE		
Y4 (copper-nickel) 17.5mm		
1941...............100,000		$2.50
25 ØRE		
Y5 (copper-nickel) 22.5mm		
1941...............100,000		2.50

FINLAND
(Suomi, Suomen)

In northeastern Europe on the Baltic Sea. Was under Russian control until 1917. Some coins do not bear name of country; these will be inscribed: "PENNI, PENNIA, MARKKA, or MARKKAA."

100 Penniä = 1 Markka

1 PENNI
Alexander II (1860-1881)
Y1 (copper) 15mm

1864...............30,000	6.00
1865...............515,000	.60
1866............3,673,000	.40
1867............3,830,000	.40
1869............1,500,000	.40
1870...............500,000	.60
1871............1,000,000	.40
1872............1,000,000	.40
1873............2,000,000	.40
1874............1,450,000	.40
1875............1,550,000	.40
1876............2,005,000	.40
1881...............600,000	.50

Alexander III (1881-1894)
Y10

1882...............100,000	1.25
1883............3,900,000	.30
1884...............404,000	.60
1888............2,500,000	.30
1891............1,000,000	.30
1892............1,525,000	.30
1893............2,290,000	.30

1894............1,825,000	.30

Nicholas II (1894-1917)
Y18

1895...............880,000	.35
1898............1,430,000	.25
1899............1,540,000	.25
1900............3,545,000	.25
1901............1,515,000	.25
1902............1,000,000	.25
1903...............920,000	.30
1904...............725,000	.50
1905............1,355,000	.25
1906............1,020,000	.25
1907............2,485,000	.25
1908...............880,000	.30
1909............3,120,000	.25
1911............2,450,000	.25
1912............2,450,000	.25
1913............1,645,000	.25
1914............1,895,000	.25
1915............2,250,000	.25
1916............3,040,000	.25

Civil War (1917-1918)
Y27

1917............1,645,000	1.50

	Mintage	Value		Mintage	Value
Republic (1918 to date)			*Republic*		
Y33			**Y34** Lion		
1919	1,195,000	$ .25	1918	4,270,000	$ .20
1920	720,000	.40	1919	4,640,000	.20
1921	510,000	.60	1920	7,710,000	.20
1922	1,060,000	.25	1921	5,914,000	.20
1923	985,000	.40	1922	8,544,000	.20
1924	2,175,000	.25	1927	1,518,000	.25
			1928	2,110,000	.20
5 PENNIÄ			1929	1,500,000	.25
			1930	2,140,000	.20
Alexander II			1932	2,130,000	.20
Y2 (copper) 25.5mm			1934	2,176,000	.20
1865	438,000	.75	1935	1,610,000	.25
1866	2,520,000	.40	1936	2,610,000	.20
1867	1,984,000	.40	1937	3,826,000	.20
1870	300,000	1.00	1938	4,296,000	.20
1872	500,000	.60	1939	2,270,000	.20
1873	1,000,000	.40	1940	1,612,000	.25
1875	1,000,200	.40			
			Y40 holed 16mm		
Alexander III			1941	5,948,000	.20
Y12			1942	4,284,000	.20
1888	600,000	.60	1943	1,532,000	.30
1889	1,070,000	.50			
1892	330,000	1.00	**10 PENNIÄ**		
			Alexander II		
Nicholas II			**Y3** (copper) 30mm		
Y19			1865	247,000	1.50
1896	414,000	.60	1866	850,000	.75
1897	592,000	.50	1867	1,322,000	.75
1898	1,154,000	.30	1876	301,000	1.25
1899	856,000	.40			
1901	996,000	.30	*Alexander III*		
1905	624,000	.50	**Y12**		
1906	960,000	.30	1889	100,000	2.50
1907	766,000	.35	1890	100,000	2.50
1908	1,656,000	.30	1891	300,000	1.50
1910	66,000	3.50			
1911	1,054,000	.30	*Nicholas II*		
1912	456,000	.60	**Y20**		
1913	1,058,000	.30	1895	212,000	1.50
1914	824,000	.40	1896	295,000	1.25
1915	2,078,000	.30	1897	503,000	.75
1916	4,468,000	.30	1898	37,000	4.00
1917	4,072,000	.35	1899	436,000	.75
			1900	524,000	.75
Civil War			1905	507,000	.75
Y28			1907	503,000	.75
1917	inc. above	2.00	1908	226,000	1.50
1918	87,120	5.00	1909	275,000	1.25
			1910	241,000	1.25
Communist Government (1918)			1911	367,000	1.00
Y32 Trumpets and Banner			1912	191,000	1.75
1918	34,880	15.00	1913	148,000	2.00

	Mintage	Value
1914	605,000	$ .75
1915	418,000	.75
1916	1,952,000	.60
1917	1,598,000	.60

Civil War
Y29

1917	inc. above	2.50

Republic
Y35 22mm

1919	3,674,000	.25
1920	2,379,000	25
1921	3,974,000	.25
1922	2,180,000	.25
1923	909,000	.40
1924	2,103,000	.25
1926	1,694,000	.25
1927	1,327,000	.30
1928	1,006,000	.30
1929	1,560,000	.25
1930	645,000	.75
1931	1,040,000	.30
1934	1,676,000	.25
1935	1,685,000	.25
1936	2,013,000	.25
1937	2,419,000	.25
1938	2,942,000	.25
1939	2,096,000	.25
1940	2,014,000	.25

Y41 holed, 18.5mm

1941	3,610,000	.35
1942	4,968,000	.35
1943	1,858,000	.50

Y41a (iron) 16mm

1943	1,426,000	.60
1944	3,038,000	.60
1945	1,808,000	.60

25 PENNIÄ

Alexander II
Y4 (silver) 16mm

1865	688,000	.50
1866	824,000	.50
1867	400,000	.60
1868	136,000	1.25
1869	264,000	.75
1871	150,000	1.00
1872	400,000	.60
1873	800,000	.50
1875	808,000	.50

Alexander III
Y13

1889	400,000	.60

	Mintage	Value
1890	800,000	$ .50
1891	280,000	.75
1894	816,000	.50

Nicholas II
Y21

1897	448,000	.75
1898	448,000	.75
1899	312,000	1.00
1901	992,000	.50
1902	208,000	1.50
1906	176,000	2.00
1907	696,000	.60
1908	336,000	1.00
1909	816,000	.50
1910	392,000	1.00
1913	832,000	.50
1915	2,400,000	.35
1916	6,392,000	.35
1917	8,036,000	.35

Civil War
Y30

1917	inc. above	1.50

Republic
Y36 (copper-nickel)

1921	20,096,000	.25
1925	1,248,000	.30
1926	2,816,000	.25
1927	1,120,000	.30
1928	2,920,000	.25
1929	200,000	1.00
1930	1,904,000	.25
1934	1,264,000	.30
1935	2,192,000	.25
1936	2,296,000	.25
1937	4,016,000	.25
1938	4,496,000	.25
1939	2,712,000	.25
1940	72,000	3.00

Y36a (bronze)

1940	4,840,000	.25
1941	5,976,000	.25
1942	6,464,000	.25
1943	4,912,000	.25

Y36b (iron)

1943	2,696,000	.25
1944	5,480,000	.25
1945	6,808,000	.25

50 PENNIÄ

Alexander II
Y5 (silver) 18.5mm

1864		5.00

	Mintage	Value
1865	1,288,000	$ .75
1866	360,000	1.00
1868	140,000	1.50
1869	128,000	1.50
1871	300,000	1.00
1872	200,000	1.25
1874	402,000	1.00

Alexander III
Y14

	Mintage	Value
1889	312,000	1.25
1890	688,000	.75
1891	284,000	1.25
1892	346,000	1.25
1893	400,000	1.00

Nicholas II
Y22

	Mintage	Value
1907	256,000	1.50
1908	352,000	1.25
1911	616,000	.75
1914	600,000	.75
1915	1,000,000	.60
1916	4,752,000	.60
1917	4,544,000	.60

Civil War
Y31

	Mintage	Value
1917	inc. above	2.00

Republic
Y37 (copper-nickel)

	Mintage	Value
1921	10,072,000	.25
1923	6,000,000	.25
1929	984,000	.30
1934	612,000	.50
1935	612,000	.50
1936	1,516,000	.25
1937	2,348,000	.25
1938	2,328,000	.25
1939	1,276,000	.25
1940	3,152,000	.25

Y37a (copper)

	Mintage	Value
1941	3,856,000	.25
1942	5,900,000	.25
1943	3,140,000	.25

Y37b (iron)

	Mintage	Value
1943	1,580,000	.25
1944	7,600,000	.25
1945	4,696,000	.25
1946	2,632,000	.25
1947	1,748,000	.25
1948	1,112,000	.25

1 MARKKA
Alexander II
Y6 (silver) 24mm

	Mintage	Value
1864	27,000	$12.50
1865	1,721,000	1.00
1866	2,012,310	1.00
1867	848,000	1.50
1872	500,000	2.00
1874	500,000	2.00
1875	502,000	2.00

Alexander III
Y15

	Mintage	Value
1890	840,000	1.25
1892	484,300	1.75
1893	256,000	2.50

Nicholas II
Y23

	Mintage	Value
1907	348,000	2.50
1908	152,000	3.50
1915	1,212,000	1.50

Republic
Y38 (copper-nickel)

	Mintage	Value
1921	10,048,000	.40
1922	10,000,000	.40
1923	1,776,000	.60
1924	3,266,000	.50

Y39 21mm

	Mintage	Value
1928	3,000,000	.25
1929	3,862,000	.25
1930	10,284,000	.25
1931	2,828,000	.25
1932	4,138,000	.25
1933	4,032,000	.25
1936	562,000	.50
1937	4,926,000	.25
1938	4,410,000	.25
1939	3,066,000	.25
1940	84,000	1.50

Y39a (bronze)

	Mintage	Value
1940	3,372,000	.25
1941	8,966,000	.25
1942	11,200,000	.25
1943	7,460,000	.25

Y39b (iron)

	Mintage	Value
1943	7,460,000	.25
1944	12,826,000	.25
1945	21,946,000	.25
1946	2,632,000	.25
1947	1,748,000	.35

	Mintage	Value
1948	20,504,000	$ .25
1949	17,357,000	.25
1950	14,654,000	.25
1951	21,378,000	.25
1952	5,410,000	.25

Y47 16mm

	Mintage	Value
1952	22,048,000	.10
1953	28,568,000	.10

Y47a

	Mintage	Value
1954	36,400,000	.10
1955	9,894,000	.10
1956	35,596,000	.10
1957	29,108,000	.10
1958	19,940,000	.10
1959	23,920,000	.10
1960	22,016,000	.10
1961	32,220,000	.10
1962	29,040,000	.10

2 MARKKAA

Alexander II

Y7 (silver) 27mm

	Mintage	Value
1865	202,000	3.00
1866	678,000	3.00
1867	146,000	3.50
1870	500,000	3.00
1872	250,000	3.00
1874	502,500	3.00

Nicholas II

Y24

	Mintage	Value
1905	24,000	10.00
1906	226,000	5.00
1907	100,000	6.00
1908	150,000	6.00

5 MARKKAA

Republic

Y42 (aluminum-bronze) 23mm

	Mintage	Value
1928	576,000	.75
1929	inc. above	.75
1930	592,000	.60
1931	3,088,000	.35
1932	844,000	.40
1933	1,048,000	.35
1935	436,000	.75
1936	470,000	.75
1937	1,032,000	.35
1938	912,000	.40
1939	752,000	.40
1940	818,000	.40
1941	1,452,000	.35

	Mintage	Value
1942	1,386,000	$ .35
1946	6,156,000	.35

Y42a (brass)

	Mintage	Value
1946	inc. above	1.00
1947	6,550,000	.30
1948	8,210,000	.30
1949	inc. above	.30
1950 (copper)	4,762,000	.30
1951	7,798,000	.30
1952	1,210,000	.30

Y48 (iron) 18mm

	Mintage	Value
1952	10,820,000	.15
1953	9,772,000	.15

Y48a (iron-nickel)

	Mintage	Value
1954	6,696,000	.15
1955	9,894,000	.15
1956	8,220,000	.15
1957	4,276,000	.15
1958	3,300,000	.15
1959	5,874,000	.15
1960	3,066,000	.15
1961	7,254,000	.15
1962	4,542,000	.15

10 MARKKAA

Republic

Y43 (aluminum-bronze) 27mm

	Mintage	Value
1928	725,000	.90
1929	inc. above	.90
1930	258,000	1.00
1931	1,533,000	.65
1932	1,003,000	.65
1934	154,000	1.25
1935	81,000	2.00
1936	304,000	.90
1937	181,000	1.00
1938	631,000	.75
1939	133,000	1.00

Y49 20mm

	Mintage	Value
1952	6,390,000	.25
1953	22,650,000	.25
1954	2,452,000	.25
1955	2,342,000	.25
1956	4,238,000	.25
1958	3,292,000	.25
1960	740,000	.35
1961	3,576,000	.25
1962	1,852,000	.25

20 MARKKAA

Republic

Y44 (aluminum-bronze) 31mm

	Mintage	Value
1931	16,000	7.50

	Mintage	Value		Mintage	Value
1932	14,500	$7.50	1961	1,811,000	$ .85
1934	389,500	1.50	1962	405,000	.85
1935	249,000	2.00			
1936	114,000	2.50			

100 MARKKAA

Republic

Y53 (silver) 23mm

	Mintage	Value		Mintage	Value
1937	509,000	1.50	1956	3,012,000	.75
1938	364,000	1.50	1957	2,228,000	.75
1939	955,000	1.25	1958	1,704,000	.75

Y50 22.5mm

	Mintage	Value		Mintage	Value
1952	83,000	2.00	1959	1,266,000	.75
1953	2,883,000	.50	1960	290,000	1.25

200 MARKKAA

Republic

Y54 (silver) 27.5mm

	Mintage	Value		Mintage	Value
1954	17,034,000	.50	1956	1,552,000	1.50
1955	2,796,000	.50	1957	2,157,000	1.50
1956	2,536,000	.50	1958	1,511,000	1.50
1957	1,052,000	.50	1959	70,500	2.50
1958	515,000	.60			

500 MARKKAA

Republic

Y52 (silver) 32mm

1951 Olympic Games

	Mintage	Value		Mintage	Value
1959	1,582,000	.50	1952	18,500	15.00
1960	3,849,000	.50	1952	586,500	5.00
1961	4,432,000	.50			

1000 MARKKAA

Republic

Y55 (silver) 32mm

	Mintage	Value
1962	2,276,000	.50
1960 commem	201,000	6.00

50 MARKKAA

Republic

Y51 (aluminum-bronze) 25mm

	Mintage	Value
1952	991,000	.90
1953	10,308,000	.85
1954	1,167,000	.90
1955	583,000	1.00
1956	792,000	1.00
1958	242,000	1.00
1960	106,000	1.25

FRANCE
(Francaise)

Large country in Western Europe. The Third Republic was formed in 1870 and lasted until World War II. The country was then occupied by Germany for 4 years. After the Allied victory in 1945 the Fourth Republic was established. In 1959 the Fifth Republic was formed and a new monetary system evolved in which the new Heavy Franc was equal to 100 Old Francs.

Mint marks:

A — Paris
B — Rouen (to 1857)
B — Beaumont-Le-Roger (from 1939)
BB — Strasbourg (to 1870)
C — Castelsarrasin (1914 and later)
D — Lyon (to 1857)
K — Bordeaux (to 1878)
MA — Marseilles (to 1857)
W — Lille (to 1857)
Horn and Torch (Paris)
Thunderbolt and Torch (Poissy — 1922 to 1924)

From 1879 all coins were minted in Paris and bear that mint mark except where noted.

100 Centimes = 1 Franc

	Mintage	Value
1 CENTIME		
Napoleon III (1852-1870)		
Y14 (bronze) 18mm		
1853A	4,075,587	$ .30
1853B	824,017	.60
1853BB	2,558,213	.30
1853D	964,100	.50
1853K	404,922	.75
1853MA	224,966	2.00
1853W	1,634,410	.30
1854A	2,750,119	.30
1854B	1,709,110	.30
1854BB	1,447,370	.30
1854D	1,545,967	.30
1854K	1,150,448	.30
1854MA	1,976,110	.30
1854W	1,399,448	.30
1855A	6,023,791	.30
1855B	1,970,886	.30
1855BB	248,450	1.75
1855D	2,466,045	.30
1855K	1,454,860	.30
1855MA	2,838,936	.30
1855W	3,101,845	.30
1856A	2,878,348	.30
1856B	4,373,216	.30
1856BB	1,873,557	.30
1856D	880,122	.50
1856K	2,062,305	.30
1856MA	305,227	1.25
1856W	2,706,577	.30
1857A	2,000,001	.30
1857B	3,000,003	.30
1857D	1,000,000	.40
1857K	1,000,000	.40
1857MA	1,500,000	.30
1857W	2,499,994	.30
Y18		
1861A	7,397,660	.25
1861BB	3,011,938	.30
1861K	1,998,709	.30
1862A	14,766,248	.25
1862BB	4,492,691	.30
1862K	3,556,553	.30
1863A	794,667	.50
1863K	3,864,326	.30
1870A	1,000,000	.35

	Mintage	Value
Third Republic (1870-1940)		
Y41		
1872A	1,250,000	$ .25
1872K	750,000	.50
1874A	1,000,000	.25
1875A	1,000,000	.25
1875K	2,000,000	.25
1877A	1,000,000	.25
1878A	1,500,000	.25
1878K	288,950	1.00
1879	800,000	.40
1882	419,000	.75
1884	400,000	.75
1885	400,000	.75
1886	400,000	.75
1887	400,000	.75
1888	400,000	.75
1889	400,000	.75
1890	400,000	.75
1891	1,400,000	.25
1892	800,000	.40
1893	300,000	1.00
1894	500,000	.50
1895	3,000,000	.25
1896	3,000,000	.25
1897	2,000,000	.25
Y58 new design		
1898	250,000	1.50
1899	1,500,000	.25
1900	221,090	2.00
1901	1,000,000	.25
1902	1,000,000	.25
1903	2,000,000	.20
1904	1,000,000	.25
1908	4,500,000	.25
1909	1,500,000	.25
1910	1,500,000	.25
1911	5,000,000	.20
1912	2,000,000	.25
1913	1,500,000	.25
1914	1,000,000	.25
1916	1,995,900	.25
1919	2,406,282	.25
1920	2,593,599	.25
2 CENTIMES		
Napoleon III		
Y15 (bronze) 20mm		
1853A	609,659	.60

	Mintage	Value		Mintage	Value
1853B	538,750	$ .60	1888	400,000	$ .60
1853BB	168,440	2.00	1889	600,000	.50
1853K	116,675	3.00	1890	300,000	1.00
1853MA	162,823	2.00	1891	300,000	1.00
1853W	70,269	5.00	1892	500,000	.50
1854A	3,118,341	.30	1893	250,000	1.50
1854B	1,995,474	.30	1894	150,000	2.50
1854BB	2,002,783	.30	1895	1,000,000	.25
1854D	2,524,264	.30	1896	1,000,000	.25
1854K	1,545,389	.30	1897	1,250,000	.25
1854MA	1,311,775	.30			
1854W	3,402,328	.30	**Y59** new design		
1855A	5,417,123	.30	1898	125,000	2.50
1855B	1,753,924	.30	1899	750,000	.35
1855BB	2,135,372	.30	1900	100,802	3.00
1855D	2,553,728	.30	1901	1,000,000	.25
1855K	1,068,497	.30	1902	750,000	.35
1855MA	2,437,805	.30	1903	750,000	.35
1855W	939,340	.40	1904	500,000	.50
1856A	1,738,098	.30	1907	250,000	1.00
1856B	4,324,121	.30	1908	3,500,000	.20
1856BB	1,281,577	.30	1909	1,750,000	.25
1856D	774,471	.50	1910	1,750,000	.25
1856K	2,280,752	.30	1911	5,000,000	.25
1856MA	2,780,834	.30	1912	1,500,000	.25
1856W	2,580,746	.30	1913	1,750,000	.25
1857A	1,250,000	.30	1914	2,000,000	.25
1857B	2,000,000	.30	1916	500,000	.50
1857D	1,000,000	.30	1919	901,726	.30
1857K	750,002	.50	1920	598,274	.40
1857MA	1,250,001	.30			
1857W	2,250,000	.30			

Y19

	Mintage	Value
1861A	4,054,111	.30
1861BB	2,440,101	.30
1861K	3,290,917	.30
1862A	7,078,131	.25
1862BB	2,807,203	.30
1862K	4,378,775	.30
1863A	437,065	.75
1863K	9,312,741	.25

Third Republic

Y42

	Mintage	Value
1877A	500,000	.50
1878A	750,000	.40
1878K	362,500	.75
1879	600,000	.50
1882	290,500	1.00
1883	500,000	.50
1884	300,000	1.00
1885	300,000	1.00
1886	300,000	1.00
1887	300,000	1.00

5 CENTIMES

Napoleon III

Y16 (bronze) 25.5mm

	Mintage	Value
1853A	13,928,277	.25
1853B	4,423,790	.25
1853BB	4,148,220	.25
1853D	5,013,281	.25
1853K	1,652,452	.30
1853MA	1,654,175	.30
1853W	5,397,860	.25
1854A	28,761,211	.25
1854B	16,354,246	.25
1854BB	20,379,850	.25
1854D	18,597,039	.25
1854K	13,608,015	.25
1854MA	14,834,662	.25
1854W	14,956,850	.25
1855A	26,932,005	.25
1855B	18,289,782	.25
1855BB	17,108,381	.25
1855D	14,250,229	.25
1855K	15,761,108	.25
1855MA	15,417,041	.25

	Mintage	Value		Mintage	Value
1855W	17,473,389	$ .25	1882	1,600,000	$ .25
1856A	25,798,854	.25	1883	2,400,000	.25
1856B	14,813,162	.25	1884	1,680,000	.25
1856BB	10,371,931	.25	1885	2,000,000	.25
1856D	7,669,470	.25	1886	1,680,000	.25
1856K	14,775,231	.25	1887	1,007,852	.30
1856MA	16,996,668	.25	1888	1,660,000	.25
1856W	15,472,473	.25	1889	1,660,000	.25
1857A	5,728,827	.25	1890	1,680,000	.25
1857B	1,843,290	.30	1891	1,600,000	.25
1857BB	1,662,339	.30	1892	1,600,000	.25
1857D	1,531,209	.30	1893	1,600,000	.25
1857K	2,416,989	.30	1894	2,240,000	.25
1857MA	4,187,969	.30	1896	6,695,350	.20
1857W	1,841,828	.30	1897	12,600,000	.20
			1898	1,200,000	.30

Y20

	Mintage	Value
1861A	6,857,228	.25
1861BB	1,662,339	.25
1861K	6,581,742	.25
1862A	5,299,543	.25
1862BB	8,583,899	.25
1862K	7,065,340	.25
1863A	12,128,389	.25
1863BB	2,323,076	.25
1863K	9,437,336	.25
1864A	3,053,076	.25
1864BB	6,109,686	25
1864K	5,831,202	.25
1865A	2,618,914	.25
1865BB	7,225,650	.25

Y60 new design

	Mintage	Value
1898	7,900,000	.20
1899	7,400,000	.20
1900	7,400,000	.20
1901	6,000,000	.20
1902	7,900,000	.20
1903	2,879,219	.25
1904	8,000,000	.20
1905	2,100,000	.25
1906	8,394,000	.20
1907	7,900,000	.20
1908	6,090,000	.20
1909	8,000,000	.20
1910	4,000,000	.20
1911	15,386,000	.15
1912	20,000,000	.15
1913	12,603,000	.15
1914	7,000,000	.20
1915	6,032,140	.20
1916	41,531,365	.15
1917	16,962,837	.15
1920	8,010,587	.20
1921	141,751	2.50

Third Republic

Y43

	Mintage	Value
1871A	2,238,382	.25
1871K	15,521	10.00
1872A	4,262,747	.25
1872K	4,064,479	.25
1873A	1,491,503	.25
1873K	1,997,000	.25
1874A	1,730,247	.25
1874K	1,325,520	.30
1875A	1,193,226	.30
1875K	760,000	.60
1876A	2,480,530	.25
1876K	1,597,000	.25
1877A	765,793	.60
1877K	1,193,000	.30
1878A	300,000	1.00
1878K	166,000	2.00
1879	1,954,530	.25
1880	1,172,286	.30
1881	2,502,000	.25

Y71 (copper-nickel) holed 19mm

	Mintage	Value
1917	10,453,389	.15
1918	35,591,616	.15
1919	43,847,770	.15
1920	51,321,082	.15

Y72 (copper-nickel) 17mm

	Mintage	Value
1920	inc. above	.15
1921	32,907,986	.10
1922 Paris	31,699,909	.10
1922 Poissy	17,716,885	.15
1923 Paris	23,321,946	.15
1923 Poissy	45,097,296	.10
1924 Paris	47,419,579	.10

	Mintage	Value
1924 Poissy	21,210,078	$ .15
1925 Paris	66,838,410	.10
1926	19,819,520	.15
1927	6,043,846	.25
1929	22,300	6.00
1930	31,902,116	.10
1931	34,711,236	.10
1932	31,111,633	.10
1933	12,970,114	.20
1934	27,143,993	.10
1935	57,221,458	.10
1936	64,340,897	.10
1937	26,329,202	.10

Y72a (nickel-bronze or nickel)

	Mintage	Value
1938	47,944,631	.10
1939 (nickel)	52,672,500	.10

10 CENTIMES

Napoleon III

Y17 (bronze) 30mm

	Mintage	Value
1852A	577,254	1.00
1853A	12,255,762	.25
1853B	3,545,922	.30
1853BB	4,582,018	.30
1853D	3,708,759	.30
1853K	1,203,400	.40
1853MA	889,145	.75
1853W	3,106,743	.30
1854A	13,327,345	.25
1854B	8,064,845	.30
1854BB	8,432,882	.30
1854D	8,487,153	.30
1854K	7,083,098	.30
1854MA	7,994,737	.30
1854W	8,242,102	.30
1855A	14,816,347	.25
1855B	9,960,323	.30
1855BB	11,953,131	.25
1855D	12,099,074	.25
1855K	11,796,779	.25
1855MA	11,309,128	.25
1855W	9,837,026	.25
1856A	19,149,261	.25
1856B	11,636,712	.25
1856BB	7,780,895	.30
1856D	4,419,354	.30
1856K	8,871,277	.30
1856MA	10,936,634	.25
1856W	11,401,708	.25
1857A	3,096,015	.30
1857B	1,619,866	.40
1857BB	1,685,320	.40
1857D	698,830	.75

	Mintage	Value
1857K	1,179,068	$ .40
1857MA	2,051,927	.40
1857W	1,858,457	.40

Y21

	Mintage	Value
1861A	3,638,378	.30
1861BB	4,624,867	.25
1861K	4,363,004	.25
1862A	4,736,264	.25
1862BB	4,702,093	.40
1862K	5,243,776	.25
1863A	4,873,059	.25
1863BB	1,340,302	.40
1863K	4,520,929	.25
1864A	1,556,490	.40
1864BB	3,052,802	.30
1864K	3,075,038	.30
1865A	1,607,515	.40
1865BB	4,796,851	.25

Third Republic

Y44

	Mintage	Value
1870A	888,915	.50
1871A	1,839,905	.40
1871K	26,500	6.00
1872A	4,399,016	.25
1872K	4,358,500	.25
1873A	2,096,370	.30
1873K	2,001,500	.30
1874A	1,194,044	.40
1874K	1,337,240	.40
1875A	1,433,870	.40
1875K	430,000	1.00
1876A	457,732	1.00
1876K	601,500	.75
1877A	392,268	1.00
1877K	403,500	1.00
1878A	150,000	2.00
1878K	100,000	2.50
1879A	822,735	.50
1880	1,413,857	.40
1881	749,000	.75
1882	1,100,000	.40
1883	700,000	.75
1884	1,060,000	.40
1885	900,000	.50
1886	1,060,000	.40
1887	874,104	.50
1888	1,050,000	.40
1889	1,010,000	.40
1890	1,060,000	.40
1891	1,000,000	.40
1892	1,020,000	.40

Mintage	Value
1893............1,120,000	$ .40
1894.............800,000	.50
1895.............600,000	.75
1896...........4,447,261	.25
1897...........7,250,000	.25
1898...........1,400,000	.40

Y61 new design

1898...........4,000,000	.25
1899...........4,000,000	.25
1900...........5,000,000	.25
1901...........2,700,000	.35
1902...........3,800,000	.25
1903...........3,650,000	.35
1904...........3,800,000	.35
1905.............950,000	.60
1906...........3,000,000	.35
1907...........4,000,000	.25
1908...........3,500,000	.30
1909...........2,932,625	.35
1910...........3,567,375	.30
1911...........7,903,000	.25
1912...........9,500,000	.25
1913...........9,000,000	.25
1914...........6,000,000	.25
1915...........4,362,468	.25
1916..........22,477,154	.20
1917..........11,913,589	.25
1920...........4,118,828	.25
1921...........1,896,225	.75

Y73 (nickel, holed) 21mm

1914...............3,972	15.00

Y73a (copper) nickel, 21mm

1917...........8,171,364	.25
1918..........30,605,494	.10
1919..........33,488,706	.10
1920..........38,844,555	.10
1921..........42,767,538	.10
1922 Paris......23,033,127	.15
1922 Poissy.....12,412,130	.15
1923 Paris......18,701,104	.15
1923 Poissy.....30,015,701	.10
1924 Paris......47,419,579	.10
1924 Poissy.....13,591,403	.15
1925 Paris......46,265,731	.10
1926..........25,660,053	.15
1927..........16,202,876	.15
1928...........6,966,552	.30
1929..........24,530,971	.15
1930..........22,146,099	.15
1931..........49,107,469	.10
1932..........30,317,387	.10
1933..........13,041,516	.15

Mintage	Value
1934..........24,067,353	$ .15
1935..........47,486,969	.10
1936..........57,738,080	.10
1937..........25,307,883	.15
1938..........41,214,151	.10
1939..........62,268,500	.10

Y73b (zinc)

1941.........235,875,200	.10

Y-V91 new design

1941..........70,860,000	.10
1942.........139,598,400	.10
1943..........48,957,600	.10

Y-V93 smaller, 17mm

1943..........24,638,000	.30
1944..........52,533,740	.25

Y74 prewar

1944...........5,929,160	2.00
1945..........46,553,360	1.00
1945B..........7,246,000	1.50
1946B.........10,566,000	1.50

20 CENTIMES

Napoleon III

Y22 (silver) 15mm

1853A...........680,103	.60
1854A.........1,682,581	.60
1855A...........362,245	1.00
1856A...........603,156	1.00
1856D...........395,702	1.00
1856BB...........13,342	7.50
1857A...........840,139	.60
1858A...........704,356	.60
1859A.........3,619,689	.50
1860A.........6,536,391	.50
1860BB.........2,986,177	.50
1862A............53,926	2.50
1863BB...........397,985	1.00

Y27 reverse: Crown

1864A...........268,255	1.50
1864BB...........112,372	2.00
1864K............58,360	2.50
1866A.........1,459,920	.50
1866BB...........843,156	.60
1866K...........412,859	1.00

Y28 larger, 16mm

1867A.........5,611,381	.40
1867BB.........3,114,264	.40
1867K............90,566	2.50
1868A...........352,510	1.00
1869BB...........200,000	1.50

	Mintage	Value
Vichy French State		
Y-V90 (zinc) 24.5mm		
1941 VINGT	54,044,000	$ .50
Y-V92 20		
1941	31,397,000	.15
1942	112,868,000	.15
1943	64,138,000	.15
1944	5,249,855	1.00
Y-V92a (iron)		
1944	695,000	5.00
Y75 prewar type (zinc)		
1945	6,402,295	1.50
1946	8,187,000	1.50

25 CENTIMES

	Mintage	Value
Y69 (nickel) 24mm		
1903	16,000,000	.25
Y70 new design		
1904	16,000,000	.25
1905	8,000,000	.25
Y76 new design, holed		
1914	941,133	.75
1915	535,237	1.00
1916	99,608	2.50
1917 (Cmes)	65,038	3.00
Y76a (copper-nickel)		
1917 (Cmes)	3,084,721	.40
1918	18,329,894	.20
1919	5,106,398	.40
1920	18,108,122	.20
1921	18,531,221	.20
1922	17,766,341	.20
1923	19,718,498	.20
1924	24,534,899	.20
1925	17,807,055	.20
1926	13,226,392	.25
1927	13,464,651	.25
1928	9,959,805	.25
1929	12,887,322	.25
1930	28,362,913	.20
1931	22,120,626	.20
1932	30,363,976	.20
1933	26,565,236	.20
1934	1,936,931	1.00
1936	4,657,312	.50
1937	6,117,120	.35
1938	6,833,666	.35
1939 (nickel)	42,964,500	.20
1940	3,466,375	.40

50 CENTIMES
(silver) 18.5mm

	Mintage	Value
Napoleon III		
Y11 Louis Napoleon		
1852A	1,010,267	$1.00
Y23 Napoleon III		
1853A	153,830	2.00
1854A	1,080,234	.60
1855A	400,259	1.00
1856A	1,436,299	.60
1856BB	1,195,698	.60
1856D	1,245,407	.60
1857A	1,631,861	.60
1858A	5,558,511	.50
1859A	3,380,473	.50
1859BB	1,112,271	.60
1860A	2,656,824	.50
1860BB	1,555,418	.60
1861BB	354,565	1.25
1862A	1,545,468	.60
1862BB	1,007,489	.60
1863BB	137,011	2.50
1864A	7,597,756	.50
1864BB	4,625,849	.50
1864K	1,827,936	.75
1865A	7,397,612	.50
1865BB	5,174,945	.50
1865K	4,900,892	.50
1866A	5,921,157	.50
1866BB	5,255,966	.50
1866K	3,500,433	.50
1867A	14,528,438	.50
1867BB	9,991,704	.50
1867K	4,691,729	.50
1868A	2,788,512	.60
1869BB	1,800,000	.75
Third Republic		
Y48		
1871A	235,803	1.50
1871K	722,980	.90
1872A	4,243,047	.50
1872K	1,643,470	.60
1873A	925,715	.75
1873K	166,009	2.50
1874A	1,227,957	.60
1881	5,390,890	.50
1882	2,319,719	.50
1886	308,758	1.00
1887	1,865,694	.60
1888	4,517,106	.50
1894	3,600,000	.50
1895	7,200,000	.50

	Mintage	Value
Y62 new design		
1897	88,000	$6.00
1898	30,000,000	.30
1899	18,000,000	.30
1900	9,194,767	.35
1901	4,960,000	.50
1902	3,778,172	.60
1903	2,221,828	.75
1904	4,000,000	.60
1905	2,380,861	.75
1906	2,679,144	.75
1907	7,331,819	.35
1908	14,304,058	.30
1909	9,900,044	.35
1910	15,922,600	.30
1911	1,329,503	1.00
1912	16,000,000	.30
1913	14,000,000	.30
1914	9,656,841	.35
1915	40,892,772	.30
1916	52,962,657	.30
1917	48,628,732	.30
1918	36,491,942	.30
1919	24,298,732	.30
1920	8,503,560	.35
Y77 (aluminum-bronze)		
1921	8,691,867	.25
1922	86,225,994	.15
1923	119,583,707	.10
1924	97,036,160	.15
1925	48,016,611	.15
1926	46,446,919	.15
1927	23,702,858	.15
1928	10,329,430	.15
1929	6,668,514	.25
Y80 new design		
1931	62,775,175	.10
1932	108,839,108	.10
1933	41,937,281	.10
1936	16,602,087	.15
1937	43,950,032	.10
1938	55,706,650	.10
1939	96,594,500	.10
1939B	inc. above	.15
1940	15,384,397	.15
1941	82,957,663	.10
1947	2,170,000	1.00
Y80a (aluminum)		
1941	24,294,231	.10
Y-V94 (aluminum)		
1942	105,464,000	.10
1943	106,417,703	.10
1943B	inc. above	1.00
1944	47,671,782	.10

	Mintage	Value
1944B	27,334,000	$ .20
1944C	27,173,356	.20
Y80a prewar type		
1944	9,898,000	.25
1944B	inc. w/1944B V94	.30
1944C	inc. w/1944C V94	.30
1945	26,224,000	.25
1945B	6,356,819	.40
1945C	2,967,000	.60
1946	21,764,000	.25
1946B	29,344,000	.25
1946C	2,840,644	.60
1947	51,744,000	.15
1947B	18,504,000	.25

1 FRANC
(silver) 23.5mm

Napoleon III

	Mintage	Value
Y12 Louis Napoleon		
1852A	1,015,402	2.00
Y24 Napoleon III		
1853A	182,508	3.00
1854A	763,973	1.25
1855A	757,000	1.25
1856A	1,195,942	1.00
1856BB	1,634,576	1.00
1856D	1,227,141	1.00
1857A	1,680,695	1.00
1858A	5,606,916	1.00
1859A	3,829,558	1.00
1859BB	1,333,333	1.00
1860A	2,740,231	1.00
1860BB	1,333,333	1.00
1861A	2,012,484	1.00
1861BB	217,793	2.50
1862BB	1,124,489	1.00
1863A	18,900	10.00
1863BB	54,173	5.00
1864A	22,202	10.00
Y30 new design		
1866A	14,638,380	.90
1866BB	7,203,690	1.00
1866K	1,402,685	1.25
1867A	12,131,428	.90
1867BB	7,294,757	1.00
1867K	6,091,869	1.00
1868A	14,942,298	.90
1868BB	10,230,151	.90
1868K	21,829	10.00
1869A	2,934,947	1.00
1869BB	3,094,263	1.00
1870A	788,324	1.50
1870BB	1,991,998	1.25

	Mintage	Value
Third Republic		
Y49		
1871A	2,979,881	$ .90
1871K	1,251,748	.90
1872A	10,178,914	.90
1872K	5,779,419	.90
1873K	19,101	10.00
1881A	2,010,000	.90
1887	3,291,930	.90
1888	3,244,069	.90
1894	1,600,000	.90
1895	3,200,000	.90
Y63 new design		
1898	15,000,000	.40
1899	11,000,000	.40
1900	99,079	2.50
1901	6,200,000	.40
1902	6,000,000	.40
1903	472,283	1.00
1904	7,000,000	.40
1905	6,003,526	.40
1906	1,908,100	.50
1907	2,562,745	.50
1908	3,961,222	.50
1909	10,923,790	.40
1910	7,725,318	.40
1911	5,542,000	.40
1912	10,001,000	.40
1913	18,654,148	.40
1914	14,361,102	.40
1914C	43,421	15.00
1915	47,955,158	.35
1916	92,029,179	.35
1917	57,153,034	.35
1918	50,112,330	.35
1919	46,111,525	.35
1920	19,321,795	.35
Y78 (aluminum-bronze)		
1920	590,049	1.00
1921	54,571,959	.15
1922	111,342,910	.15
1923	140,137,683	.15
1924	87,714,563	.15
1925	36,522,732	.15
1926	1,579,575	.50
1927	11,330,486	.20
1928	485,259	1.00
Y81 new design		
1931	15,503,990	.20
1932	29,768,441	.15
1933	15,356,367	.20
1934	17,285,800	.20
1935	1,666,038	.60

	Mintage	Value
1936	23,816,782	$ .15
1937	30,940,378	.15
1938	66,164,560	.15
1939	48,434,500	.15
1940	25,525,512	.15
1941	34,705,492	.15
Y81a (aluminum)		
1941	11,705,741	.15
Y-V95 (aluminum)		
1942	140,438,000	.15
1943	273,645,897	.15
1943B	inc. above	1.00
1944	50,604,850	.15
1944B	13,622,075	.30
1944C	74,859,005	.20
Y81a prewar type		
1944	22,608,000	.20
1944B	inc. w/1944B V95	.30
1944C	inc. w/1944C V95	.20
1945	61,780,000	.10
1945B	4,250,866	.30
1945C	5,219,806	.30
1946	52,516,000	.10
1946B	26,493,000	.15
1946C	9,869,157	.25
1947	110,448,000	.10
1947B	31,562,000	.15
1948	96,092,000	.10
1948B	45,481,000	.10
1949	41,090,000	.10
1949B	35,840,000	.10
1950	27,882,286	.10
1950B	18,800,000	.15
1957	16,497,000	.10
1957B	63,976,000	.10
1958	21,197,000	.10
1958B	13,412,000	.10
1959	41,985,000	.10

2 FRANCS

Napoleon III

	Mintage	Value
Y25 (silver) 27.5mm		
1853A	48,968	6.00
1854A	215,103	2.50
1855A	82,431	4.00
1856A	240,847	2.50
1856BB	693,369	2.50
1856D	288,578	2.50
1857A	338,964	2.50
1858A	1,288	25.00
1859A	894	40.00

	Mintage	Value
Y31 new design		
1866A	3,225,798	$1.50
1866BB	3,089,824	1.50
1866K	437,055	2.50
1867A	3,695,153	1.50
1867BB	3,470,737	1.50
1867K	1,743,984	1.50
1868A	3,762,479	1.50
1868BB	733,227	2.00
1868K	87,135	5.00
1869A	1,104,428	1.50
1869BB	366,773	2.50
1870A	3,187,168	1.50
1870BB	1,001,307	1.50

Third Republic
Y45

	Mintage	Value
1870A	238,750	5.00
1870K	559,817	3.50
1871K	1,215,072	2.00

Y50 w/LIBERTE, EGALITE, FRATERNITE

	Mintage	Value
1870A	1,324,250	2.00
1871A	4,757,257	2.00
1871K	1,255,958	2.00
1872A	2,306,361	1.50
1872K	1,467,427	2.00
1873A	528,076	3.00
1881	1,014,000	2.00
1887	2,342,903	1.50
1888	130,501	6.00
1894	300,000	4.00
1895	600,000	3.00

Y64 new design

	Mintage	Value
1898	5,000,000	.90
1899	3,500,000	.90
1900	500,000	1.50
1901	1,860,000	1.00
1902	2,000,000	1.00
1904	1,500,000	1.00
1905	2,000,000	1.00
1908	2,501,808	1.00
1909	1,000,265	1.25
1910	2,190,000	1.00
1912	1,000,000	1.25
1913	500,000	1.50
1914	5,718,526	.90
1914C	461,647	2.00
1915	13,963,409	.75
1916	17,886,653	.75
1917	16,555,357	.75
1918	12,026,147	.75

	Mintage	Value
1919	9,260,934	$ .75
1920	3,013,677	.90
Y79 (aluminum-bronze)		
1920	inc. above	1.00
1921	14,362,786	.20
1922	29,462,887	.20
1923	43,960,369	.20
1924	29,631,410	.20
1925	31,606,872	.20
1926	2,962,351	.40
1927	1,678,263	.50
Y82 new design		
1931	1,717,167	.50
1932	8,942,689	.20
1933	8,412,770	.20
1934	6,895,782	.20
1935	297,633	1.50
1936	12,394,328	.20
1937	11,054,992	.20
1938	28,071,831	.20
1939	25,403,000	.20
1940	9,715,881	.20
1941	16,683,717	.20
Y82a (aluminum)		
1941		.20
Y-V96 (aluminum)		
1943	148,704,271	.15
1943B	inc. above	1.00
1944	25,545,825	.20
1944B	10,297,863	.50
1944C	19,470,267	.50
Y89 (brass) 27mm		
1944	50,000,000	1.25
Y82a prewar type		
1944	7,224,000	.25
1944B	inc. w/1944B V96	.50
1944C	inc. w/1944C V96	.50
1945	16,635,896	.20
1945B	1,726,144	.60
1945C	1,164,705	.60
1946	34,929,500	.15
1946B	6,017,500	.40
1946C	1,533,377	.60
1947	78,984,000	.15
1947B	26,219,500	.15
1948	32,354,500	.15
1948B	39,090,000	.15
1949	13,583,500	.15
1949B	23,955,000	.15
1950	12,190,508	.15
1950B	18,185,000	.15

	Mintage	Value
1958	9,906,000	$ .15
1959	17,744,500	.15

5 FRANCS
(silver) 37.5mm

Napoleon III

Y13 Louis Napoleon

	Mintage	Value
1852A	16,106,664	5.00
1852BB	41,377	30.00

Y26 Napoleon III

	Mintage	Value
1854A	10,615	40.00
1855A	4,075,121	4.00
1855BB	786,052	6.00
1856A	4,682,694	4.00
1856BB	2,223,387	5.00
1856D	2,249,130	5.00
1857A	93,406	10.00
1858A	21,790	30.00
1859A	3,365	50.00

Y32 new design

	Mintage	Value
1861A	22,093	20.00
1862A	21,129	20.00
1863A	21,687	20.00
1864A	32,168	15.00
1865A	24,577	20.00
1865BB	72,557	10.00
1866A	37,893	15.00
1867A	6,586,442	3.50
1867BB	4,223,870	4.00
1868A	6,633,998	3.50
1868BB	12,090,112	3.50
1869A	2,055,891	4.50
1869BB	9,596,966	3.50
1870A	6,620,297	3.50
1870BB	2,054,764	4.50

Third Republic

Y46 Liberty head

	Mintage	Value
1870A	64,200	12.50
1870K	544,309	6.00

Y51 similar: LIBERTE, EGALITE, FRATERNITE reverse

	Mintage	Value
1870A	1,185,000	4.00
1871K	629,666	7.50

Y52 3 human figures

	Mintage	Value
1870A	261,000	10.00
1871A	237,906	10.00
1871K	74,609	$15.00
1872A	56,844	15.00
1872K	20,994	25.00
1873A	27,076,954	3.00
1873K	3,852,855	4.00
1874A	7,999,202	3.50
1874K	4,000,000	4.00
1875A	13,338,560	3.00
1875K	1,661,440	5.00
1876A	8,800,000	3.50
1876K	1,732,263	5.00
1877A	2,631,994	4.50
1877K	660,863	7.50
1878A	1,154	75.00
1878K	263,130	15.00

Y53 as Y52 with 3 pronged spearhead left of A reverse

	Mintage	Value
1871A	256,410	30.00

Y83 (nickel) 23mm

	Mintage	Value
1933	160,078,170	1.00

Y84 new design, 31mm

	Mintage	Value
1933	403,385	2.00
1934	56,280,025	.50
1935	54,281,974	.50
1937	6,902,595	.60

Y84a (aluminum-bronze)

	Mintage	Value
1939	2,028,880	1.00
1940	7,751,600	.75
1945	5,990,169	.75
1945B	2,378,000	1.25
1945C	....	1.50
1946	24,451,837	.75
1946C	inc. above	1.25

Y84b (aluminum)

	Mintage	Value
1945	95,398,800	.20
1945B	6,043,200	.40
1945C	2,208,114	.60
1946	61,332,000	.20
1946B	13,360,400	.30
1946C	1,268,907	1.00
1947	46,575,600	.20
1947B	30,838,800	.25
1948	104,473,500	.20
1948B	28,046,800	.25
1949	203,251,600	.20
1949B	48,414,000	.20
1950	128,371,600	.20
1950B	28,952,000	.25
1952	4,000,000	.75

	Mintage	Value

Y-V97 Petain, 22mm

1941. 13,782,000	$12.50

(this coin did not enter circulation)

10 FRANCS

Y86 (silver) 28mm

	Mintage	Value
1930. 36,986,163	.75
1931. 35,467,583	.75
1932. 40,287,667	.75
1933. 31,145,963	.75
1934. 52,000,776	.75
1937. 52,368	6.00
1938. 14,090,181	1.00
1939. 8,299,260	1.25

Y86a (copper-nickel) 26mm

	Mintage	Value
1945. 6,757,000	.75
1946. 24,409,000	.60
1946B. 8,452,000	.75
1947. 41,627,000	.60
1947B. 17,187,500	.60
1948. 155,945,000	.50
1948B. 40,499,500	.60
1949. 111,972,500	.50
1949B. 29,517,500	.60

Y98 (aluminum-bronze) 20mm

	Mintage	Value
1950. 13,534,000	.15
1950B. 4,807,500	.25
1951. 153,689,000	.15
1951B. 106,866,344	.15
1952. 76,810,000	.15
1952B. 72,345,846	.15
1953. 46,272,000	.15
1953B. 36,465,856	.15
1954. 2,207,000	.40
1954B. 24,202,454	.15
1955. 47,466,000	.15
1957. 26,351,000	.15
1958. 27,213,000	.15

20 FRANCS

Y87 (silver) 35mm

	Mintage	Value
1933. 24,447,048	3.00
1934. 11,832,803	3.50
1937. 1,189,205	7.50
1938. 10,913,979	3.50

Y99 (aluminum-bronze) 23.5mm

	Mintage	Value
1950. 126,435,000	.30
1950B. 43,355,000	.30
1951. 97,922,000	.30
1951B. 46,814,790	.30

	Mintage	Value
1952. 130,281,000	$ .30
1952B. 54,381,160	.30
1953. 58,522,000	.30
1953B. 42,409,050	.30
1954. 1,573,000	1.00

50 FRANCS

Y100 (aluminum-bronze) 27mm

	Mintage	Value
1951. 68,629,600	.60
1951B. 11,829,121	.60
1952. 74,211,600	.60
1952B. 13,432,229	.60
1953. 63,171,600	.60
1953B. 23,375,768	.60
1954. 996,800	1.50
1954B. 6,530,882	.75
1958. 500,738	1.50

100 FRANCS

Y101 (copper-nickel) 24mm

	Mintage	Value
1954. 97,285,500	1.00
1954B. 86,260,628	1.00
1955. 152,517,500	1.00
1955B. 136,584,872	1.00
1956. 7,578,334	1.25
1956B. 19,154,500	1.00
1957. 11,312,000	1.00
1957B. 25,702,000	1.00
1958. 5,902,500	1.25
1958B. 54,071,500	1.00

Fifth Republic
Heavy Franc System
1 CENTIME

Y102 (stainless steel) 15mm

1962. 34,200,000	.10

5 CENTIMES

Y103 (stainless steel) 19mm

1962. 205,360,000	.10

10 CENTIMES

Y104 (aluminum-bronze) 20mm

1962. 29,100,000	.15

20 CENTIMES

Y105 (aluminum-bronze) 23mm

1962. 48,200,000	.20

50 CENTIMES

Y106 (aluminum-bronze) 25mm

1962. 37,560,000	.40

	Mintage	Value

1 FRANC

Y108 (nickel) 24mm
1960..........344,055,000 $ .75
1961..........119,611,306 .75
1962...........14,013,694 .75

5 FRANCS

Y110 (silver) 29mm
1960...........37,974,000 $2.00
1961...........15,630,000 2.00
1962...........42,500,000 2.00

FRENCH COCHIN-CHINA
(Cochin Chine Francaise)

Southernmost state of Indo-China. Now part of Vietnam. Coinage obsolete.

100 Centimes = 1 Piastre

SAPEQUE

Y1 (bronze, square hole) 20mm
1879.................... 1.50

1 CENTIME

Y2 (bronze) 31mm
1875.................... 1.50
1879.................... 1.50
1884..............444,269 1.50

10 CENTIMES

Y3 (silver) 17.5mm
1879.................... 2.50
1884..............510,000 2.50

20 CENTIMES

Y4 (silver) 25mm
1879.................... 3.50
1884..............320,000 3.50

50 CENTIMES

Y5 (silver) 29mm
1879.................... 6.00
1884...............10,000 6.00

The 1 Piastre (silver) 39.5mm 1879 is a pattern, and the 1885 was struck in proof only for the Antwerp Exposition.

FRENCH EQUATORIAL AFRICA
(Afrique Equatoriale Francaise)

Formerly a French Overseas Possession in Central Africa.

100 Centimes = 1 Franc

50 CENTIMES

Y1 (brass) 17.5mm
1942............8,000,000 .75

Y1a (bronze)
1943...........16,000,000 .75

1 FRANC

Y2 (brass) 22mm
1942............3,000,000 1.00

Y2a (bronze)
1943............6,000,000 1.00

Y6 (aluminum) 23mm
1948...........15,000,000 .25

2 FRANCS

Y7 (aluminum) 27mm
1948............5,040,000 .40

See Cameroons for integrated coinage, 1958.

FRENCH INDO-CHINA
(Indochine Francaise)

A former French colony in Southeast Asia. In 1953 Indo-China was partitioned into Cambodia, Laos, South Vietnam, and North Vietnam. The silver coins minted in San Francisco in 1920 and 1921 do not show weight and fineness. The 1939-40 10 and 20 centimes in nickel are sharper in appearance and slightly thicker than the copper-nickel coins, and the 20 centimes 1939 in nickel is with security edge. During World War II various older issues were coined in zinc. These were made from dies created from molds of existing coins and were issued as emergency coinage. There has been no attempt to list any of these.

Mint marks:

A — Paris

Horn and torch — Paris

B — Beaumont le Roger

C — Castelsarrasin

H — Birmingham

S — San Francisco

Thunderbolt and torch — Poissy

Except where noted all coins were minted in Paris and have A or horn and torch mint mark.

5 Sapeques = 1 Centime

100 Centimes = 1 Piastre

	Mintage	Value
SAPEQUE		
Y1 (bronze) square hole, 20mm		
1887 5,000,000		$1.00
1888 5,000,000		1.00
1892 1,635,767		1.50
1893 864,233		2.50
1894 2,500,000		1.00
1897 2,828,536		1.00
1898 2,171,464		1.00
1899 5,000,000		1.00
1900 2,656,614		1.00
1901 4,843,486		1.00
1902 2,500,000		1.00
½ CENTIME		
Y20 (bronze) holed, 21mm		
1935 26,365,135		.25
1936 23,634,865		.25
1937 10,243,527		.25
1938 16,665,473		.25
1939 17,305,000		.25
1940 11,218,000		.60
Y20a (zinc)		
1940 185,000		10.00
1 CENTIME		
Y2 (bronze) 31mm		
1885 3,673,190		1.00

	Mintage	Value
1886 1,882,541		$1.25
1887 2,362,388		1.00
1888 2,564,148		1.00
1889 1,573,464		1.25
1892 2,647,680		1.00
1893 1,852,320		1.00
1894 465,000		2.50
Y3 holed, 27.5mm		
1896 5,980,009		.75
1897 11,054,991		.60
1898 5,000,000		.75
1899 8,000,000		.50
1900 3,000,100		.75
1901 9,750,000		.50
1902 5,050,000		.50
1903 8,000,000		.50
1906 2,000,000		.75
1908 3,000,000		.75
Y4 new design, 26mm		
1908 . . . . inc. above		3.50
1909 5,000,000		.50
1910 7,703,000		.40
1911 15,234,000		.35
1912 17,027,300		.35
1913 3,945,392		.50

	Mintage	Value
1914	11,026,799	$ .25
1916	1,311,570	.50
1917	9,761,559	.25
1918	2,371,528	.40
1919	9,147,572	.25
1920A	18,305,304	.25
1920 no mint mark — San Francisco	15,000,000	.25
1921A	14,721,854	.25
1922A	8,850,117	.25
1922 thunderbolt — (Poissy)	9,475,720	.25
1923A	1,079,468	.35
1923 (Poissy)	27,891,109	.25
1924 (Poissy)	7,633,171	.25
1926A	11,672,270	.25
1927	3,327,730	.35
1930	4,682,208	.25
1931	5,317,791	.25
1937	8,901,992	.25
1938	15,499,008	.25
1939	17,589,000	.25

5 CENTIMES

Y5 (copper-nickel) holed, 25mm

	Mintage	Value
1923	1,610,926	.75
1924	3,389,074	.50
1925	6,000,000	.50
1930	4,000,000	.25
1937	10,000,000	.25
1938	1,480,000	.75

Y5a (w/zinc) thinner

	Mintage	Value
1938	50,569,000	.25
1939	38,501,000	.25

10 CENTIMES

Y6 (silver) 19mm

	Mintage	Value
1885	2,040,000	.90
1888	1,000,000	1.00
1892	200,000	3.00
1893	600,000	1.50
1894	500,000	1.50
1895 2Gr721 obv	600,000	1.50

Y10

	Mintage	Value
1895 2Gr7 obv	300,000	2.50
1896	650,000	1.50
1897	900,000	1.25

Y14

	Mintage	Value
1898	500,000	1.50
1899	4,100,000	1.00
1900	3,600,100	1.00
1901	2,950,000	1.00
1902	7,050,000	.90
1903	1,300,000	1.25

	Mintage	Value
1908	1,000,000	$1.25
1909	1,000,000	1.25
1910	2,689,000	1.00
1911	2,310,839	1.00
1912	2,500,000	1.00
1913	4,846,605	.90
1914	2,667,393	1.00
1916	2,000,000	1.00
1917	1,500,000	1.00
1919	1,500,000	1.00
1920 no mint mark — San Francisco	10,000,000	2.50
1921A	12,515,504	.75
1922	22,380,600	.75
1923	21,755,368	.75
1924	2,819,659	.80
1925	4,909,029	.75
1927	6,470,800	.75
1928	1,592,863	.90
1929	5,830,820	.75
1930	6,607,520	.75
1937	25,000,000	.60

Y21 (nickel) 18mm

	Mintage	Value
1939	16,841,000	.25
1940	25,270,000	.25

Y21a (copper-nickel)

	Mintage	Value
1940	2,237,000	.40
1941S	30,745,000	.25

20 CENTIMES

Y7 (silver) 26mm

	Mintage	Value
1885	1,280,000	1.50
1887	250,000	3.00
1892	200,000	3.00
1893	200,000	3.00
1894	250,000	3.00
1895 5Gr443 obv	300,000	3.00

Y11

	Mintage	Value
1895 5Gr4 obv	250,000	3.00
1896	300,000	3.00
1897	300,000	3.00

Y15

	Mintage	Value
1898	250,000	2.50
1899	2,050,000	1.50
1900	1,750,100	1.50
1901	1,375,000	1.50
1902	3,525,000	1.25
1903	675,000	2.00
1908	500,000	2.50
1909	500,000	2.50
1911	2,339,850	1.50
1912	160,150	3.00
1913	1,251,570	1.50

	Mintage	Value
1914	2,500,000	$1.50
1916	1,000,000	1.75
1920 no mint mark —		
San Francisco	4,000,000	3.50
1921A	3,663,041	1.25
1922	5,812,311	1.00
1923	7,109,028	1.00

Y17

	Mintage	Value
1924	1,399,682	1.75
1925	2,555,854	1.25
1927	3,244,523	1.25
1928	794,289	2.00
1929	643,750	2.00
1930	5,576,331	1.25
1937	17,500,000	1.00

Y22 (nickel) 24mm

	Mintage	Value
1939	344,500	20.00

Y22a (copper-nickel)

	Mintage	Value
1940	14,676,000	.35
1941S	25,000,000	.35

50 CENTIMES

Y8 (silver) 29mm

	Mintage	Value
1885	40,000	10.00
1894	100,000	3.50
1895	100,000	3.50

Y12

	Mintage	Value
1896	110,000	3.50
1936	4,000,000	1.75

1 PIASTRE

Y9 (silver) 39mm

	Mintage	Value
1885	799,511	17.50
1886	3,215,771	5.50
1887	3,076,410	5.50
1888	947,615	17.50
1889	1,239,884	12.50
1890	6,108	150.00
1893	794,723	17.50
1894	1,308,437	10.00
1895 27.215Gr obv.	1,782,012	10.00

Y13

	Mintage	Value
1895 27Gr obv	11,858,018	4.00
1896	3,798,452	5.00
1897	2,511,128	6.00
1898	4,303,953	4.00
1899	4,681,244	4.00
1900	13,318,856	4.00
1901	3,150,000	4.50
1902	3,326,554	4.50
1903	10,076,893	4.00

	Mintage	Value
1904	5,750,712	$4.00
1905	3,560,882	4.50
1906	10,194,060	4.00
1907	14,061,745	4.00
1908	13,986,340	4.00
1909	9,201,143	4.00
1910	760,718	10.00
1913	3,244,089	4.50
1921 no mint mark —		
San Francisco	4,850,000	4.50
1921H	3,580,000	5.00
1922 no mint mark —		
San Francisco	1,150,000	25.00
1922H	7,420,289	4.00
1924 Paris	2,831,349	8.00
1925	2,882,193	7.50
1926	3,382,656	6.00
1927	8,184,076	7.50
1928	5,289,957	15.00

Y18 new design

	Mintage	Value
1931	16,000,000	7.50

Vichy French Government
¼ CENTIME

Y-V31 (zinc) holed, 20mm

	Value
1942	4.50
1943	7.50

1 CENTIME

Y-V30 (zinc) holed, 28mm

	Value
1940	2.00
1941	1.00

Y-V32 (aluminum) 17mm

	Value
1943	.25

5 CENTIMES

Y-V33 (aluminum) holed, 21mm

	Value
1943	.35

Postwar Coinage
5 CENTIMES

Y26 (aluminum) 18mm

	Mintage	Value
1946	28,000,000	.25
1946B	22,000,000	.25

10 CENTIMES

Y27 (aluminum) 23mm

	Mintage	Value
1945	40,170,000	.25
1945B	9,830,000	.30

	Mintage	Value
20 CENTIMES		
Y28 (aluminum) 27mm		
1945	15,412,000	$ .35
1945B	6,665,000	.50
1945C	22,423,000	.35
50 CENTIMES		
Y23 (copper-nickel) 29mm		
1946	32,292,000	1.75

	Mintage	Value
1 PIASTRE		
Y24 (copper-nickel) 35mm		
1946 security edge		
	2,520,000	$5.00
1947	42,218,750	6.00
Y25 reeded edge		
1947	inc. above	2.50

FRENCH OCEANIA
(Establissements Francais De L'Oceanie)

A French possession, consisting of islands in the South Pacific.

100 Centimes = 1 Franc

	Mintage	Value
50 CENTIMES		
Y1 (aluminum) 18mm		
1949	700,000	.20
1 FRANC		
Y2 (aluminum) 23mm		
1949	2,000,000	.30

	Mintage	Value
2 FRANCS		
Y3 (aluminum) 27mm		
1949	1,000,000	.40
5 FRANCS		
Y4 (aluminum) 32mm		
1952	2,000,000	.75

FRENCH SOMALILAND
(Cote Francaise Des Somalis)

A French possession in Northeast Africa. Coins dated 1948-1952 are inscribed. "Republic Francaise Union Francaise"; those dated 1959 are inscribed: "Republic Francaise."

100 Centimes = 1 Franc

	Mintage	Value
1 FRANC		
Y1 (aluminum) 23mm		
1948	200,000	.50
Y5		
1959	500,000	.25
2 FRANCS		
Y2 (aluminum) 27mm		
1948	200,000	.75
Y6		
1959	200,000	.35

	Mintage	Value
5 FRANCS		
Y3 (aluminum) 32mm		
1948	500,000	1.00
Y7		
1959	500,000	.50
20 FRANCS		
Y4 (aluminum-bronze) 24mm		
1952	500,000	1.25

FRENCH WEST AFRICA
(Afrique Occidentale Francaise)

Former French possessions in West Africa. Now broken into several states within the French community of Nations.

100 Centimes = 1 Franc

	Mintage	Value
50 CENTIMES		
Y1 (aluminum-bronze) 18mm		
1944 10,000,000		$2.00
1 FRANC		
Y2 (aluminum-bronze) 23mm		
1944 15,000,000		1.50
Y3 (aluminum)		
1948 22,829,000		.25
2 FRANCS		
Y42 (aluminum) 27mm		
1948 10,909,000		.35
5 FRANCS		
Y5 (aluminum-bronze) 19mm		
1956 85,000,000		.25

	Mintage	Value
10 FRANCS		
Y6 (aluminum-bronze) 23mm		
1956 44,133,000		$ .35
25 FRANCS		
Y7 (aluminum-bronze) 27mm		
1956 37,876,800		.65
Integrated Coinage —		
French West Africa-Togo		
10 FRANCS		
Y8 (aluminum-bronze) 23mm		
1957 5,867,000		.50
25 FRANCS		
Y9 (aluminum-bronze) 27mm		
1957 12,123,200		.85

GERMAN EAST AFRICA
(Deutsch Ostafrika)

A former German colony in southeast Africa. Coinage obsolete.

64 Pesa = 1 Rupie
100 Heller = 1 Rupie

German East Africa Company
(DEUTSCH OSTAFRIKANISCHE GESELLSCHAFT)

1 PESA		
Y1 (copper) 25.2mm		
1890 1,000,000		3.00
1891 12,550,946		1.50
1892 27,541,389		1.50
¼ RUPIE		
Y2 (silver) 19.2mm		
1891 76,688		3.50
1898 100,000		3.00
1901 350,000		2.50
½ RUPIE		
Y3 (silver) 24.4mm		
1891 68,342		3.50

1897 75,000		3.50
1901 215,000		2.50
1 RUPIE		
Y4 (silver) 30.5mm		
1890 154,394		5.00
1891 126,258		5.00
1892 359,735		5.00
1893 142,355		5.00
1894 48,200		7.50
1897 244,030		5.00
1898 356,722		5.00
1899 226,754		5.00
1900 209,289		5.00
1901 319,022		5.00
1902 151,019		5.00

	Mintage	Value
2 RUPIE		
Y5 (silver) 35mm		
1893	32,854	$50.00
1894	18,000	60.00

German East Africa
(DEUTSCH OSTAFRIKA)
½ HELLER

	Mintage	Value
Y6 (bronze) 17.5mm		
1904A	1,200,858	1.00
1905A	7,192,410	.75
1905J	4,000,000	.75
1906J	6,000,000	.75

1 HELLER

	Mintage	Value
Y7 (bronze) 20mm		
1904A	10,255,763	1.00
1904J	2,500,000	1.50
1905A	3,759,519	1.50
1905J	7,566,000	1.50
1906A	3,003,694	1.50
1906J	1,962,000	1.50
1907J	17,790,000	1.00
1908J	12,205,366	1.00
1909J	1,698,000	1.50
1910J	5,096,439	1.50
1911J	6,420,000	1.50
1912J	7,011,789	1.50
1913A		1.50
1913J	5,186,457	1.50

5 HELLER

	Mintage	Value
Y8 (bronze) 37mm		
1908J	600,000	10.00
1909J	756,106	10.00
Y11 (copper-nickel) 21mm		
1913A		3.00
1913J	1,000,000	3.00
1914J	1,000,000	3.00

10 HELLER

	Mintage	Value
Y12 (copper-nickel) 26mm		
1908J	12,000	10.00
1909J	1,988,526	3.00
1910J	500,000	4.00
1911A		3.00
1914J	200,000	5.00

¼ RUPIE

	Mintage	Value
Y13 (silver) 19.2mm		
1904A	300,000	3.00
1906A	300,000	3.00

	Mintage	Value
1906J	100,000	$4.00
1907J	200,000	3.00
1909A	200,000	3.00
1910J	600,000	3.00
1912J	400,000	3.00
1913A		3.00
1913J	400,000	3.00
1914J	200,000	3.00

½ RUPIE

	Mintage	Value
Y14 (silver) 24.4mm		
1904A	400,000	3.50
1906A	50,000	5.00
1906J	50,000	5.00
1907J	140,000	4.00
1909A	100,000	4.00
1910J	300,000	4.00
1912J	200,000	4.00
1913A		4.00
1913J	200,000	4.00
1914J	100,000	4.00

1 RUPIE

	Mintage	Value
Y15 (silver) 30.5mm		
1904A	1,000,000	5.00
1905A	300,000	7.00
1905J	1,000,000	5.00
1906A	950,000	5.00
1906J	700,000	6.00
1907J	880,000	5.00
1908J	500,000	6.00
1909A	200,000	7.00
1910J	270,000	7.00
1911A		7.00
1911J	1,400,000	5.00
1912J	300,000	7.00
1913A		7.00
1913J	1,400,000	5.00
1914J	500,000	6.00

Provisional Issue
Struck at Tabora

5 HELLER

	Mintage	Value
Y9 (brass) 21mm		
1916	302,000	3.00

20 HELLER

	Mintage	Value
Y10 (copper) 29mm		
1916	325,000	2.50
Y10a (brass)		
1916	1,307,760	1.25

GERMAN NEW GUINEA
(Neu-Guinea Compagnie)

A former German colony on the eastern end of the island of New Guinea. Now under U. N. Trusteeship. Coinage obsolete.

100 Pfennig = 1 Mark

	Mintage	Value			Mintage	Value
1 PFENNIG				**1 MARK**		
Y1 (copper) 15.5mm				Y5 (silver) 23mm		
1894	32,785	$10.00		1894	33,331	$20.00
2 PFENNIG				**2 MARK**		
Y2 (copper) 20mm				Y6 (silver) 28mm		
1894	16,786	10.00		1894	13,404	25.00
10 PFENNIG				**5 MARK**		
Y3 (copper) 31mm				Y7 (silver) 37mm		
1894	23,930	10.00		1894	19,094	200.00
½ MARK						
Y4 (silver) 20mm						
1894	16,236	25.00				

GERMANY
(Deutsches Reich, Deutschland)

Until 1871, Germany was made up of independent states and cities which had separate coinage. After the German Empire was formed the issuance of coins was in two classes. Gold and silver coins of 2, 3, and 5 Marks continued to be issued by separate states and cities, while minor coins from 1 Pfennig through 1 Mark were issued by the central government. In 1918 the regular coinage of cities and states came to an end.

Mint Marks:

A — Berlin	E — Dresden
B — Hanover (until 1878)	F — Stuttgart
B — Vienna (1938-1945)	G — Karlsruhe
C — Frankfort (until 1879)	H — Darmstadt (until 1882)
D — Munich	J — Hamburg

100 Pfennig = 1 Mark

	Mintage	Value		Mintage	Value
1 PFENNIG			1874G	4,768,000	.35
Empire			1874H	2,013,000	.40
			1875A	64,854,000	.35
Y1 (copper) 17.5mm			1875B	27,617,000	.30
1873A	184,000	2.00	1875C	22,770,000	.30
1873B	95,000	3.00	1875D	13,342,000	.30
1873D	51,000	5.00	1875E	7,778,000	.35
1874A	26,224,000	.35	1875F	15,270,000	.30
1874B	8,742,000	.35	1875G	12,020,000	.30
1874C	15,627,000	.35	1875H	3,515,000	.35
1874D	7,074,000	.35	1875J	7,241,000	.35
1874E	4,522,000	.35	1876A	34,890,000	.25
1874F	3,985,000	.35			

	Mintage	Value		Mintage	Value
1876B	5,994,000	$ .35	1892G	2,688,000	$ .25
1876C	11,043,000	.30	1892J	3,980,000	.25
1876D	12,641,000	.30	1893A	18,966,000	.20
1876E	6,531,000	.30	1893D	7,026,000	.20
1876F	11,404,000	.30	1893E	1,218,000	.25
1876G	3,331,000	.35	1893F	1,460,000	.25
1876H	2,998,000	.35	1893G	700,000	.50
1876J	1,165,000	1.00	1893J	1,824,000	.25
1877A	472,000	1.00	1894A	17,592,000	.20
1877B	88,000	3.00	1894D	5,530,000	.20
1885A	5,447,000	.25	1894E	5,040,000	.20
1885E	430,000	1.00	1894F	4,206,000	.25
1885G	1,100,000	.45	1894G	2,351,000	.25
1885J	1,696,000	.40	1894J	2,619,000	.25
1886A	14,114,000	.20	1895A	20,156,000	.20
1886D	2,873,000	.30	1895D	1,495,000	.30
1886E	2,059,000	.30	1895E	1,190,000	.30
1886F	1,726,000	.35	1895F	4,365,000	.25
1886G	814,000	.50	1895G	3,051,000	.25
1886J	1,592,000	.35	1895J	3,838,000	.25
1887A	15,923,000	.20	1896A	27,094,000	.20
1887D	5,176,000	.25	1896D	7,025,000	.20
1887E	2,314,000	.25	1896E	3,725,000	.25
1887F	6,345,000	.20	1896F	3,450,000	.25
1887G	814,000	.50	1896G	3,028,000	.25
1887J	2,082,000	.25	1897A	8,533,000	.20
1888A	19,936,000	.20	1897D	2,600,000	.25
1888D	3,277,000	.25	1897E	1,294,000	.30
1888E	1,310,000	.35	1897F	2,389,000	.25
1888F	584,000	.50	1897G	1,122,000	.30
1888G	1,384,000	.35	1897J	4,490,000	.25
1888J	2,803,000	.25	1898A	18,563,000	.20
1889A	20,749,000	.20	1898D	4,430,000	.25
1889D	8,433,000	.20	1898E	2,431,000	.25
1889E	4,330,000	.25	1898F	4,193,000	.25
1889F	5,010,000	.25	1898G	1,950,000	.25
1889G	3,410,000	.30	1898J	3,231,000	.25
1889J	3,307,000	.30	1899A	22,009,000	.20
Y31 design changed			1899D	4,590,000	.25
1890A	17,294,000	.20	1899E	3,725,000	.25
1890D	7,030,000	.20	1899F	4,300,000	.25
1890E	4,189,000	.25	1899G	2,550,000	.25
1890F	4,189,000	.25	1899J	2,416,000	.25
1890G	3,050,000	.25	1900A	51,804,000	.15
1890J	2,246,000	.25	1900D	14,634,000	.15
1891A	12,040,000	.20	1900E	7,886,000	.20
1891D	875,000	.50	1900F	7,886,000	.20
1891E	528,000	.75	1900G	6,137,000	.20
1891F	1,263,000	.30	1900J	9,916,000	.20
1891G	360,000	1.00	1901A	21,045,000	.15
1891J	1,836,000	.30	1901D	5,337,000	.20
1892A	22,340,000	.20	1901E	1,397,000	.25
1892D	6,139,000	.20	1901F	2,934,000	.20
1892E	3,195,000	.25	1901G	1,997,000	.25
1892F	5,013,000	.25	1901J	2,011,000	.20

	Mintage	Value		Mintage	Value
1902A	7,474,000	$ .20	1911D	8,656,000	$ .15
1902D	2,811,000	.20	1911E	5,235,000	.15
1902E	1,183,000	.25	1911F	5,780,000	.15
1902F	1,250,000	.25	1911G	2,075,000	.20
1902G	880,000	.40	1911J	5,594,000	.15
1902J	12,000	10.00	1912A	42,693,000	.15
1903A	12,690,000	.15	1912D	10,173,000	.15
1903D	3,140,000	.20	1912E	5,688,000	.15
1903E	1,955,000	.25	1912F	7,441,000	.15
1903F	2,945,000	.20	1912G	5,525,000	.15
1903G	1,376,000	.25	1912J	5,014,000	.15
1903J	2,832,000	.20	1913A	32,671,000	.15
1904A	28,625,000	.15	1913D	8,160,000	.15
1904D	4,118,000	.20	1913E	2,257,000	.20
1904E	2,778,000	.20	1913F	6,620,000	.15
1904F	3,620,000	.20	1913G	3,309,000	.20
1904G	3,231,000	.20	1913J	1,455,000	.25
1904J	4,467,000	.20	1914A		.15
1905A	19,630,000	.15	1914D		.25
1905D	6,083,000	.20	1914E	800,000	.50
1905E	3,564,000	.20	1914F	3,315,000	.20
1905F	5,053,000	.20	1914G	1,100,000	.25
1905G	3,051,000	.20	1914J		.25
1905J	4,085,000	.20	1915A		.15
1906A	46,921,000	.15	1915D		.25
1906D	5,633,000	.20	1915E		.25
1906E	7,277,000	.20	1915F	1,411,000	.25
1906F	6,895,000	.20	1915G		.25
1906G	5,193,000	.20	1915J		.25
1906J	3,622,000	.25	1916A		.15
1907A	33,710,000	.15	1916D		.25
1907D	14,690,000	.15	1916E		.25
1907E	3,718,000	.25	1916F	1,103,000	.25
1907F	7,303,000	.20	1916G		.25
1907G	3,051,000	.25	1916J		.25
1907J	6,721,000	.25	**Y19** (aluminum) 16mm		
1908A	21,921,000	.15	1916A		2.50
1908D	10,628,000	.15	1916F		2.50
1908E	3,400,000	.25	1916G		2.50
1908F	6,111,000	.25	1917A		.20
1908G	3,662,000	.25	1917D		.20
1908J	5,580,000	.25	1917E		.20
1909A	21,430,000	.15	1917F		.20
1909D	2,813,000	.25	1917G		.20
1909E	2,562,000	.25	1917J		.20
1909F	2,425,000	.25	1918A	3,564,107	2.00
1909G	1,220,000	.30	1918D	320,000	2.50
1909J	1,633,000	.25			
1910A	10,760,000	.15	*Republic — Rentenpfennig*		
1910D	4,220,000	.20	**Y32** (bronze) 17.5mm		
1910E	1,600,000	.25	1923A		.50
1910F	3,008,000	.20	1923D		.50
1910G	1,830,000	.25	1923E		.50
1910J	2,450,000	.20	1923F		.50
1911A	38,172,000	.15	1923G		.50

	Mintage	Value		Mintage	Value
1923J		$ .50	1934E		$ .20
1924A		.20	1934F		.20
1924D		.20	1934G		.20
1924E		.20	1934J		.20
1924F		.20	1935A		.20
1924G		.20	1935D		.20
1924J		.20	1935E		.20
1925A (error)		10.00	1935F		.20
1929A (error)		10.00	1935G		.20
1929F (error)		10.00	1935J		.20
			1936A		.20
Reichspfennig			1936D		.20
			1936E		.20
Y37			1936F		.20
1924A		.20	1936G		.20
1924D		.20	1936J		.20
1924E		.20			
1924F		.20			
1924G		.20	*Nazi Regime (Swastika)*		
1924J		.20			
1925A		.20	**Y88**		
1925D		.20	1936A		1.50
1925E		.20	1936E		1.50
1925F		.20	1936F		1.50
1925G		.20	1936G		1.50
1925J		.20	1936J		1.50
1927A		.20	1937A		.25
1927D		.20	1937D		.25
1927E		.20	1937E		.25
1927F		.20	1937F		.25
1927G		.20	1937G		.25
1928A		.20	1937J		.25
1928D		.20	1938A		.25
1928F		.20	1938B	2,378,000	1.00
1928G		.20	1938D		.25
1929A		.20	1938E		.25
1929D		.20	1938F		.25
1929E		.20	1938G		.25
1929F		.20	1938J		.25
1929G		.20	1939A		.25
1930A		.20	1939B	22,732,400	.25
1930D		.20	1939D		.25
1930E		.20	1939E		.25
1930F		.20	1939F		.25
1930G		.20	1939G		.25
1931A		.20	1939J		.25
1931D		.20	1940A		.40
1931E		.20	1940F		.40
1931F		.20	1940G		1.25
1931G		1.25	1940J		1.25
1932A		.20			
1933A		.20	**Y88a** (zinc)		
1933E		.20	1940A		.25
1933F		.20	1940B		.25
1934A		.20	1940D		.25
1934D		.20	1940E		.25
			1940F		.25

	Mintage	Value
1940G		$1.00
1940J		.25
1941A		.25
1941B		.25
1941D		.25
1941E		.25
1941F		.25
1941G		.25
1941J		.25
1942A		.25
1942B		.25
1942D		.25
1942E		.25
1942F		.25
1942G		.25
1942J		.25
1943A		.25
1943B		.25
1943D		.25
1943E		1.00
1943F		.25
1943G		.25
1943J		.25
1944A		.25
1944B		1.00
1944D		.25
1944E		.25
1944F		.25
1944G		.25
1945A		1.00
1945E		2.50

Post World War II —
Swastika Removed

Y98

	Mintage	Value
1944D (coined in 1945)		10.00
1945F		3.50
1946F		5.00
1946G	90,000	5.00

Currency Reform —
Bank Deutscher Lander

Y101 (bronze coated steel) 16.5mm

	Mintage	Value
1948D	45,500,000	.10
1948F	68,200,000	.10
1948G	45,600,000	.10
1948J	79,300,000	.10
1949D	100,600,000	.10
1949F	129,900,000	.10
1949G	50,500,000	.10
1949J	101,900,000	.10

Bundesrepublik Deutschland
Y105

	Mintage	Value
1950D	622,058,000	.10

	Mintage	Value
1950F	744,890,000	$ .10
1950G	458,612,000	.10
1950J	638,637,000	.10

Note: 1 PF. continue to be minted each year but are dated 1950. Above figures (1950) are through 1963.

2 PFENNIG

Empire

Y2 (copper) 20mm

	Mintage	Value
1873A	877,000	.75
1873B	289,000	1.50
1873C	160,000	2.00
1873D	2,359,000	.35
1873F	22,000	7.50
1873G	118,000	2.50
1874A	37,360,000	.25
1874B	10,310,000	.25
1874C	17,474,000	.25
1874D	5,237,000	.30
1874E	5,090,000	.30
1874F	6,404,000	.30
1874G	6,127,000	.30
1874H	2,706,000	.35
1875A	28,962,000	.25
1875B	15,843,000	.25
1875C	35,540,000	.25
1875D	11,159,000	.25
1875E	7,872,000	.30
1875F	9,827,000	.30
1875G	11,902,000	.25
1875H	3,309,000	.30
1875J	14,210,000	.25
1876A	18,906,000	.25
1876B	7,096,000	.30
1876C	12,279,000	.25
1876D	10,296,000	.25
1876E	4,988,000	.30
1876F	7,206,000	.30
1876G	3,502,000	.30
1876H	3,630,000	.30
1876J	1,995,000	.35
1877A	9,827,000	.25
1877B	60,000	4.50

Y4 design changed

	Mintage	Value
1904A	5,414,000	.20
1904D	1,404,000	.30
1904E	744,000	.50
1904F	1,002,000	.30
1904G	495,000	.75
1904J	43,000	5.00
1905A	5,171,000	.20
1905D	1,571,000	.30
1905E	9,244,000	.20

	Mintage	Value		Mintage	Value
1905F	1,115,000	$ .30	1916D		$ .25
1905G	1,030,000	.30	1916E		.25
1905J	1,608,000	.30	1916F	451,000	.75
1906A	8,459,000	.20	1916G		.25
1906D	3,539,000	.25	1916J		.25
1906E	2,055,000	.25			
1906F	2,839,000	.25	*Republic — Rentenpfennig*		
1906G	1,526,000	.30	**Y33** (bronze)		
1906J	1,907,000	.25	1923A		.20
1907A	13,467,000	.20	1923D		.20
1907D	1,921,000	.25	1923F		1.00
1907E	744,000	.50	1923G		.20
1907F	1,058,000	.30	1923J		.20
1907G	610,000	.60	1924A		.20
1907J	951,000	.50	1924D		.20
1908A	5,421,000	.20	1924E		.20
1908D	1,407,000	.30	1924F		.20
1908E	744,000	.50	1924G		.20
1908F	791,000	.50	1924J		.20
1908G	610,000	.60			
1908J	816,000	.50	*Reichspfennig*		
1910A	5,421,000	.20	**Y38**		
1910D	1,406,000	.30	1923F (error)		10.00
1910E	745,000	.50	1924A		.20
1910F	552,000	.60	1924D		.20
1910G	517,000	.60	1924E		.20
1910J	568,000	.60	1924F		.20
1911A	8,186,000	.20	1924G		.20
1911D	2,100,000	.25	1924J		.20
1911E	1,132,000	.30	1925A		.20
1911F	1,490,000	.30	1925D		.20
1911G	1,313,000	.30	1925E		.20
1911J	1,882,000	.30	1925F		.20
1912A	13,580,000	.20	1925G		.20
1912D	3,108,000	.25	1936A		.20
1912E	1,807,000	.30	1936D		.20
1912F	2,366,000	.25	1936E		.20
1912G	1,395,000	.30	1936F		.20
1912J	1,605,000	.30			
1913A	4,211,000	.25	*Nazi Regime (Swastika)*		
1913D	2,525,000	.25	**Y89**		
1913E	412,000	.75	1936A		1.50
1913F	1,601,000	.30	1936D		1.50
1913G	740,000	.50	1936F		1.50
1913J	1,233,000	.30	1937A		.25
1914A	1,500,000	.30	1937D		.25
1914E	457,000	.75	1937E		.25
1914F	157,000	2.00	1937F		.25
1914G	10,000	10.00	1937G		.25
1914J	600,000	.60	1937J		.25
1915A		.25	1938A		.25
1915D		.25	1938B	2,714,000	1.00
1915E		.25	1938D		.25
1915F	903,000	.50	1938E		.25
1916A		.25	1938F		.25

Mintage	Value		Mintage	Value
1938G...................	$ .25	1874B............5,053,000	$ .25
1938J....................	.25	1874C............3,611,000	.25
1939A...................	.25	1874D............2,446,000	.35
1939B............9,360,740	.25	1874E............5,465,000	.25
1939D...................	.25	1874F............3,561,000	.25
1939E...................	.25	1874G............2,721,000	.35
1939F...................	.25	1875A...........30,843,000	.20
1939G...................	.25	1875B...........11,657,000	.20
1939J....................	.25	1875C...........18,178,000	.20
1940A...................	.25	1875D...........12,379,000	.20
1940D...................	1.25	1875E............6,745,000	.25
1940E...................	1.25	1875F............9,757,000	.25
1940G...................	1.25	1875G...........10,219,000	.20
1940J....................	1.25	1875H.............702,000	.75
		1875J............9,780,000	.20

Bundesrepublik Deutschland

Y106 (bronze coated steel)

1950D...........26,262,000	.10	1876A...........22,342,000	.20
1950F...........30,278,000	.10	1876B............8,924,000	.20
1950G...........17,151,000	.10	1876C............8,679,000	.20
1950J...........27,216,000	.10	1876D...........14,467,000	.25
1958D...........15,088,000	.10	1876E............6,898,000	.25
1958F...........24,122,000	.10	1876F............6,826,000	.25
1958G...........13,112,000	.10	1876G............6,942,000	.25
1958J...........21,250,000	.10	1876H............3,026,000	.25
1959D...........22,526,000	.10	1876J...........11,920,000	.20
1959F...........25,017,000	.10	1888A............7,366,000	.25
1959G...........15,422,000	.10	1888D............1,966,000	.35
1959J...........32,231,000	.10	1888E............1,016,000	.35
1960D...........20,515,000	.10	1888F............1,412,000	.35
1960F...........13,060,000	.10	1888G.............853,000	.50
1960G............5,732,000	.10	1888J............1,129,000	.35
1960J...........12,609,000	.10	1889A...........10,803,000	.20
1961D...........12,278,000	.10	1889D............2,816,000	.35
1961F...........24,990,000	.10	1889E............1,491,000	.35
1961G...........17,321,000	.10	1889F............2,010,000	.35
1961J...........19,886,000	.10	1889G............1,220,000	.35
1962D...........20,481,000	.10	1889J............1,635,000	.35
1962F...........42,189,000	.10		

Y8 design changed

1962G...........25,029,000	.10	1890A............4,547,000	.25
1962J...........31,632,000	.10	1890D............2,813,000	.35
		1890E............1,086,000	.35

4 REICHSPFENNIG

Y39 (bronze) 22.5mm

1890F............1,068,000	.35
1932A......... ⎫	1.00	1890G.............948,000	.50
1932D......... ⎪	1.00	1890J............1,629,000	.35
1932E......... ⎬40,000,000	2.50	1891A............6,313,000	.25
1932F......... ⎪	1.00	1891E.............173,000	1.50
1932G......... ⎪	1.00	1891F.............942,000	.50
1932J......... ⎭	1.00	1891G.............942,000	1.25
		1892A............2,278,000	.35
		1892D.............920,000	.50

5 PFENNIG

Empire

Y5 (copper-nickel) 18mm

		1892E.............546,000	.75
		1892F.............264,000	1.00
		1892G.............800,000	.50
		1892J..............93,000	2.00
		1893A............8,571,000	.25
1874A...........10,002,000	.20	1893D.............920,000	.50

	Mintage	Value		Mintage	Value
1893E	1,148,000	$ .35	1903E	1,113,000	$ .35
1893F	1,546,000	.35	1903F	1,209,000	.35
1893G	421,000	1.00	1903G	610,000	.75
1893J	1,544,000	.35	1903J	816,000	.50
1894A	10,830,000	.20	1904A	3,791,000	.25
1894D	2,812,000	.35	1904D	1,408,000	.35
1894E	802,000	.50	1904E	745,000	.75
1894G	280,000	1.00	1904F	905,000	.50
1894J	1,634,000	.35	1904G	610,000	.75
1895E	686,000	.75	1904J	817,000	.50
1895F	2,004,000	.35	1905A	8,128,000	.20
1895G	940,000	.50	1905D	2,109,000	.35
1896A	1,459,000	.35	1905E	1,116,000	.35
1896E	658,000	.75	1905F	1,504,000	.35
1896F	400,000	1.00	1905G	914,000	.50
1896G	inc. w/1897G	3.00	1905J	1,225,000	.35
1896J	1,633,000	.35	1906A	18,970,000	.15
1897A	9,390,000	.25	1906D	4,921,000	.25
1897D	2,812,000	.35	1906E	2,605,000	.35
1897E	852,000	.50	1906F	3,511,000	.25
1897F	1,609,000	.35	1906G	2,135,000	.35
1897G	1,609,000	.35	1906J	2,859,000	.35
1897J	1,220,000	.35	1907A	11,929,000	.15
1898A	10,836,000	.15	1907D	2,112,000	.35
1898D	2,812,000	.35	1907E	1,517,000	.35
1898E	1,492,000	.35	1907F	1,844,000	.35
1898F	2,006,000	.35	1907G	915,000	.50
1898G	1,220,000	.35	1907J	1,635,000	.35
1898J	1,634,000	.35	1908A	22,114,000	.15
1899A	10,883,000	.15	1908D	4,491,000	.25
1899D	2,812,000	.35	1908E	2,918,000	.35
1899E	1,487,000	.35	1908F	5,123,000	.25
1899F	2,005,000	.35	1908G	3,346,000	.25
1899G	1,221,000	.35	1908J	3,263,000	.25
1899J	1,633,000	.35	1909A	5,796,000	.25
1900A	18,941,000	.10	1909D	2,758,000	.35
1900D	4,254,000	.25	1909E	983,000	.50
1900E	2,235,000	.35	1909F	251,000	1.00
1900F	3,208,000	.25	1909J	1,632,000	.35
1900G	2,135,000	.35	1910A	7,343,000	.20
1900J	2,859,000	.35	1910D	2,813,000	.35
1901A	8,155,000	.20	1910E	1,290,000	.35
1901D	2,779,000	.35	1910F	1,581,000	.35
1901E	1,492,000	.35	1910G	1,222,000	.35
1901F	1,810,000	.35	1910J	152,000	1.50
1901G	914,000	.50	1911A	15,660,000	.15
1901J	1,225,000	.35	1911D	2,220,000	.35
1902A	8,949,000	.20	1911E	1,770,000	.35
1902D	2,812,000	.35	1911F	1,814,000	.35
1902E	1,120,000	.35	1911G	1,833,000	.35
1902F	1,800,000	.35	1911J	3,115,000	.25
1902G	1,220,000	.35	1912A	19,300,000	.15
1902J	1,636,000	.35	1912D	4,015,000	.25
1903A	5,932,000	.25	1912E	2,568,000	.25
1903D	1,406,000	.35	1912F	3,529,000	.25

	Mintage	Value
1912G	2,440,000	$ .35
1912J	3,020,000	.25
1913A	15,705,000	.15
1913D	5,519,000	.25
1913E	2,373,000	.35
1913F	2,053,000	.35
1913G	1,230,000	.35
1913J	252,000	1.00
1914A	12,000,000	.15
1914D		.25
1914E		.25
1914F	2,205,000	.35
1914G		.25
1914J		.25
1915D		.25
1915E		.25
1915F	1,893,000	.35
1915G		.25
1915J		.25

Y21 new design (iron) 17.5mm

		Value
1915A		.15
1915D		.15
1915E		.15
1915F		.15
1915G		.15
1915J		.15
1916A		.15
1916D		.15
1916E		.15
1916F		15
1916G		.15
1916J		.15
1917A		.15
1917D		.15
1917E		.15
1917F		.15
1917G		.15
1917J		.15
1918A		.15
1918D		.15
1918E		.15
1918F		.15
1918G		.15
1918J		.15

Y23 similar

		Value
1919A		.15
1919D		.15
1919E		.15
1919F		.15
1919G		.15
1919J		.15
1920A		.15
1920D		.15
1920E		.15

	Mintage	Value
1920F		$ .15
1920G		.15
1920J		.15
1921A		.15
1921D		.15
1921E		.15
1921F		.15
1921G		.15
1921J		.15
1922D		.15
1922E		.15
1922F		.15
1922G		.15
1922J		.15

Republic — Rentenpfennig
Y34 (aluminum-bronze) 18mm

		Value
1923A		.15
1923D		.15
1923F		1.50
1923G		.15
1924A		.15
1924D		15
1924E		.15
1924F		.15
1924G		.15
1924J		.15

Reichspfennig
Y40

	Mintage	Value
1924A		20
1924D		.20
1924E		.20
1924F		.20
1924G		.20
1924J		.20
1925A		.20
1925D		.20
1925E		.20
1925F		.20
1925G		.20
1925J		.20
1926A		.20
1926E		.20
1926F		.20
1930A	6,737,012	.20
1935A		.20
1935D		.20
1935E		.20
1935F		.20
1935G		.20
1935J		.20
1936A		.20
1936D		.20
1936E		.20

	Mintage	Value
1936F		$ .20
1936G		.20
1936J		.20

Nazi Regime (Swastika)
Y90

		Value
1936A		1.00
1936D		1.00
1936G		1.00
1937A		.25
1937D		.25
1937E		.25
1937F		.25
1937G		.25
1937J		.25
1938A		.25
1938B		.25
1938D		.25
1938E		.25
1938F		.25
1938G		.25
1938J		.25
1939A		.25
1939B		.25
1939D		.25
1939E		.25
1939F		.25
1939G		.25
1939J		.25

Y90a (zinc)

		Value
1940A		.25
1940B		.25
1940D		.25
1940E		.25
1940F		.25
1940G		.25
1940J		.25
1941A		.25
1941B		.25
1941D		.25
1941E		.25
1941F		.25
1941G		.25
1941J		.25
1942A		.25
1942B		.25
1942D		.25
1942E		.25
1942F		.25
1942G		.25
1943A		1.00
1943B		1.00
1943D		1.00
1943E		1.00
1943F		.50

	Mintage	Value
1943G		$ .50
1944A		2.50
1944B		2.50
1944D		.50
1944E		.50
1944F		.50
1944G		2.50

Post World War II —
Swastika Removed
Y99

		Value
1947A		3.50
1947D	2,900,000	6.00
1947E		8.00
1948A		4.00
1948E		8.00

Currency Reform —
Bank Deutscher Lander
Y102 (brass coated steel) 18.5mm

	Mintage	Value
1949D	62,483,000	.10
1949F	28,350,000	.10
1949G	52,080,000	.10
1949J	68,977,000	.10

Bundesrepublik Deutschland
Y107

	Mintage	Value
1950D	211,209,000	.10
1950F	320,172,000	.10
1950G	157,629,000	.10
1950J	221,509,000	.10

Note: See 1 PF. (1950) above.

10 PFENNIG
Empire
Y6 (copper-nickel) 21mm

	Mintage	Value
1873A	930,000	.50
1873B	332,000	1.00
1873C	522,000	.75
1873D	471,000	1.00
1873F	476,000	1.00
1873G	518,000	.75
1873H	43,000	3.50
1874A	7,664,000	.20
1874B	2,669,000	.25
1874C	12,029,000	.20
1874D	3,585,000	.25
1874E	3,157,000	.25
1874F	7,309,000	.20
1874G	5,550,000	.20
1874H	3,323,000	.25
1875A	15,522,000	.20
1875B	4,120,000	.25
1875C	8,304,000	.20
1875D	13,365,000	.20
1875E	9,832,000	.20

	Mintage	Value		Mintage	Value
1875F	7,974,000	$ .20	1898D	2,813,000	$ .25
1875G	5,389,000	.20	1898E	805,000	.50
1875H	4,267,000	.25	1898F	2,006,000	.35
1875J	9,406,000	.20	1898G	570,000	.75
1876A	34,175,000	.20	1898J	1,635,000	.25
1876B	10,120,000	.20	1899A	10,837,000	.20
1876C	13,214,000	.20	1899D	3,813,000	.25
1876D	16,787,000	.20	1899E	2,175,000	.35
1876E	6,160,000	.20	1899F	2,008,000	.35
1876F	7,034,000	.20	1899G	1,292,000	.35
1876G	6,222,000	.20	1899J	1,635,000	.35
1876H	3,222,000	.25	1900A	34,558,000	.15
1876J	11,314,000	.20	1900D	8,694,000	.15
1888A	8,519,000	.20	1900E	4,490,000	.25
1888D	2,493,000	.25	1900F	5,932,000	.20
1888E	1,268,000	.35	1900G	4,239,000	.25
1888F	1,340,000	.35	1900J	5,720,000	.20
1888G	1,081,000	1.00	1901A	10,200,000	.15
1888J	1,436,000	.35	1901D	3,252,000	.25
1889A	11,451,000	.20	1901E	1,863,000	.35
1889D	2,813,000	.25	1901F	2,594,000	.25
1889E	1,492,000	.35	1901G	1,526,000	.35
1889F	2,432,000	.25	1901J	1,225,000	.35
1889G	1,222,000	.35	1902A	5,878,000	.20
1889J	1,637,000	.35	1902D	1,406,000	.35
			1902E	501,000	.75
Y9 design changed			1902F	1,002,000	.35
1890A	6,878,000	.20	1902G	609,000	.75
1890F	784,000	.50	1902J	815,000	.50
1890G	976,000	.50	1903A	5,130,000	.20
1890J	1,637,000	.35	1903D	1,406,000	.35
1891A	4,239,000	.25	1903E	987,000	.50
1891D	2,812,000	.25	1903F	1,002,000	.35
1891E	1,489,000	.35	1903G	610,000	.75
1891F	1,226,000	.35	1903J	816,000	.50
1891G	246,000	1.50	1904A	5,189,000	.20
1892A	2,413,000	.25	1904D	1,055,000	.35
1892D	2,812,000	.25	1904E	558,000	.75
1892E	810,000	.50	1904F	752,000	.50
1892F	663,000	.75	1904G	457,000	1.00
1892G	300,000	1.00	1904J	612,000	.75
1893A	8,435,000	.20	1905A	8,649,000	.15
1893E	362,000	1.00	1905D	1,846,000	.35
1893F	1,345,000	.35	1905E	979,000	.50
1893G	920,000	.50	1905F	1,310,000	.35
1893J	1,635,000	.35	1905G	642,000	.75
1894E	259,000	1.50	1905J	1,429,000	.35
1896A	4,996,000	.25	1906A	14,369,000	.15
1896D	2,812,000	.25	1906D	4,132,000	.25
1896E	1,495,000	.35	1906E	2,188,000	.35
1896F	2,008,000	.35	1906F	2,953,000	.25
1896G	200,000	1.50	1906G	1,952,000	.35
1896J	1,632,000	.35	1906J	2,042,000	.35
1897A	5,842,000	.20	1907A	17,970,000	.15
1897G	1,019,000	.35	1907D	2,812,000	.25
1898A	10,833,000	.20			

	Mintage	Value
1907E	2,290,000	$ .35
1907F	3,205,000	.25
1907G	1,888,000	.35
1907J	2,750,000	.25
1908A	20,409,000	.15
1908D	6,772,000	.20
1908E	2,490,000	.25
1908F	3,535,000	.25
1908G	1,707,000	.35
1908J	2,649,000	.25
1909A	2,269,000	.25
1909D	966,000	.50
1909E	805,000	.50
1909F	780,000	.50
1909G	980,000	.50
1909J	724,000	.50
1910A	3,734,000	.25
1910D	1,406,000	.35
1910E	300,000	1.00
1910F	1,002,000	.35
1910G	610,000	.75
1911A	13,554,000	.15
1911D	2,507,000	.25
1911E	2,245,000	.25
1911F	2,235,000	.25
1911G	1,678,000	.35
1911J	3,062,000	.25
1912A	21,312,000	.15
1912D	6,988,000	.20
1912E	2,648,000	.25
1912F	3,786,000	.25
1912G	2,441,000	.25
1912J	2,740,000	.25
1913A	13,466,000	.15
1913D	3,164,000	.25
1913E	1,477,000	.35
1913F	1,990,000	.35
1913G	1,372,000	.35
1913J	1,549,000	.35
1914A	13,000,000	.15
1914D	4,500,000	.25
1914E	2,000,000	.35
1914F	4,514,000	.25
1914G	3,000,000	.25
1914J	3,000,000	.25
1915A	6,846,000	.20
1915D	1,886,000	.35
1915E	730,000	.50
1915F	1,507,000	.35
1915G	404,000	1.00
1915J	150,000	2.00
1916D	179,000	1.75

Y22 new design (iron)

	Mintage	Value
1915A		2.50
1916A		.20

	Mintage	Value
1916D		$ .20
1916E		.20
1916F		.20
1916G		.20
1916J		.20
1917A		.20
1917D		.20
1917E		.20
1917F		.20
1917G		.20
1917J		.20
1918D	42,054	2.50

Y24 similar

	Mintage	Value
1921A		1.00
1922D		1.00
1922E		1.00
1922F		1.00
1922G		1.00
1922J		1.00

Y20 design changed (zinc)
no mint mark

	Mintage	Value
1917	121,547,000	.15
1918	166,369,000	.15

Y25 similar

	Mintage	Value
1919	189,702,000	.15
1920	245,321,000	.15
1921	357,979,000	.15
1922	162,474,000	.15

Republic — Rentenpfennig
Y35 (aluminum-bronze)

	Mintage	Value
1923A		.15
1923D		.15
1923F		1.00
1923G		.15
1924A		.15
1924D		.15
1924E		.15
1924F		.15
1924G		.15
1924J		.15
1925F	about 12,500	7.50

Reichspfennig
Y41

	Mintage	Value
1924A		.20
1924D		.20
1924E		.20
1924F		.20
1924G		.20
1924J		.20
1925A		.20
1925D		.20

	Mintage	Value		Mintage	Value
1925E		$ .20	1937A		$ .25
1925F		.20	1937D		.25
1925G		.20	1937E		25
1925J		.20	1937F		25
1926A		.20	1937G		.25
1926G		.20	1937J		.25
1928A		.20	1938A		.25
1928G		.20	1938B		.25
1929A		.20	1938D		.25
1929D		.20	1938E		.25
1929E		.20	1938F		.25
1929F		.20	1938G		.25
1929G		.20	1938J		.25
1929J		.20	1939A		.25
1930A		.20	1939B		.25
1930D		.20	1939D		.25
1930E		.20	1939E		.25
1930F		.20	1939F		.25
1930G		.20	1939G		.25
1930J		.20	1939J		.25
1931A		.20			
1931D		.20	**Y91a** (zinc)		
1931F		.20	1940A		.25
1931G		.20	1940B		.25
1932A		.20	1940D		.25
1932D		.20	1940E		.25
1932E	1,490,518	1.00	1940F		.25
1932F		.20	1940G		.25
1932G		1.00	1940J		.25
1933A		.20	1941A		.25
1933G		20	1941B		.25
1933J		.20	1941D		.25
1934A		.20	1941E		.25
1934D		.20	1941F		.25
1934E		.20	1941G		.25
1934F		.20	1941J		.25
1934G		.20	1942A		.25
1935A		.20	1942B		.25
1935D		.20	1942D		.25
1935E		.20	1942E		.25
1935F		.20	1942F		.25
1935G		.20	1942G		.25
1935J		.20	1942J		.25
1936A		.20	1943A		.25
1936D		.20	1943B		2.50
1936E		.20	1943D		.25
1936F		.20	1943E		.25
1936G		.20	1943F		.25
1936J		.20	1943G		.25
			1943J		.25
			1944A		.25
Nazi Regime (Swastika)			1944B		.25
Y91			1944D		.25
1936A		1.00	1944E		.25
1936E		1.00	1944F		.25
1936G		1.00	1944G		.25

	Mintage	Value
1945A		$1.00
1945E		1.00

Post World War II —
Swastika Removed

Y100

	Mintage	Value
1945F		2.00
1946F		3.00
1946G	144,000	3.00
1947A		2.50
1947E		5.00
1947F		3.00
1948A		4.00
1948E		6.00
1948F		4.00

Currency Reform —
Bank Deutscher Lander

Y103 (brass coated steel) 21.5mm

	Mintage	Value
1949D	125,898,000	.10
1949F	120,932,000	.10
1949G	87,852,000	.10
1949J	154,095,000	.10

Bundesrepublik Deutschland

Y108

	Mintage	Value
1950D	331,561,000	.10
1950F	425,676,000	.10
1950G	260,176,000	.10
1950J	314,403,000	.10

Note: See 1 PF. (1950) above.

20 PFENNIG

Empire

Y12 (silver) 16mm

	Mintage	Value
1873A	2,157,000	.75
1873B	664,000	1.50
1873C	903,000	1.50
1873D	1,200,000	1.00
1873E	10,000	15.00
1873F	449,000	2.00
1873G	763,000	1.50
1873H	54,000	6.00
1874A	8,829,000	.50
1874B	9,222,000	.50
1874C	1,303,000	1.00
1874D	10,086,000	.50
1874E	2,281,000	.75
1874F	7,222,000	.50
1874G	3,281,000	.75
1874H	1,841,000	1.00
1875A	9,034,000	.50
1875B	2,768,000	.75
1875C	5,938,000	.50
1875D	15,031,000	.50

	Mintage	Value
1875E	1,486,000	$1.00
1875F	7,667,000	.50
1875G	3,939,000	.75
1875H	1,340,000	1.00
1875J	3,501,000	.75
1876A	6,959,000	.50
1876B	5,088,000	.50
1876C	5,911,000	.50
1876D	14,151,000	.50
1876E	11,648,000	.50
1876F	13,635,000	.50
1876G	7,820,000	.50
1876H	1,432,000	1.00
1876J	10,272,000	.50
1877F	700,000	2.00

Y7 new design (nickel) 23mm

	Mintage	Value
1887A	2,711,000	1.00
1887D	703,000	1.00
1887E	372,000	3.00
1887F	502,000	2.00
1887G	305,000	3.00
1887J	408,000	2.00
1888A	5,426,000	1.00
1888D	1,406,000	1.00
1888E	744,000	1.50
1888F	1,005,000	1.00
1888G	610,000	1.50
1888J	818,000	1.00

Y10 reverse design changed

	Mintage	Value
1890A	2,715,000	1.00
1890D	703,000	1.00
1890E	373,000	2.00
1890F	502,000	1.00
1890G	305,000	2.00
1890J	409,000	1.50
1892A	2,712,000	1.00
1892D	703,000	1.00
1892E	372,000	2.00
1892F	502,000	1.00
1892G	304,000	2.00
1892J	408,000	1.50

25 PFENNIG

Empire

Y11 (nickel) 23mm

	Mintage	Value
1909A	962,000	1.50
1909D	1,406,000	1.25
1909E	250,000	2.25
1909F	400,000	2.00
1909G	609,000	1.50
1909J	10,000	12.50
1910A	9,522,000	1.00
1910D	1,408,000	1.25
1910E	1,241,000	1.25

	Mintage	Value
1910F	1,604,000	$1.25
1910G	329,000	2.00
1910J	1,561,000	1.25
1911A	3,178,000	1.00
1911D	506,000	1.75
1911E	747,000	1.50
1911G	892,000	1.50
1911J	516,000	1.75
1912A	2,590,000	1.25
1912D	900,000	1.50
1912F	1,002,000	1.25
1912J	362,000	2.00

50 PFENNIG

Empire

Y13 (silver) 20mm

	Mintage	Value
1875A	7,094,000	.75
1875B	2,799,000	1.00
1875C	2,046,000	1.00
1875D	4,668,000	.75
1875E	352,000	1.75
1875F	813,000	1.50
1875G	2,033,000	1.00
1875H	175,000	2.00
1875J	2,411,000	1.00
1876A	34,475,000	.60
1876B	11,016,000	.60
1876C	10,945,000	.60
1876D	3,641,000	1.00
1876E	4,127,000	1.00
1876F	4,488,000	1.00
1876G	1,796,000	1.25
1876H	1,876,000	1.25
1876J	3,588,000	1.00
1877A	3,248,000	1.00
1877B	3,690,000	1.00
1877C	2,387,000	1.25
1877D	3,004,000	1.00
1877E	1,120,000	1.25
1877F	1,310,000	1.25
1877H	621,000	1.50
1877J	1,525,000	1.25

Y14 small eagle in wreath

	Mintage	Value
1877A	6,745,000	2.00
1877B	3,096,000	2.00
1877C	2,819,000	2.00
1877D	5,315,000	2.00
1877E	2,296,000	2.00
1877F	2,145,000	2.00
1877G	2,060,000	2.00
1877H	1,510,000	2.00
1877J	1,332,000	2.00
1878E	364,000	5.00

Y15 large eagle

	Mintage	Value
1896A	388,945	$5.00
1898A	387,000	5.00
1900J	191,792	5.00
1901A	194,341	5.00
1902F	95,355	6.00
1903A	384,187	5.00

½ MARK

Y16 (silver) 20mm

	Mintage	Value
1905A	37,765,000	.30
1905D	7,636,000	.35
1905E	4,907,000	.35
1905F	6,310,000	.35
1905G	3,866,000	.35
1905J	6,315,000	.35
1906A	29,753,000	.25
1906D	11,976,000	.25
1906E	5,821,000	.35
1906F	8,035,000	.35
1906G	4,272,000	.35
1906J	2,179,000	.50
1907A	14,168,000	.25
1907D	2,883,000	.50
1907E	600,000	1.50
1907F	1,702,000	.75
1907G	926,000	1.00
1907J	3,268,000	.50
1908A	5,018,000	.35
1908D	400,000	1.75
1908E	591,000	1.50
1908F	——	7.50
1908G	675,000	1.50
1908J	1,308,000	.75
1909A	5,403,000	.35
1909D	1,000,000	.75
1909E	745,000	1.00
1909F	999,000	1.00
1909G	606,000	1.50
1909J	815,000	1.00
1911A	2,709,000	.50
1911D	703,000	1.50
1911E	375,000	1.75
1911F	501,000	1.50
1911G	610,000	1.50
1911J	417,000	1.75
1912A	2,709,000	.50
1912D	703,000	1.50
1912E	369,000	1.75
1912F	502,000	1.50
1912J	399,000	1.75
1913A	5,419,000	.35
1913D	1,406,000	.75
1913E	745,000	1.00
1913F	1,003,000	.75

	Mintage	Value
1913G	610,000	$1.50
1913J	367,000	1.75
1914A		.35
1914D	26,562,000	.35
1914J		.35
1915A		.35
1915D		.35
1915E		.35
1915F	5,309,000	.35
1915G		.35
1915J		.35
1916A		.35
1916D		.35
1916E		.35
1916F	2,410,000	.50
1916G		.35
1916J		.35
1917A		.35
1917D		.35
1917E		.35
1917F	450,000	1.75
1917G		.35
1917J		.35
1918A		.35
1918D		.35
1918E		.35
1918F	4,010,000	.35
1918G		.35
1918J		.35

Y27

	Mintage	Value
1919A		1.00
1919D		1.00
1919E		2.00
1919F	1,559,000	1.00
1919J		1.00

50 PFENNIG

Y26 (aluminum) 23mm

	Value
1919A	.15
1919D	1.00
1919Œ	1.00
1919F	1.00
1919G	1.00
1919J	1.00
1920A	.15
1920D	.15
1920Œ	.15
1920F	.15
1920G	.15
1920J	.15
1921A	.15
1921D	.15
1921Œ	.15
1921F	.15

	Mintage	Value
1921G		$ .15
1921J		.15
1922A		.15
1922D		.15
1922Œ		.15
1922F		.15
1922G		.15
1922J		.15

Rentenpfennig

Y36 (aluminum-bronze) 24mm

	Value
1923A	.35
1923D	.35
1923F	.35
1923G	.35
1923J	1.00
1924A	.35
1924D	.35
1924E	.35
1924F	.35
1924G	.35
1924J	.35

Reichspfennig

Y42

	Mintage	Value
1924A		20.00
1924E	1,805,000	20.00
1924F	55,432	20.00
1924G	11,224	20.00
1925E	inc. w/1924E	20.00
1925F	inc. w/1924F	20.00

Y43 new design (nickel) 20mm

	Mintage	Value
1927A		.30
1927D		.30
1927E	27,300,000	.30
1927F		.30
1927G		.30
1927J		.30
1928A		.30
1928D		.30
1928E	89,200,000	.30
1928F		.30
1928G		.30
1928J		.30
1929A		.30
1929D	13,400,000	.30
1929F		.30
1930A		.30
1930D		.30
1930E	7,700,000	.30
1930F		.30
1930G		.30
1930J		.30

	Mintage	Value
1931A.........		$ .30
1931D.........		.30
1931F.........	8,500,000	.30
1931G.........		.30
1931J.........		.30
1932E.........	300,000	1.00
1932G.........		1.00
1933G.........	1,400,000	.30
1933J.........		.30
1935A.........		.30
1935D.........		.30
1935E.........		.30
1935F.........		.30
1935G.........		.30
1935J.........		.30

Y80 (aluminum) 22mm

1935A.........		.25
1935D.........		.25
1935E.........		.25
1935F.........		.25
1935G.........		.25
1935J.........		.25

Y43

1936A.........		.30
1936D.........		.30
1936E.........		.30
1936F.........		.30
1936G.........		.30
1936J.........		.30
1937A.........		.30
1937D.........		.30
1937F.........		.30
1937J.........		.30
1938E.........		.30
1938G.........		.30
1938J.........		.30

Nazi Regime (Swastika)

Y93

1938A.........		7.50
1938B.........		7.50
1938D.........		7.50
1938E.........		7.50
1938F.........		7.50
1938G.........		7.50
1938J.........		7.50
1939A.........		7.50
1939B.........		17.50
1939D.........		7.50
1939E.........		7.50
1939F.........		7.50
1939G.........		7.50
1939J.........		7.50

Y92 (aluminum) 23mm

	Mintage	Value
1939A.........		$ .30
1939B.........		1.00
1939D.........		.30
1939E.........		.30
1939F.........		.30
1939G.........		.30
1939J.........		.30
1940A.........		.30
1940B.........		.30
1940D.........		.30
1940E.........		.30
1940F.........		.30
1940G.........		1.00
1940J.........		.20
1941A.........		.20
1941B.........		.20
1941D.........		.20
1941E.........		.20
1941F.........		.20
1941G.........		.20
1941J.........		.20
1942A.........		.20
1942B.........		.20
1942D.........		.20
1942E.........		.20
1942F.........		.20
1942G.........		.20
1943A.........		.20
1943B.........		.20
1943D.........		.20
1943G.........		.20
1943J.........		.20
1944B.........		.30
1944D.........		1.00
1944F.........		.30
1944G.........		1.00

Bank Deutscher Lander

Y104 (copper-nickel) 20mm

	Mintage	Value
1949D..........	39,080,000	.30
1949F..........	45,118,000	.30
1949G..........	25,058,000	.30
1949J..........	28,050,000	.30
1950G..........	30,000	3.50

Bundesrepublik Deutschland

Y109

	Mintage	Value
1950D..........	71,466,000	.25
1950F..........	115,461,000	.25
1950G..........	49,058,000	.25
1950J..........	73,292,000	.25

Note: See 1 PF. (1950) above.

Mintage	Value
1 MARK	
Empire	
Y17 (silver) 24mm	
1873A............929,000	$1.00
1873B.............89,000	3.50
1873C.............18,000	7.50
1873D............244,000	2.00
1873F............109,000	3.00
1874A..........6,310,000	.50
1874B..........2,672,000	.75
1874C............840,000	1.25
1874D..........7,079,000	.50
1874E..........3,239,000	.60
1874F..........6,155,000	.50
1874G..........4,209,000	.60
1874H..........1,892,000	.75
1875A.........30,340,000	.50
1875B..........7,689,000	.50
1875C..........6,209,000	.50
1875D..........7,538,000	.50
1875E..........4,645,000	.60
1875F..........7,073,000	.50
1875G..........6,072,000	.50
1875H..........2,727,000	.75
1875J..........2,299,000	.75
1876A.........17,296,000	.50
1876C..........4,789,000	.60
1876D..........2,955,000	.75
1876F..........4,160,000	.60
1876G..........2,332,000	.75
1876H..........1,108,000	1.00
1876J..........2,481,000	.75
1877A............697,000	1.50
1877B.............48,000	4.50
1878A..........1,526,000	.75
1878B............581,000	1.50
1878C............600,000	1.50
1878E............317,000	2.00
1878F..........1,038,000	.75
1878G............525,000	1.50
1878J............895,000	1.25
1879A............156,000	2.50
1880A..........1,071,000	1.00
1880D............337,000	2.00
1880E............172,719	2.50
1880F............223,000	2.50
1880G............145,000	2.50
1880H............196,000	2.50
1880J............163,000	2.50
1881A..........6,386,000	.50
1881D..........2,040,000	.75
1881E..........1,333,184	1.00
1881F..........1,203,000	1.00
1881G............426,000	1.75
1881H............790,000	1.25

Mintage	Value
1881J............386,000	$1.75
1882A..........1,474,000	.75
1882F............252,000	2.00
1882G............458,000	1.75
1882H............397,000	1.75
1882J............109,000	3.00
1883A............809,000	1.25
1883D............208,000	2.50
1883E............112,000	3.00
1883F............147,000	2.50
1883G.............91,000	3.50
1883J............120,000	3.00
1885A..........1,467,000	.75
1885G............468,000	1.75
1885J............413,000	1.75
1886A..........1,100,000	1.00
1886D..........1,445,000	.75
1886E............764,000	1.25
1886F..........1,030,000	1.00
1886G............160,000	2.50
1886J............427,000	1.75
1887A..........3,005,000	.60
Y18 reverse design changed	
1891A............711,000	1.00
1891D........inc. w/1892D	20.00
1892A............908,000	.75
1892D............418,000	1.25
1892E............222,000	2.00
1892F............301,000	1.50
1892G............182,000	2.50
1892J............236,000	2.00
1893A..........1,603,000	.50
1893D............425,000	1.25
1893E............224,000	2.00
1893F............299,000	2.00
1893J............253,000	2.00
1894G............183,000	2.50
1896A..........2,159,000	.50
1896D............562,000	1.00
1896E............296,000	2.00
1896F............400,000	1.25
1896G............243,000	2.00
1896J............326,000	1.50
1898A..........1,000,000	.50
1899A..........1,438,000	.50
1899D............632,000	1.00
1899E............335,000	1.50
1899F............392,000	1.50
1899G............273,000	2.00
1899J............367,000	1.50
1900A..........1,625,000	.50
1900D............420,000	1.25
1900E............223,000	2.00
1900F............300,000	1.50
1900G............183,000	2.50

	Mintage	Value
1900J	245,000	$2.00
1901A	3,821,000	.50
1901D	914,000	.75
1901E	484,000	1.25
1901F	802,000	.75
1901G	579,000	1.00
1901J	530,000	1.00
1902A	5,222,000	.50
1902D	1,546,000	.50
1902E	818,000	.75
1902F	952,000	.75
1902G	269,000	2.00
1902J	898,000	.75
1903A	3,965,000	.50
1903D	914,000	.75
1903E	485,000	1.25
1903F	652,000	1.00
1903G	613,000	1.00
1903J	531,000	1.00
1904A	3,242,000	.50
1904D	1,761,000	.50
1904E	961,000	.75
1904F	about 750,000	1.00
1904G	663,000	1.00
1904J	1,020,000	.50
1905A	10,303,000	.50
1905D	1,759,000	.50
1905E	931,000	.75
1905F	about 500,000	1.25
1905G	859,000	.75
1905J	1,021,000	.50
1906A	5,413,000	.50
1906D	1,412,000	.50
1906E	745,000	1.00
1906F	2,256,000	.50
1906G	609,000	1.00
1906J	372,000	1.50
1907A	9,201,000	.50
1907D	2,387,000	.50
1907E	1,255,000	.50
1907F	1,703,000	.50
1907G	1,035,000	.50
1907J	1,833,000	.50
1908A	4,331,000	.50
1908D	1,126,000	.50
1908E	596,000	1.00
1908F	801,000	.75
1908G	488,000	1.25
1908J	653,000	1.00
1909A	4,150,000	.50
1909D	1,968,000	.50
1909E		5.00
1909G	854,000	.75
1909J	53,000	5.00
1910A	5,869,000	.50

	Mintage	Value
1910D	1,406,000	$ .50
1910E	1,050,000	.50
1910F	1,631,000	.50
1910G	610,000	1.00
1910J	1,094,000	.50
1911A	5,693,000	.35
1911D	126,000	2.50
1911E	737,000	1.00
1911F	773,000	1.00
1911G	305,000	1.50
1911J	812,000	.75
1912A	1,928,000	.50
1912D	632,000	1.00
1912E	707,000	1.00
1912F	502,000	1.00
1912J	408,000	1.25
1913F	450,000	2.50
1913G	274,000	2.50
1913J	367,000	2.50
1914A	11,500,000	.50
1914D	3,515,000	.50
1914E	1,762,000	.50
1914F	2,300,000	.50
1914G	1,500,000	.50
1914J	1,900,000	.50
1915A	9,167,000	.50
1915D	704,000	1.00
1915E	566,000	1.00
1915F	2,910,000	.50
1915G	799,000	.75
1915J	1,234,000	.50
1916F	306,000	1.50

Coinage Reform

Y44 22.5mm

	Mintage	Value
1924A		1.00
1924D		1.00
1924E		1.00
1924F		1.00
1924G		1.00
1924J		1.00
1925A		1.00
1925D		1.00

Reichsmark

Y45

	Mintage	Value
1925A		1.00
1925D		1.00
1925E	104,000,000	1.00
1925F		1.00
1925G		1.00
1925J		1.00

	Mintage	Value		Mintage	Value
1926A	⎫	$1.00	1954D	5,201,000	$ .50
1926D	⎪	1.00	1954F	6,000,000	.50
1926E	⎬ 51,000,000	1.00	1954G	3,459,000	.50
1926F	⎪	1.00	1954J	5,340,000	.50
1926G	⎪	1.00	1955D	3,100,000	.50
1926J	⎭	1.00	1955F	4,909,000	.50
1927A	⎫	12.50	1955G	2,500,000	.50
1927F	⎬ 4,800,000	2.00	1955J	3,000,000	.50
1927J	⎭	1.00	1956D	12,230,000	.50

Y81 new design (nickel) 23mm

	Value		Mintage	Value
1933A	.60	1956F	14,699,000	.50
1933D	.60	1956G	8,362,000	.50
1933E	.60	1956J	11,477,000	.50
1933F	.60	1957D	6,820,000	.50
1933G	.60	1957F	6,389,000	.50
1934A	.60	1957G	3,840,000	.50
1934D	.60	1957J	6,631,000	.50
1934E	.60	1958D	4,150,000	.50
1934F	.60	1958F	4,109,000	.50
1934G	.60	1958G	3,459,000	.50
1934J	.60	1958J	4,656,000	.50
1935A	.60	1959D	10,406,000	.50
1935E	.60	1959F	11,972,000	.50
1935J	.60	1959G	6,921,000	.50
1936A	.60	1959J	10,690,000	.50
1936D	.60	1960D	5,462,000	.50
1936E	.60	1960F	5,709,000	.50
1936F	.60	1960G	3,610,000	.50
1936G	.60	1960J	5,608,000	.50
1936J	.60	1961D	6,124,000	.50
1937A	.60	1961F	6,029,000	.50
1937D	.60	1961G	3,958,000	.50
1937E	.60	1961J	6,008,000	.50
1937F	.60	1962D	8,187,000	.50
1937G	.60	1962F	11,122,000	.50
1937J	.60	1962G	5,565,000	.50
1938A	1.50	1962J	8,676,000	.50
1938E	.60			
1938F	.60			
1938G	.60			

Post World War I Issues

2 MARK

Y46 (silver) 26mm

	Value		Mintage	Value
1938J	60	1925A	⎫	1.25
1939A	2.50	1925D	⎪	1.25
1939B	2.50	1925E	⎬ 26,000,000	1.25
1939D	2.50	1925F	⎪	1.25
1939E	2.50	1925G	⎪	1.25
1939F	2.50	1925J	⎭	1.25
1939G	2.50	1926A	⎫	1.25
1939J	2.50	1926D	⎪	1.25
		1926E	⎬ 65,000,000	1.25

Bundesrepublik Deutschland

Y110 (copper-nickel) 23.5mm

	Mintage	Value		Mintage	Value
			1926F	⎪	1.25
			1926G	⎪	1.25
1950D	60,466,000	.50	1926J	⎭	1.25
1950F	69,182,000	.50	1927A	⎫	1.50
1950G	39,825,000	.50	1927D	⎬ 8,500,000	1.50
1950J	61,483,000	.50	1927E	⎭	1.50

	Mintage	Value
1927F	} inc. above	$1.50
1927J		1.50
1931D		2.00
1931E		2.00
1931F	} 6,800,000	2.00
1931G		2.00
1931J		2.00

Y78 Martin Luther, 25mm

	Mintage	Value
1933A	541,900	2.50
1933D	140,600	2.50
1933E	74,500	3.00
1933F	100,300	2.50
1933G	61,000	3.00
1933J	81,700	3.00

Y83 Potsdam Church

	Mintage	Value
1934A	2,709,500	2.50
1934D	703,000	3.00
1934E	372,500	3.00
1934F	501,500	3.00
1934G	305,500	3.00
1934J	408,500	3.00

Y86 Friedrich Schiller

	Mintage	Value
1934F	300,000	3.00

Y96 Hindenburg and Swastika

	Mintage	Value
1936D		.60
1936E		.60
1936G		.60
1936J		.60
1937A		.60
1937D		.60
1937E		.60
1937F		.60
1937G		.60
1937J		.60
1938A		.60
1938B	10,300,000	2.00
1938D		.60
1938E		.60
1938F		.60
1938G		.60
1938J		.60
1939A		.60
1939B	6,300,000	.60
1939D		.60
1939E		5.00
1939F		.60
1939G		.60
1939J		.60

Bundesrepublik Deutschland

Y11 (copper-nickel) 25.5mm

	Mintage	Value
1951D	19,564,000	.85
1951F	22,608,000	.85
1951G	13,011,000	$ .85
1951J	20,104,000	.85

Y117 Max Planck

	Mintage	Value
1957D	7,452,000	.85
1957F	6,337,000	.85
1957G	2,598,000	.85
1957J	9,407,000	.85
1958D	12,623,000	.75
1958F	16,824,000	.75
1958G	10,744,000	.75
1958J	9,407,000	.75
1959D	874,000	1.00
1959F	203,000	1.50
1960D	3,685,000	.75
1960F	3,692,000	.75
1960G	1,731,000	.75
1960J	4,672,000	.75
1961D	3,090,000	.75
1961F	3,872,000	.75
1961G	2,075,000	.75
1961J	2,603,000	.75
1962D	3,988,000	.75
1962F	3,344,000	.75
1962G	3,227,000	.75
1962J	2,340,000	.75

3 MARK
(aluminum) 28mm

Y29 no legend on reverse

	Mintage	Value
1922A		1.50
1922E	2,000	10.00

Y28 legend on reverse

	Mintage	Value
1922A		.25
1922D		5.00
1922E	2,440,000	.25
1922F	6,023,793	.25
1922G		.25
1922J	8,987,000	.25
1923E	2,030,000	1.00

Y47 (silver) 30mm

	Mintage	Value
1924A		2.00
1924D		2.00
1924E		2.00
1924F		2.00
1924G		2.00
1924J		2.00
1925D	7,928,000	2.00

Y50 Rhineland

	Mintage	Value
1925A	3,052,156	10.00
1925D	1,122,520	10.00
1925E	441,000	12.00
1925F	172,875	15.00
1925G	299,664	12.00
1925J	492,000	12.00

	Mintage	Value
Y52 700 year Lubeck		
1926..............200,000		$12.00
Y53 Bremerhaven		
1927..............150,000		20.00
Y55 Nordhausen		
1927..............100,000		12.50
Y56 Marburg		
1927..............130,000		10.00
Y57 Tubingen		
1927..............50,000		12.50
Y59 Durer		
1928..............50,000		22.50
Y60 Naumburg		
1928..............100,000		10.00
Y61 Dinkelsbuhl		
1928..............40,000		22.50
Y62 Lessing		
1929A..............216,760		9.00
1929D..............56,240		10.00
1929E..............29,800		10.00
1929F..............40,120		10.00
1929G..............24,400		10.00
1929J..............32,680		10.00
Y64 Waldeck-Prussia		
1929..............170,000		17.50
Y65 Constitution		
1929A..............1,420,561		7.50
1929D..............499,114		8.00
1929E..............122,155		10.00
1929F..............370,257		8.00
1929G..............255,590		8.00
1929J..............342,323		8.00
Y67 Meissen		
1929..............200,000		6.00
Y69 Graf Zeppelin		
1930A..............541,900		17.50
1930D..............140,600		20.00
1930E..............74,500		25.00
1930F..............100,300		20.00
1930G..............61,000		25.00
1930J..............81,700		25.00
Y71 von der Vogelweide		
1930A..............162,570		11.00
1930D..............42,180		12.50
1930E..............22,350		12.50
1930F..............30,090		12.50
1930G..............18,300		13.50
1930J..............24,510		12.50
Y72 Rhineland		
1930A..............1,734,080		8.50
1930D..............449,920		10.00

	Mintage	Value
1930E..............38,400		$12.50
1930F..............320,960		10.00
1930G..............195,200		10.00
1930J..............261,440		10.00
Y74 Magdeburg		
1931..............100,000		12.50
Y75 Stein		
1931..............150,000		10.00
Y48 regular		
1931A....		2.00
1931D....		2.00
1931E.... about 25,000,000		5.00
1931F....		2.00
1931G....		2.00
1931J....		2.00
1932A....		3.00
1932D....		3.00
1932F.... about 20,000,000		5.00
1932G....		5.00
1932J....		5.00
1933G..............152,000		5.00
Y76 Goethe		
1932A..............216,760		17.50
1932D..............56,240		20.00
1932E..............29,800		25.00
1932F..............40,220		25.00
1932G..............24,400		25.00
1932J..............32,680		25.00

5 MARK
(silver) 36mm

	Mintage	Value
Y51 Rhineland		
1925A..............912,780		22.50
1925D..............236,815		25.00
1925E..............125,481		25.00
1925F..............173,484		25.00
1925G..............102,743		25.00
1925J..............133,011		25.00
Y49 regular issue		
1927A....................		4.00
1927D....................		4.00
1927E....................		4.00
1927F....................		4.00
1927G....................		4.00
1927J....................		4.00
1928A....................		4.00
1928D....................		4.00
1928E....................		4.00
1928F....................		4.00
1928G....................		4.00
1928J....................		4.00
1929A....................		4.00
1929D....................		7.50
1929E....................		4.00

	Mintage	Value
1929F		$4.00
1929G		4.00
1929J		7.50
1930A		4.00
1930D		7.50
1930E		7.50
1930F		7.50
1930G		7.50
1930J		7.50
1931A		4.00
1931D		4.00
1931E		4.00
1931F		4.00
1931G		4.00
1931J		4.00
1932A		4.00
1932D		4.00
1932E		4.00
1932F		4.00
1932G		4.00
1932J		4.00
1933J	1,634,000	10.00

Y54 Bremerhaven

	Mintage	Value
1927A	50,000	47.50

Y58 Tubingen

	Mintage	Value
1927F	40,000	35.00

Y63 Lessing

	Mintage	Value
1929A	86,704	32.50
1929D	22,496	35.00
1929E	11,920	45.00
1929F	16,048	40.00
1929G	9,760	50.00
1929J	13,072	40.00

Y66 Constitution

	Mintage	Value
1929A	325,140	35.00
1929D	84,360	40.00
1929E	44,700	45.00
1929F	60,180	45.00
1929G	36,600	45.00
1929J	49,020	45.00

Y68 Meissen

	Mintage	Value
1929E	120,000	27.50

Y70 Graf Zeppelin

	Mintage	Value
1930A	216,760	30.00
1930D	56,240	40.00
1930E	29,800	40.00
1930F	40,120	40.00
1930G	24,400	40.00
1930J	32,680	40.00

Y73 Rhineland

	Mintage	Value
1930A	325,140	15.00
1930D	84,360	17.50
1930E	44,700	17.50

	Mintage	Value
1930F	60,180	$17.50
1930G	36,600	17.50
1930J	49,020	17.50

Y77 Goethe

	Mintage	Value
1932A	10,838	75.00
1932D	2,812	90.00
1932E	1,490	100.00
1932F	2,006	90.00
1932G	1,220	100.00
1932J	1,634	100.00

Y79 Martin Luther, 29mm

	Mintage	Value
1933A	108,380	4.50
1933D	28,120	6.00
1933E	16,900	6.00
1933F	20,060	6.00
1933G	12,200	6.00
1933J	16,340	6.00

Y84 21 Marz, 1933

	Mintage	Value
1934A	2,167,600	5.00
1934D	562,400	5.00
1934E	298,000	5.00
1934F	401,200	5.00
1934G	244,000	5.00
1934J	326,800	5.00

Y85 church, no date

	Mintage	Value
1934A		1.50
1934D		1.50
1934E		1.50
1934F		1.50
1934G		1.50
1934J		1.50
1935A		1.50
1935D		1.50
1935E		1.50
1935F		1.50
1935G		1.50
1935J		5.00

Y87 Schiller

	Mintage	Value
1934F	100,000	5.00

Y82 Hindenburg

	Mintage	Value
1935A		1.25
1935D		1.25
1935E		1.25
1935F		1.25
1935G		1.25
1935J	2,830,300	1.25
1936A		1.25
1936D		1.25
1936E		1.25
1936F		1.25
1936G		1.25
1936J	4,343,800	1.25

	Mintage	Value
Y97 Hindenburg and Swastika		
1936A		$1.25
1936D		1.25
1936E		1.25
1936F		1.25
1936G		1.25
1936J		1.25
1937A		1.25
1937D		1.25
1937E		1.25
1937F		1.25
1937G		1.25
1937J		1.25
1938A		1.25
1938D		1.25
1938E		1.25
1938F		1.25
1938G		1.25
1938J		1.25
1939A		1.25
1939B	1,942,000	5.00
1939D		1.25
1939E		1.25
1939F		1.25
1939G		1.25
1939J		1.25

Bundesrepublik Deutschland

Y112	Mintage	Value
1951D	20,600,000	2.00
1951F	24,000,000	2.00
1951G	13,840,000	2.00
1951J	21,160,000	2.00
1956D	1,092,000	2.00
1956F	1,200,000	2.00
1956J	1,068,000	2.00
1957D	566,000	2.00
1957F	2,100,000	2.00
1957G	692,000	2.00
1957J	1,630,000	2.00
1958D	1,226,000	2.00
1958F	600,000	2.00

	Mintage	Value
1958G	1,557,000	$2.00
1958J	60,000	3.00
1959D	520,000	2.00
1959G	224,000	2.00
1959J	1,343,000	2.00
1960D	1,039,000	2.00
1960F	932,000	2.00
1960G	1,024,000	2.00
1960J	1,468,000	2.00
1961D	1,040,000	2.00
1961F	1,467,000	2.00
1961G	136,000	2.50
1961J	668,000	2.00
Y113 Nurnburg		
1952	200,000	7.50
Y114 Von Schiller		
1955	200,000	6.00
Y115 Von Baden		
1955	200,000	5.00
Y116 Von Eichendorff		
1957	200,000	4.50

Postwar Inflationary Coinage
200 MARK

Y30 (aluminum) 23mm		
1923A		.25
1923D		.25
1923E		.25
1923F		.25
1923G		.25
1923J		.25

500 MARK

Y31 (aluminum) 27mm		
1923A		.35
1923D		.35
1923E		.35
1923F		.35
1923G		.35
1923J		1.00

GERMANY — States

2, 3 and 5 Marks Silver Coinage of the Individual States under the Empire (1874-1918). Name of issuing state on obverse. Most have DEUTSCHES REICH, eagle, value and date on reverse. "S" numbers refer to *Catalog of Modern World Coins,* 6th Edition.

Anhalt

2 MARK

Y-S12 28mm		
1876	200,000	5.00

Y-S13		
1896	50,000	6.00

Y-S18		
1904	50,000	3.00

	Mintage	Value
3 MARK		
Y-S19 33mm		
1909	100,000	$2.00
1911	100,000	2.00
Y-S20		
1914	200,000	2.00
5 MARK		
Y-S14 38mm		
1896	10,000	15.00
Y-S21		
1914	30,000	6.00

Baden

	Mintage	Value
2 MARK		
Y-S18 28mm		
1876	1,739,038	6.00
1877	763,927	8.00
1880	74,000	10.00
1883	45,493	15.00
1888	75,279	7.50
Y-S20		
1892	106,750	3.00
1894	106,750	3.00
1896	213,520	2.50
1898	87,442	3.00
1899	327,061	2.50
1900	222,219	2.50
1901	401,322	2.50
1902	5,368	7.50
YS-22 50th year of reign		
1902	375,018	3.00
Y-S24 head facing right		
1902	198,250	2.50
1903	493,989	2.00
1904	1,121,754	2.00
1905	609,835	2.00
1906	107,549	5.00
1907	913,024	2.00
Y-S26 Golden Wedding		
1906	350,000	1.50
Y-S28 1826-1907		
1907	350,000	2.00
Y-S38 Friedrich II		
1911	77,000	7.50
1913	137,250	6.00
3 MARK		
Y-S39 33mm		
1908	304,927	1.50
1909	760,716	1.50
1910	674,640	1.50
1911	382,039	1.50

	Mintage	Value
1912	835,199	$1.50
1914	412,804	1.50
1915	169,533	3.00
5 MARK		
Y-S19 38mm		
1875	314,186	5.00
1876	472,806	5.00
1888	30,111	10.00
Y-S21		
1891	42,700	7.00
1893	42,700	6.00
1894	60,915	5.00
1895	73,418	4.00
1898	131,341	4.00
1899	61,073	4.00
1900	128,352	4.00
1901	128,131	4.00
1902	42,708	4.00
Y-S23 50th year of reign		
1902	50,024	7.50
Y-S25 head facing right		
1902	128,100	4.00
1903	439,105	4.00
1904	237,914	4.00
1907	243,821	4.00
Y-S27 Golden Wedding		
1906	60,000	6.00
Y-S29 Death of Friedrich		
1907 (1826-1907)	60,000	6.00
Y-S40		
1908	184,000	4.00
1913	244,000	4.00

Bavaria (Bayern)

	Mintage	Value
2 MARK		
Y-S26 28mm		
1876	5,370,139	2.00
1877	1,511,500	3.00
1880	168,000	5.00
1883	104,217	8.00
Y-S33		
1888	172,368	6.00
Y-S35		
1891	246,050	4.00
1893	246,050	4.00
1896	492,131	4.00
1898	201,476	3.00
1899	753,396	1.50
1900	722,484	1.50
1912	213,652	2.50
1913	97,698	3.00

	Mintage	Value
1901	829,064	$1.50
1902	1,340,781	1.50
1903	1,406,067	1.50
1904	2,320,238	1.50
1905	1,406,100	1.50
1906	1,054,500	1.50
1907	2,106,712	1.50
1908	632,700	1.50

Y-S38 Birthday

1911	640,000	1.50

Y-S45

1914	573,533	1.50

3 MARK

Y-S36 33mm

1908	680,529	2.00
1909	827,460	2.00
1910	1,496,091	2.00
1911	843,437	2.00
1912	1,013,650	2.00
1913	731,275	2.00

Y-S39 Birthday

1911	639,721	2.00

Y-S46

1914	717,460	1.50

5 MARK

Y-S27 38mm

1874	84,960	4.00
1875	656,751	3.50
1876	1,129,555	3.00

Y-S34

1888	68,947	15.00

Y-S37

1891	98,420	4.00
1893	98,420	3.50
1894	140,652	3.50
1895	140,639	3.50
1896	28,120	20.00
1898	303,040	3.00
1899	140,640	3.00
1900	295,241	3.00
1901	295,371	3.00
1902	506,049	3.00
1903	1,012,097	2.50
1904	548,340	3.00
1906	70,249	4.00
1907	752,658	3.00
1908	576,579	3.00
1913	520,000	3.00

Y-S40 Birthday

1911	160,000	5.00

Y-S47

	Mintage	Value
1914	142,400	$6.00

Bremen

2 MARK

Y-S10 28mm

1904	100,000	2.00

5 MARK

Y-S11 38mm

1906	40,846	6.50

Brunswick (Braunschweig)

3 MARK

Y-S8 Wedding, 33mm

1915	1,700	25.00

Y-S10 U.Luneb added

1915	31,634	6.00

5 MARK

Y-S9 Wedding, 38mm

1915	1,400	40.00

Y-S11 U.Luneb added

1915	8,600	15.00

Hamburg

2 MARK

Y-S2 28mm

1876	2,325,000	3.00
1877	499,631	3.50
1878	349,578	3.50
1880	98,936	5.00
1883	60,446	6.00
1888	99,820	5.00

Y-S4

1892	140,925	3.00
1893	145,800	3.00
1896	286,434	2.00
1898	117,843	3.00
1899	286,360	2.00
1900	576,669	2.00
1901	482,408	2.00
1902	778,880	2.00
1903	817,215	2.00
1904	1,248,330	1.50
1905	204,040	1.75
1906	1,224,910	1.50
1907	1,225,503	1.50
1908	367,750	1.75
1911	204,250	1.75
1912	78,500	2.00
1913	105,325	1.75
1914	327,758	1.75

	Mintage	Value

3 MARK

Y-S5 33mm

1908.............408,475	$1.00
1909...........1,388,892	1.00
1910.............525,500	1.00
1911.............922,000	1.00
1912.............491,088	1.00
1913.............343,900	1.00
1914.............575,111	1.00

5 MARK

Y-S3 38mm

1875.............285,661	8.00
1876.............930,000	5.00
1888..............40,363	10.00

Y-S6

1891..............59,409	6.00
1893..............54,660	6.00
1894..............81,700	4.00
1895..............81,700	4.00
1896..............16,340	20.00
1898.............175,974	3.50
1899..............81,700	3.50
1900.............171,859	3.00
1901.............171,603	3.00
1902.............294,034	3.00
1903.............588,335	3.00
1904.............318,640	3.00
1907.............325,534	3.00
1908.............457,974	3.00
1913.............326,800	3.00

Hesse (Hessen)

2 MARK

Y-S6 28mm

1876.............202,108	8.00
1877.............338,000	8.00

Y-S13

1888..............22,350	12.00

Y-S15

1891..............62,650	8.00

Y-S21

1895..............53,700	8.00
1896...............8,950	12.00
1898..............33,950	10.00
1899..............53,250	8.00
1900...............8,950	12.00

Y-S23

1904.............100,000	3.00

3 MARK

Y-S25 33mm

1910.............200,000	1.50

5 MARK

Y-S7 38mm

1875.............148,035	$10.0(
1876.............290,450	8.0(

Y-S14

1888...............8,940	20.0

Y-S16

1891..............25,060	15.0(

Y-S22

1895..............39,380	10.00
1898..............37,480	10.00
1899...............4,475	15.00
1900..............17,900	12.50

Y-S24

1904..............40,000	9.00

Lippe-Detmold

2 MARK

Y-S6 28mm

1906..............20,000	7.00

3 MARK

Y-S7 33mm

1913..............15,000	8.00

Lubeck

2 MARK

Y-S1 28mm

1901..............25,000	5.00

Y-S2

1904..............25,000	4.00
1905..............25,000	4.00
1906..............25,000	4.00
1907..............25,000	4.00
1911..............25,000	4.00
1912..............25,000	4.00

3 MARK

Y-S3 33mm

1908..............33,334	4.00
1909..............33,334	4.00
1910..............33,334	4.00
1911..............33,334	4.00
1912..............34,000	4.00
1913..............15,000	5.00
1914..............10,000	5.00

5 MARK

Y-S4 38mm

1904..............10,000	10.00
1907..............10,000	10.00
1908..............10,000	10.00
1913...............6,000	12.50

	Mintage	Value
Mecklenburg-Schwerin		
2 MARK		
Y-S8 28mm		
1876	300,000	$8.00
Y-S13		
1901	50,000	8.00
Y-S14		
1904	100,000	3.00
3 MARK		
Y-S16 33mm		
1915	33,334	4.00
5 MARK		
Y-S15 38mm		
1904	40,000	10.00
Y-S17		
1915	10,000	15.00
Mecklenburg-Strelitz		
2 MARK		
Y-S9 28mm		
1877	100,000	12.50
Y-S14		
1905	10,000	10.00
3 MARK		
Y-S15 33mm		
1913	7,000	10.00
Oldenburg		
2 MARK		
Y-S8 28mm		
1891	100,000	8.00
Y-S10		
1900	50,000	6.00
1901	75,000	5.00
5 MARK		
Y-S11 38mm		
1900	20,000	14.00
1901	10,000	15.00
Prussia (Preussen)		
2 MARK		
Y-S30 28mm		
1876A	13,369,896	1.50
1876B	3,985,119	2.00
1876C	5,233,403	2.00
1877A	3,633,572	2.00
1877B	1,301,471	2.00

	Mintage	Value
1877C	1,321,471	$2.00
1879	29,260	7.50
1880	664,715	4.00
1883	164,472	5.00
1884	140,168	5.00
Y-S37 Friedrich		
1888	500,000	1.75
Y-S41 Wilhelm II		
1888	140,512	3.00
Y-S43		
1891	543,962	3.00
1892	181,713	5.00
1893	948,325	1.00
1896	1,771,855	1.00
1898	1,042,187	1.00
1899	2,350,920	1.00
1900	2,681,537	1.00
1901	398,486	2.00
1902	3,948,323	1.00
1903	4,078,709	1.00
1904	9,981,031	1.00
1905	6,423,135	1.00
1906	4,000,000	1.00
1907	8,085,264	1.00
1908	2,388,550	1.00
1911	1,181,475	1.00
1912	732,813	1.25
Y-S46 1701-1901		
1901	2,600,000	1.00
Y-S50 Eagle and Serpent		
1913	1,500,000	1.00
Y-S52 Wilhelm II		
1913	1,500,000	1.25
3 MARK		
Y-S44 33mm		
1908	2,858,666	.75
1909	6,343,745	.75
1910	5,790,624	.75
1911	3,241,710	.75
Y-S48 1810-1910		
1910	200,000	3.50
1912	4,626,390	.75
Y-S49 1811-1911		
1911	400,000	3.00
Y-S51 Eagle and Serpent		
1913	1,000,000	1.25
Y-S53 Wilhelm II		
1913	1,000,000	2.00
Y-S54		
1914	2,022,000	2.00

	Mintage	Value
Y-S56 Mansfelder		
1915	30,000	$8.50

5 MARK

Y-S31 38mm		
1874A	837,546	4.00
1875A	852,836	4.00
1875B	919,482	4.00
1876A	2,041,407	4.00
1876B	2,098,368	4.00
1876C	812,361	4.00
Y-S38 Friedrich		
1888	200,000	5.00
Y-S42 Wilhelm II		
1888	56,204	10.00
Y-S45		
1891	130,261	7.50
1892	224,009	4.00
1893	215,300	4.00
1894	440,203	4.00
1895	831,025	3.50
1896	45,925	12.50
1898	1,333,590	3.00
1899	528,960	3.00
1900	1,079,874	3.00
1901	667,990	3.00
1902	1,950,840	3.00
1903	3,855,795	3.00
1904	2,060,410	3.00
1906	230,963	3.50
1907	2,102,338	3.00
1908	2,230,579	3.00
Y-S47 1701-1901		
1901	460,000	3.50
Y-S55		
1913	1,961,712	3.50
1914	1,587,179	3.50

Reuss

2 MARK
28mm

Y-S6 Reuss-Greiz		
1877	20,000	8.00
Y-S7 Reuss-Schleiz		
1884	100,000	8.00
Y-S7 Reuss-Greiz		
1892	10,000	8.00
Y-S8 Reuss-Greiz		
1899	10,000	8.00
1901	10,000	8.00

	Mintage	Value
3 MARK		
33mm		
Y-S10 Reuss-Greiz		
1909	10,000	$8.00

Saxony (Sachsen)

2 MARK

Y-S28 28mm		
1876	1,613,135	2.50
1877	796,246	2.50
1879	36,110	7.50
1880	57,509	6.00
1883	55,700	6.00
1888	90,995	4.00
Y-S30		
1891	130,375	2.00
1893	130,375	2.00
1895	116,622	2.00
1896	144,180	2.00
1898	106,669	2.00
1899	401,330	2.00
1900	383,564	2.00
1901	439,724	2.00
1902	542,762	2.00
Y-S33 1828-1902		
1902	167,625	3.00
Y-S40 regular		
1903	745,501	2.00
1904	1,079,402	2.00
Y-S43 1832-1904		
1904	150,000	2.00
Y-S47		
1905	558,951	2.00
1906	558,750	2.00
1907	1,117,519	2.00
1908	632,700	2.00
1911	186,250	2.00
1912	167,225	2.00
1914	298,000	2.00
Y-S51 Univ. Leipzig		
1909	125,000	3.00

3 MARK

Y-S48 33mm		
1908	276,073	1.50
1909	1,196,719	1.50
1910	745,000	1.50
1911	581,250	1.50
1912	378,750	1.50
1913	306,509	1.50
Y-S53 Monument		
1913	1,000,000	1.50

	Mintage	Value
5 MARK		
Y-S29 38mm		
1875	481,869	$6.00
1876	635,240	6.00
1889	36,397	10.00
1891	52,150	6.00
1893	52,150	6.00
1894	74,616	5.00
1895	89,483	5.00
1898	160,348	5.00
1899	74,260	5.00
1900	156,706	5.00
1901	156,450	5.00
1902	168,200	5.00
Y-S34 1828-1902		
1902	100,000	6.50
Y-S41 regular		
1903	536,298	5.00
1904	290,643	5.00
Y-S44 1832-1904		
1904	37,200	7.50
Y-S49 regular		
1907	398,043	3.00
1908	317,301	3.00
1914	298,000	4.00
Y-S52 Univ. Leipzig		
1909	50,000	6.00

Sachsen-Altenburg

	Mintage	Value
2 MARK		
Y-S4 28mm		
1901	50,000	8.50
5 MARK		
Y-S5 38mm		
1901	20,000	12.00
Y-S6		
1903	20,000	10.00

Sachsen-Coburg-Gotha

	Mintage	Value
2 MARK		
Y-S15 28mm		
1895	15,000	10.00
Y-S18		
1905	10,000	10.00
5 MARK		
Y-S16 38mm		
1895	4,000	22.50

	Mintage	Value
Y-S19		
1907	10,000	$17.50

Sachsen-Meiningen

	Mintage	Value
2 MARK		
Y-S8 28mm		
1901	20,000	7.50
Y-S10		
1902	20,000	6.00
1913	5,000	12.50
Y-S13		
1915	30,000	3.00
3 MARK		
Y-S11 33mm		
1908	35,000	4.00
1913	20,000	4.00
Y-S14		
1915	30,000	5.00
5 MARK		
Y-S9 38mm		
1901	20,000	12.50
Y-S12		
1902	20,000	10.00
1908	60,000	8.50

Sachsen-Weimar

	Mintage	Value
2 MARK		
Y-S6 28mm		
1892	50,000	5.00
1898	100,000	5.00
Y-S8		
1901	100,000	5.00
Y-S9		
1903	40,000	5.00
Y-S11		
1908	50,000	5.00
3 MARK		
Y-S13 33mm		
1910	133,000	3.00
Y-S14		
1915	50,000	5.00
5 MARK		
Y-S10 38mm		
1903	24,000	7.50

	Mintage	Value
Y-S12		
1908	40,000	$7.50

Schaumburg-Lippe

2 MARK

Y-S12 28mm		
1898	5,000	7.50
1904	5,000	7.50

3 MARK

Y-S14 33mm		
1911	50,000	2.50

5 MARK

Y-S13 38mm		
1898	3,000	15.00
1904	3,000	15.00

Schwarzburg-Rudolstadt

2 MARK

Y-S10 28mm		
1898	100,000	5.00

Schwarzburg-Sondershausen

2 MARK

Y-S5 28mm		
1896	50,000	5.00
Y-S6		
1905	75,000	4.00

3 MARK

Y-S7 33mm		
1909	70,000	6.00

Waldeck-Pyrmont

5 MARK

Y-S5 38mm		
1903	2,000	40.00

Wurttemberg

2 MARK

Y-S13 28mm		
1876	1,550,014	5.00
1877	1,106,763	6.00
1880	128,943	8.00
1883	73,872	10.00
1888	123,140	6.00

	Mintage	Value
Y-S21		
1892	177,000	$2.00
1893	174,055	2.00
1896	351,031	2.00
1898	144,001	5.00
1899	537,571	2.00
1900	515,885	1.25
1901	591,927	1.25
1902	815,620	1.25
1903	811,383	1.25
1904	1,988,177	1.00
1905	609,835	1.25
1906	1,504,620	1.00
1907	1,504,497	1.00
1908	451,370	1.25
1912	251,224	1.25
1913	225,675	1.25
1914	315,962	1.25

3 MARK

Y-S22 33mm		
1908	300,000	1.00
1909	1,906,698	.75
1910	837,230	1.00
1911	424,820	1.00
1912	849,100	1.00
1913	267,100	1.00
1914	733,121	1.00
Y-S24 1886-1911		
1911	500,000	2.00

5 MARK

Y-S14 38mm		
1874	112,530	4.00
1875	317,851	4.00
1876	896,725	4.00
1888	49,258	5.00
Y-S23		
1892	69,333	4.00
1893	71,089	4.00
1894	20,000	20.00
1895	200,712	4.00
1898	212,262	4.00
1899	112,272	4.00
1900	210,574	4.00
1901	210,700	4.00
1902	360,881	4.00
1903	722,182	4.00
1904	391,317	4.00
1906	45,000	5.00
1907	436,321	4.00
1908	521,716	4.00
1913	341,200	4.00

Y94 and Y95 were issued for use by German Military personnel in the occupied countries of Europe during World War II. 5,000,000 5 RPf and 25,000,000 10 RPf were minted in 1940. These coins exist with other mint marks, also 1941A but it is doubtful that they entered circulation and are rare.

	Mintage	Value		Mintage	Value
5 REICHSPFENNIG			**10 REICHSPFENNIG**		
Y94 (zinc) 18mm			**Y95** (zinc) 21mm		
1940A		$10.00	1940A		$10.00

GERMAN DEMOCRATIC REPUBLIC
(Deutschland)

The eastern portion of partitioned Germany which is under Communist control.

100 Pfennig = 1 Mark

1 PFENNIG
Y1 (aluminum) 17mm
1948A	.10
1949A	10
1949E	.10
1950A	.10
1950E	.10

Y5 new design
1952A	.10
1952E	.10
1953A	.10
1953E	.10

Y11 DDR
1960A	.15
1961A	.15

5 PFENNIG
Y2 (aluminum) 19mm
1948A	.10
1949A	.10
1950A	.10

Y6 new design
1952A	.10
1952E	.10
1953A	.25
1953E	.10

10 PFENNIG
Y3 (aluminum) 21mm
1948A	.20
1949A	.20
1950A	.20
1950E	.20

Y7 new design
1952A	.20
1952E	.20
1953A	.50
1953E	.20

50 PFENNIG
Y4 (aluminum-bronze) 20mm
1950A	1.00

Y10 (aluminum) DDR
1958A	.30

1 MARK
Y8 (aluminum) 25mm DDR
1956A	.50

2 MARK
Y9 (aluminum) 27mm DDR
1957A	.75

GREECE
ΕΛΛΑΔΟΣ, ΕΛΛΗΝΩΝ, or ΕΛΛΗΝΙΚΗ
(Vasilon Tis Ellados — Kingdom of Hellas)
Southernmost of the Balkan countries, extending into the Mediterranean Sea.
Coins were minted at various European mints.

100 Lepta = 1 Drachma

	Mintage	Value
1 LEPTON		
(copper) 15mm		
George I (1863-1913)		
Y1 young head		
1869		$1.00
1870 . . . . {22,505,677	1.00
Y10 older head		
1878		1.00
1879		1.00
2 LEPTA		
(copper) 20.5mm		
George I		
Y2 young head		
1869	11,231,724	1.00
Y11 older head		
1878	inc. above	1.00
5 LEPTA		
(copper) 25.5mm		
George I		
Y3 young head		
1869		.75
1870		.75
Y12 older head {50,343,158		
1878		75
1879		.75
1882		.75
Y16 (copper-nickel) 17mm		
1894	4,000,000	.30
1895	4,000,000	.30
Y19 holed 19.5mm		
1912	25,053,946	.25
Paul I (1947-1964)		
Y38 (aluminum) 20mm		
1954	15,000,000	.15
10 LEPTA		
(copper) 30mm		
George I		
Y4 young head		
1869		1.00
1870		1.00
Y13 older head . . {38,492,162		
1878		1.00
1879		1.00
1882		1.00

	Mintage	Value
Y17 (copper-nickel) 19mm		
1894	3,000,000	$ .30
1895	3,000,000	.30
Y20 holed 21.5mm		
1912	28,973,497	.30
George II (1922-1923)		
Y29 (aluminum) 21mm		
1922	120,000,000	.25
Paul I		
Y39 22mm		
1954	48,000,000	.15
1959	20,000,000	.15
20 LEPTA		
George I		
Y5 (silver) 16mm		
1869	2,223,127	1.00
1874	inc. above	1.00
1883	1,000,000	1.00
Y18 (copper-nickel) 21mm		
1893	248,010	2.00
1894	4,751,992	.40
1895	5,000,000	.40
Y21 (nickel) holed 23mm		
1912	10,145,092	.40
Republic 1924-1935		
Y31 17mm		
1926	20,000,000	.25
Paul I		
Y40 (aluminum) holed, 24mm		
1954	24,000,000	.15
1959	20,000,000	.15
50 LEPTA		
George 1		
Y6 (silver) 18mm		
1868	4,500,633	1.00
1874	inc. above	1.00
1883	600,000	1.25
Republic		
Y32 (copper-nickel) 19mm		
1926	20,000,000	.35
1926B	20,000,000	.35

	Mintage	Value
Paul I		
Y41 18mm		
1954	37,228,000	$ .15
1957	5,108,000	.15
1959	10,160,000	.15
1962	20,500,000	.15

1 DRACHMA

George I

Y7 (silver) 23mm

1868	⎫	1.50
1873	⎬ 4,531,358	1.50
1874	⎭	1.50
1883	800,000	1.50

Y22 new design

1910	4,570,159	1.50
1911	1,881,817	1.50

Republic

Y33 (copper-nickel)

1926	20,000,000	.50
1926B	15,000,000	.50

Paul I

Y42 (copper-nickel) 21mm

1954	24,091,000	.25
1957	8,151,000	.25
1959	10,180,000	.25
1962	20,060,000	.25

2 DRACHMAI

George I

Y8 (silver) 27mm

1868	886,850	3.00
1873	inc. above	3.00
1883	250,000	3.00

Y23 new design

1911	1,500,000	2.50

Republic

Y34 (copper-nickel)

1926	11,500,000	.60
1926B	22,000,000	.60

	Mintage	Value
Paul I		
Y43		
1954	12,609,000	$ .35
1957	10,171,200	.35
1959	5,000,000	.35
1962	10,096,000	.35

5 DRACHMAI

George I

Y14 (silver) 37mm

1875	3,092,573	12.50
1876	inc. above	9.00

Republic

Y35 (nickel) 31mm

1930	25,000,000	.50

Paul I

Y44 (copper-nickel) 28mm

1954	21,000,000	.60

10 DRACHMAI

Republic

Y36 (silver) 24mm

1930	7,500,000	2.00

Paul I

Y45 (nickel) 32mm

1959	20,000,000	1.25

20 DRACHMAI

Republic

Y37 (silver) 28mm

1930	11,500,000	3.50

Paul I

Y46 26mm

1960	20,000,000	1.75

A 50 Lepta (aluminum, holed) 23mm dated 1921 exists. 2,524,227 were minted, but none entered circulation.

GREENLAND
(Grønlands)

A large island possession of Denmark in the North Atlantic. Coins dated 1926 were minted in various years. The center hole was punched in the 25 Øre during the period 1940 to 1945.

100 Øre = 1 Krone

	Mintage	Value		Mintage	Value
25 ØRE			1926 286,982		$ .75
Y5 (copper-nickel) 25mm			**Y10** new design		
1926 317,365		$ .50	1957 100,209		.75
Y6 with center hole			**Y10a** (copper-nickel)		
1926 . . . . inc. above		.50	1960 108,500		.75
50 ØRE			**5 KRONER**		
Y7 (aluminum-bronze) 22mm			**Y9** (brass) 30mm		
1926 195,837		.60	1944 Philadelphia . . . 100,000		4.00
1 KRONE					
Y8 (aluminum-bronze) 27.5mm					

GUADELOUPE

A French possession in the Caribbean Sea. Coins of France now circulating.

100 Centimes = 1 Franc

50 CENTIMES			1 FRANC		
Y1 (copper-nickel) 22mm			**Y2** (copper-nickel) 25mm		
1903 600,000		2.50	1903 700,000		4.00
1921 600,000		2.50	1921 700,000		4.00

HUNGARY
(Magyar)

Country in central Europe. Before World War I along with Austria, comprised the Austro-Hungarian Empire.

Mint marks:

BP Budapest (all from 1926)
KB Kremnitz (1868-1915)
GYF Gyulafehervar (1868-1871)
Coins of 1868 without mint mark were Gyulafehervar

100 Krajczar = 1 Forint (1868-1892)
100 Filler = 1 Korona (1892-1921)
100 Filler = 1 Pengo (1925-1945)
100 Filler = 1 Forint (1946 to date)

	Mintage	Value
Forint System		
5/10 KRAJCZAR		
Y3 (copper) 17mm		
1882KB	2,400,000	$ .40

1 KRAJCZAR		
Y1 (copper) 19mm		
1868KB	12,531,070	.25
1868 (Gyulafehervar)		
. . . . .inc. above		1.00
1869KB	5,072,736	.25
1872KB		.25
1873KB		1.50
Y4 design changed		
1878KB	4,478,154	.40
1879KB	10,100,984	.25
1881KB	12,232,831	.25
1882KB	19,799,904	.25
1883KB	8,535,127	.35
1885KB	26,605,955	.25
1886KB	17,670,993	.25
1887KB	11,988,907	.25
1888KB	10,334,145	.25
Y5 design changed		
1891KB	16,271,659	.25
1892KB	5,870,524	.40

4 KRAJCZAR		
Y2 (copper) 26.5mm		
1868KB	3,099,298	.75
1868 (Gyulafehervar)		
. . . . .inc. above		1.50

10 KRAJCZAR		
(billon) 17mm		
Y6 VALTO PENZ only		
1868KB		.75
1868GYF		1.50
Y7 MAGYAR KIRALYI VALTO PENZ		
1868KB	3,249,975	.50
1868GYF	1,011,508	1.00
1869KB	12,746,767	.35
1869GYF	2,747,272	.75
Y10 design changed		
1870KB	21,933,353	.30
1870GYF	3,031,602	.50
1871GYF	3,382,790	.50
(All KB from here on.)		
1872	1,153,922	.60
1873	1,066,053	.60

	Mintage	Value
1874	1,323,713	$ .60
1875	425,044	1.00
1876	518,486	1.00
1877	460,077	1.00
1887	25,369	5.00
1888	357,628	1.25

20 KRAJCZAR		
(billon) 20mm		
Y8 VALTO PENZ only		
1868KB		1.00
1868GYF		2.00
Y9 MAGYAR KIRALYI VALTO PENZ		
1868KB	3,224,057	.50
1868GYF	1,039,346	.75
1869KB	9,487,455	.50
1869GYF	2,298,599	.50
Y11 design changed		
1870KB	4,426,752	.50
1870GYF	7,212,703	.50
1872KB	1,285,806	.75

1 FORINT		
Y12 (silver) 28mm		
1868KB	573,584	3.50
1868GYF	266,486	5.00
1869KB	493,698	3.50
1869GYF	362,175	4.50
Y13 new reverse		
1870KB	1,253,687	4.50
1870GYF	567,922	6.00
1871KB	2,444,984	3.50
1871GYF	242,750	7.50
(All KB from here on.)		
1872	3,456,245	3.00
1873	2,338,364	3.50
1874	2,081,702	3.50
1875	2,073,958	3.50
1876	4,136,174	2.00
1877	2,241,386	3.50
1878	5,717,374	2.00
1879	25,755,927	1.50
1880	3,814,618	2.00
1881	15,494,763	1.50
Y14 new reverse		
1882	1,897,441	3.00
1883	7,040,776	2.00
1884	1,721,725	3.00
1885	1,672,086	3.00
1886	1,565,967	3.00

	Mintage	Value
1887	2,022,064	$3.00
1888	1,841,360	3.00
1889	1,974,397	3.00
1890	2,021,792	3.00

Y15 new reverse

	Mintage	Value
1890	inc. above	3.00
1891	1,469,863	3.00
1892	1,606,566	3.00

Korona System

1 FILLER

Y23 (bronze) 17mm

	Mintage	Value
1892	inc. w/1893	1.50
1893	8,152,507	.25
1894	8,641,784	.25
1895	9,121,315	.25
1896	5,396,972	.25
1897	5,156,580	.25
1898	1,419,348	.50
1899	5,065,896	.25
1900	10,461,111	.25
1901	5,993,930	.25
1902	16,299,391	.25
1903	2,291,166	.25
1906	61,246	5.00

2 FILLER

Y24 (bronze) 19mm

	Mintage	Value
1892	inc. w/1893	1.00
1893	17,176,179	.25
1894	39,150,321	.25
1895	65,016,511	.25
1896	53,715,725	.25
1897	37,296,844	.25
1898	14,072,860	.25
1899	21,569,648	.25
1900	584,444	1.25
1901	25,805,472	.25
1902	6,936,091	.30
1903	4,052,403	.35
1904	4,203,139	.35
1905	9,334,866	.30
1906	9,443,458	.30
1907	3,140,445	.35
1908	16,486,377	.25
1909	19,074,802	.25
1910	6,025,053	.30
1914		.30
1915	1,294,363	.30

Y28 (iron) 17.5mm

	Mintage	Value
1916		.25
1917		.25
1918		.25

10 FILLER

Y25 (nickel) 19.5mm

	Mintage	Value
1892	inc. w/1893	$1.50
1893	15,733,070	.25
1894	39,463,387	.25
1895	16,803,543	.25
1906	56,213	2.00
1908	6,818,747	.25
1909	17,204,205	.25

Y26 (copper, zinc, nickel) 18.5mm

	Mintage	Value
1914		.25
1915	4,400,000	.25
1916		.25

Y29 (iron)

	Mintage	Value
1915	very few	10.00
1916	very few	10.00
1918		.30

Y-E36

	Mintage	Value
1920	3,000,000	2.50

20 FILLER

Y27 (nickel) 21.5mm

	Mintage	Value
1892	695,598	.75
1893	27,187,060	.25
1894	26,117,342	.25
1906	66,948	2.00
1907	1,247,694	.50
1908	10,770,033	.25
1914		.50

Y30 (iron)

	Mintage	Value
1916		.35
1917		.35
1918		.35

Y-F36

	Mintage	Value
1920		2.50
1921	very few	10.00

1 KORONA

Y32 (silver) 22.5mm

	Mintage	Value
1892	15,000	12.50
1893	24,385,503	1.00
1894	12,077,290	1.00
1895	18,544,465	1.00
1896	3,982,502	1.50
1906	50,114	5.00

Y31 commemorative

	Mintage	Value
1896	1,000,000	2.00

Y32a smaller head

	Mintage	Value
1912	4,004,094	1.50

	Mintage	Value
1913	5,214	$20.00
1914		2.00
1915	4,400,000	1.50
1916		2.00

2 KORONA

Y33 (silver) 28mm

	Mintage	Value
1912	4,000,268	1.50
1913	3,000,325	1.50
1914		1.50

5 KORONA

Y34 (silver) 36mm

	Mintage	Value
1900	3,840,000	3.50
1906	1,263	30.00
1907	500,221	5.00
1908	1,742,452	4.00
1909	1,298,970	4.00

Y35 Coronation

1907	300,032	7.50

Pengo System
1 FILLER

Y37 (bronze) 17mm

	Mintage	Value
1926	6,471,003	.25
1927	16,528,997	.25
1928	7,000,000	.25
1929	417,538	1.00
1930	3,733,838	.35
1931	10,848,624	.25
1932	5,000,000	.30
1933	5,000,000	.30
1934	3,110,810	.35
1935	6,889,190	.25
1936	10,000,000	.25
1938	10,575,000	.25
1939	10,425,000	.25

2 FILLER

Y38 (bronze) 19mm

	Mintage	Value
1926	17,777,273	.20
1927	44,836,270	.15
1928	11,448,448	.20
1929	8,994,922	.20
1930	6,943,087	.25
1931	825,640	1.00
1932	4,174,360	.25
1933	501,340	1.25
1934	9,498,660	.20
1935	10,000,000	.20
1936	2,049,397	.35
1937	7,950,603	.25
1938	14,125,000	.20

	Mintage	Value
1939	16,875,000	$ .20
1940	7,000,000	.25

Y50 (steel) 17mm

1940	78,000,000	.50

Y50a

1940	inc. above	.20
1941	12,000,000	.50
1942		.50

Y51 (zinc)

1943		.15
1944		.15

10 FILLER

Y39 (nickel) 19.5mm

1926	20,510,000	.15
1927	12,255,020	.20
1935	4,739,887	.25
1936	3,004,583	.25
1938	6,700,000	.25
1939	4,460,000	.25
1940	960,000	.75

Y52 (steel)

1940	45,926,665	.15
1941	24,963,335	.15
1942	45,000,000	.15

20 FILLER

Y40 (nickel) 21.5mm

1926	25,000,000	.20
1927	829,690	1.00
1938	20,150,000	.20
1939	2,020,310	.50
1940	2,470,000	.50

Y53 (steel, holed)

1941	75,007,415	.25
1943		.25
1944		.25

50 FILLER

Y41 (copper-nickel) 22mm

1926	14,921,474	.30
1938	20,078,526	.30
1939	2,770,000	.75
1940	6,230,000	.45

1 PENGO

Y42 (silver) 18mm

1926	15,000,000	1.00
1927	18,000,000	1.00
1937	4,000,000	1.50
1938	5,000,000	1.50
1939	13,000,000	1.00

	Mintage	Value
Y54 (aluminum) 19.5mm		
1941 80,000,000		$ .25
1942		.25
1943		.25
1944		.25

2 PENGO
(silver) 27mm

	Mintage	Value
Y43 Madonna		
1929 5,000,000		1.25
1931 1,000		25.00
1932 711,611		2.00
1933 1,051,195		1.75
1935 50,154		6.00
1936 711,040		2.00
1937 1,500,000		1.75
1938 8,520,000		1.25
1939		1.50
Y45 Pazmany		
1935 50,000		7.50
Y46 Rakoczi		
1935 100,000		4.00
Y47 Liszt		
1936 200,000		4.00
Y55 (aluminum)		
1941 24,000,000		.50
1942		.50
1943		.50

5 PENGO
(silver) 36mm

	Mintage	Value
Y44 Horthy 10th Year		
1930 3,650,000		4.00
Y48 St. Stephan		
1938 600,000		4.00
Y49 Horthy		
1939 407,800		4.00
Y57 Horthy (aluminum)		
1943 2,000,000		1.50
Y56 regular, 32.5mm		
1945		2.00

Forint System —
Communist Regime
2 FILLER

	Mintage	Value
Y58 (bronze) 17.5mm		
1946		.15
1947 23,645,290		.15
Y70 (aluminum, holed)		
1950		.15

	Mintage	Value
	5 FILLER	
Y59 (aluminum) 17mm		
1948		$ .20
1951		.20
Y71 design changed		
1953		.15
1959		.15
1961		.15
	10 FILLER	
Y60 (aluminum-bronze) 19mm		
1946		.20
1947		.20
Y72 new design (aluminum)		
1950		.15
1951		.15
	20 FILLER	
Y61 (aluminum-bronze) 22mm		
1946		.25
1947 17,610,114		.25
1948		.25
Y73 new design (aluminum)		
1953		.25
	50 FILLER	
Y62 (aluminum) 22mm		
1948		.35
Y74 new design		
1953		.30
	1 FORINT	
Y63 (aluminum) 23.5mm		
1946		.50
1947 1,526,260		.50
Y75 new design		
1949		.45
1950		.45
1956		.45
Y80 new design		
1957		.35
	2 FORINT	
Y64 (aluminum) 27mm		
1946		.75
1947 3,515,000		.75
Y76 new design		
1950		.60
1956		.60
Y81 new design		
1957		.50
	5 FORINT	
Y65 (silver) 32mm		
1946		7.50

	Mintage	Value
Y66 thinner		
1947............10,004,252		$3.50
Y67 Petoefi		
1948.............100,000		5.00

10 FORINT
(silver)

	Mintage	Value
Y68 Szechenyi, 36mm		
1948..............100,000		7.50
Y77 Currency Reform, 30mm		
1956...............22,000		5.00

20 FORINT
(silver)

	Mintage	Value
Y69 Tancsics, 40mm		
1948...............50,000		12.50

	Mintage	Value
Y78 Szechenyi Bridge, 32mm		
1956................22,000		$7.50

25 FORINT
(silver)

	Mintage	Value
Y79 Parliament Bldg., 34mm		
1956................22,000		12.50
Y82 Liszt, 32mm		
1961...............15,000		17.50
Y87 Bartok		
1961...............15,000		17.50

50 FORINT
(silver) 34mm

	Mintage	Value
Y83 Liszt		
1961...............15,000		27.50
Y88 Bartok		
1961...............15,000		27.50

ICELAND
(Island)

An island in the North Atlantic Ocean, east of Greenland. Formerly united with Denmark with king having dual role as king of each country. Now a republic. Coins to 1940 with heart mint mark were minted in Denmark. From 1940 coins were minted in England and do not have mint marks.

100 Aurar (singular Eyrir) = 1 Krona

1 EYRIR

Y1 (bronze) 15mm

		Value
1926...............405,161		.30
1931...............462,371		.30
1937...............210,560		.40
1938...............278,700		.30
1939...............305,000		.30
1940...............500,000		.25
1942............2,000,000		.20

Republic

Y11 new design

		Value
1946............4,000,000		.15
1953............4,000,000		.15
1956............2,000,000		.15
1957............2,000,000		.15
1958............2,000,000		.15
1959............1,600,000		.15

2 AURAR

Y2 (bronze) 19mm

		Value
1926..........497,978		.30

		Value
1931...............445,724		.30
1938...............206,231		.50
1940 Copenhagen....257,280		.40
1940 London........500,000		.30
1942............2,000,000		.20

5 AURAR

Y3 (bronze) 24mm

		Value
1926...............355,431		.40
1931...............311,443		.50
1940...............500,000		.35
1942............2,000,000		.25

Republic

Y12 new design

		Value
1946............4,000,000		.15
1958.............400,000		.25
1959.............600,000		.20
1960............1,200,000		.15
1961............1,200,000		.15

10 AURAR

Y4 (copper-nickel) 15mm

	Mintage	Value
1922	300,000	$ .35
1923	302,000	.35
1925	321,025	.35
1929	176,126	.50
1933	157,147	.60
1936	213,007	.40
1939	208,000	.40
1940	1,000,000	.25

Y4a (zinc)

1942	1,500,000	.30

Republic

Y13 (copper-nickel) new design

1946	4,000,000	.20
1953	4,000,000	.20
1957	1,200,000	.20
1958	2,500,000	.20
1959	1,000,000	.20
1960	1,000,000	.20
1961	2,000,000	.20
1962	3,000,000	.20

25 AURAR

Y5 (copper-nickel) 17mm

1922	300,000	.50
1923	304,000	.50
1925	207,320	.60
1933	104,182	1.00
1937	201,104	.60
1940	1,000,000	.30

Y5a (zinc)

1942	1,000,000	.40

Republic

Y14 (copper-nickel) new design

1946	2,000,000	.30
1951	2,000,000	.30
1954	2,000,000	.30

	Mintage	Value
1957	1,000,000	$ .30
1958	1,500,000	.30
1959	1,000,000	.30
1960	1,000,000	.30
1961	1,200,000	.30
1962	2,000,000	.30

1 KRONA

Y6 (aluminum-bronze) 22.5mm

1925	252,000	1.25
1929	154,244	2.00
1940 Copenhagen	209,495	1.75
1940 England	1,000,000	.75

Republic

Y15 (aluminum-bronze) new design

1946	4,062,500	.75

Y15a (nickel,-brass)

1957	1,000,000	.50
1959	500,000	.50
1961	500,000	.50
1962	1,000,000	.50

2 KRONUR

Y7 (aluminum-bronze) 28mm

1925	126,000	2.00
1929	77,087	3.00
1940	1,000,000	1.00

Republic

Y16 new design

1946	2,087,000	1.00

Y16a (nickel-brass)

1958	500,000	.75
1962	500,000	.75

Medals struck in bronze and silver in Germany in 1930 were not legal tender and thus are not listed herewith.

IRELAND
(Saorstat Eireann, Eire)

An island west of England. Formerly part of the British Empire, since 1949 an independent republic.

4 Farthings = 1 Penny
12 Pence = 1 Shilling
2 Shillings = 1 Florin
5 Shillings = 1 Crown

	Mintage	Value
1 FARTHING		
(bronze) 20mm		
Y1 SAORSTAT EIREANN		
1928	300,000	$ .25
1930	288,000	.25
1931	192,000	.50
1932	192,000	.50
1933	480,000	.20
1935	192,000	.40
1936	192,000	.40
1937	480,000	.20
Y9 EIRE		
1939	768,000	.20
1940	192,000	.35
1941	480,000	20
1943	480,000	.20
1944	480,000	.20
1946	480,000	.20
1949	192,000	.25
1953	192,000	.25
1959	192,000	.25
½ PENNY		
(bronze) 25.5mm		
Y2 SAORSTAT EIREANN		
1928	2,880,000	.15
1933	720,000	.20
1935	960,000	.15
1937	960,000	.15
Y10 EIRE		
1939	240,000	.50
1940	1,680,000	.10
1941	2,400,000	.10
1942	6,931,200	.10
1943	2,668,800	.10
1946	720,000	.15
1949	1,344,000	.10
1953	2,400,000	.10
1 PENNY		
(bronze) 31mm		
Y3 SAORSTAT EIREANN		
1928	9,000,000	.15
1931	2,400,000	.20
1933	1,680,000	.20
1935	5,472,000	.15
1937	5,400,000	.15
Y11 EIRE		
1940	312,000	.75
1941	4,680,000	.15
1942	17,520,000	.10
1943	3,360,000	.15
1946	4,800,000	.15

	Mintage	Value
1948	4,800,000	$ .15
1949	4,800,000	.15
1950	2,400,000	.15
1952	2,400,000	15
1962	1,200,000	.15
3 PENCE		
(nickel) 18mm		
Y4 SAORSTAT EIREANN		
1928	1,500,000	.35
1933	320,000	.50
1934	800,000	.35
1935	240,000	.50
Y12 EIRE		
1939	64,000	1.50
1940	720,000	.35
Y12a (copper-nickel)		
1942	4,000,000	.25
1943	1,360,000	.25
1946	800,000	.35
1948	1,600,000	.25
1949	1,200,000	.25
1950	1,600,000	.25
1953	1,600,000	.25
1956	1,200,000	.25
1961	2,400,000	.25
1962	3,200,000	.25
6 PENCE		
(nickel) 21mm		
Y5 SAORSTAT EIREANN		
1928	3,201,480	.30
1934	600,000	.40
1935	520,000	.45
Y13 EIRE		
1939	876,000	.35
1940	1,120,000	.30
Y13a (copper-nickel)		
1942	1,320,000	.30
1945	400,000	.45
1946	720,000	.30
1947	800,000	.30
1948	800,000	.30
1949	600,000	.30
1950	800,000	.30
1952	800,000	.30
1953	800,000	.30
1955	600,000	.30
1956	600,000	.30
1958	600,000	.30
1959	2,000,000	.25
1960	2,020,000	.25
1961	3,000,000	.25
1962	4,000,000	.25

	Mintage	Value
1 SHILLING		
(silver) 24mm		
Y6 SAORSTAT EIREANN		
1928	2,700,000	$1.00
1930	460,000	1.50
1931	400,000	1.50
1933	300,000	1.75
1935	400,000	1.50
1937	100,000	2.50
Y14 EIRE		
1939	1,140,000	1.00
1940	580,000	1.25
1941	300,000	1.25
1942	286,000	1.25
Y14a (copper-nickel)		
1951	2,000,000	.35
1954	3,000,000	.35
1955	1,000,000	.35
1959	2,000,000	.35
1962	4,000,000	.35
1 FLORIN		
(silver) 28.5mm		
Y7 SAORSTAT EIREANN		
1928	2,025,000	1.50
1930	330,000	2.00
1931	200,000	2.50
1933	300,000	2.00
1934	150,000	2.50
1935	390,000	2.00
1937	150,000	2.50
Y15 EIRE		
1939	1,080,000	1.50

	Mintage	Value
1940	670,000	$1.75
1941	400,000	2.00
1942	109,000	2.50
Y15a (copper-nickel)		
1951	1,000,000	.70
1954	1,000,000	.70
1955	1,000,000	.70
1959	2,000,000	.70
1961	2,000,000	.70
1962	2,400,000	.70
HALF CROWN		
(silver) 32mm		
Y8 SAORSTAT EIREANN		
1928	2,160,000	2.50
1930	352,000	3.00
1931	160,000	3.50
1933	336,000	3.00
1934	480,000	3.00
1937	40,000	5.00
Y16 EIRE		
1939	888,000	2.50
1940	752,000	2.50
1941	320,000	3.00
1942	285,600	4.00
1943	inc. above	4.00
Y16a (copper-nickel)		
1951	800,000	1.00
1954	400,000	1.25
1955	1,080,000	1.00
1959	1,600,000	1.00
1961	1,600,000	1.00
1962	3,200,000	1.00

ITALIAN SOMALILAND
(Somalia Italiana)

Prior to World War II an Italian colony in northeastern Africa. After the War administered by the United Nations under Italian trusteeship. See Somalia. In 1960 Somalia became independent.

100 Bese = 1 Rupia

1 BESA		
Y1 (bronze) 20mm		
1909	2,000,000	6.00
1910	500,000	6.00
1913	200,000	6.00
1921	500,000	6.00

2 BESE		
Y2 (bronze) 25mm		
1909	500,000	7.00
1910	250,000	7.00
1913	300,000	7.00
1921	600,000	7.00

	Mintage	Value
1923	1,500,000	$7.00
1924	inc. above	7.00

4 BESE

Y3 (bronze) 30mm

	Mintage	Value
1909	250,000	8.00
1910	250,000	8.00
1913	50,000	10.00
1921	200,000	8.00
1923	1,000,000	8.00
1924	inc. above	8.00

¼ RUPIA

Y4 (silver) 19mm

1910	400,000	7.50
1913	100,000	8.00

½ RUPIA

Y5 (silver) 24mm

1910	400,000	12.50
1912	100,000	12.50
1913	100,000	12.50

	Mintage	Value
1915	50,000	$20.00
1919	200,000	12.50

1 RUPIA

Y6 (silver) 30mm

	Mintage	Value
1910	300,000	12.50
1912	600,000	12.50
1913	300,000	12.50
1914	300,000	12.50
1915	250,000	12.50
1919	400,000	12.50
1920	1,300,000	20.00
1921	943,000	25.00

5 LIRE

Y7 (silver) 25.5mm

1925	400,000	25.00

10 LIRE

Y8 (silver) 28mm

1925	100,000	37.50

ITALY
(Italia)

A large boot-shaped country in southern Europe extending into the Mediterranean Sea. Small quantities of the 20 Centesimi through 20 Lire coins were minted dated 1926 through 1938. These were presentation coins and did not enter circulation.

Mint marks:

B — Bologna (1861)
BI — Birmingham (1893-1894)
FIRENZE — Florence (1861)
H — Birmingham (1866-1867)
KB — Berlin (1894)
M — Milan (1861-1875)
N — Naples (1861-1867)
OM — Strasbourg (1866-1867)
R — Rome
T — Turin (1861-1867)
No mint mark — Parigi (1862-1866)

All coins from 1878 have R (Rome) except where noted.
100 Centesimi = 1 Lira

1 CENTESIMO

Victor Emanuel II (1861-1878)

Y6 (copper) 15mm

1861M	.50

1861N	2.00
1862N	.90
1867M	.30
1867T	1.25

Humbert I (1878-1900)

Y22

	Mintage	Value
1895	13,860,000	$ .25
1896	3,700,000	.40
1897	1,844,500	2.00
1899	1,287,474	.40
1900	10,000,000	.25

Victor Emanuel III (1900-1946)

Y35 (bronze)

1902	26,308	12.50
1903	5,655,000	.25
1904	14,623,692	.25
1905	8,505,531	.25
1908	3,916,000	.25

Y37 new design

1908	inc. above	3.50
1909	3,539,000	.25
1910	3,598,560	.25
1911	700,000	1.00
1912	3,995,000	.25
1913	3,200,000	.25
1914	11,585,000	.25
1915	9,757,440	.25
1916	17,250,000	.25
1917	2,400,000	.25
1918	2,710,000	1.00

2 CENTESIMI

Victor Emanuel II

Y7 (copper) 20mm

1861M		.50
1861N		1.00
1862N		.35
1867M		.30
1867T		1.00

Humbert I

Y23

1895	610,000	1.00
1896	296,500	1.50
1897	4,414,000	.25
1898	4,164,000	.25
1900	1,717,500	.30

Victor Emanuel III

Y36 (bronze)

1903	5,000,000	.25
1905	1,260,000	30
1906	3,145,000	.25
1907	230,000	1.25
1908	1,815,500	.25

Y38 new design

1908	inc. above	3.00

	Mintage	Value
1909	2,419,359	$ .25
1910	589,975	.40
1911	2,777,155	.25
1912	840,000	.30
1914	1,467,500	.25
1915	4,860,000	.25
1916	1,540,000	.25
1917	2,637,500	.25

5 CENTESIMI

Victor Emanuel II

Y8 (copper) 25mm

1861B		1.00
1861M		.30
1861N		.50
1862N		.30
1867M		.35
1867N		.30

Humbert I

Y24

1895	600,000	.75
1896	379,000	.75

Victor Emanuel III

Y39 (bronze)

1908	824,390	1.25
1909	1,733,610	.30
1912	743,000	.50
1913	1,964,066	.30
1915	1,038,000	.40
1918	4,242,000	.30

Y42 19.5mm

1919	13,208,000	.40
1920	33,372,000	.20
1921	80,110,889	.20
1922	42,914,000	.20
1923	29,614,000	.20
1924	20,352,000	.20
1925	40,460,000	.20
1926	21,158,000	.20
1927	15,800,475	.20
1928	16,090,000	.20
1929	29,000,000	.20
1930	22,694,000	.20
1931	20,000,000	.20
1932	11,456,007	.20
1933	20,720,000	.20
1934	16,000,000	.20
1935	11,000,000	.20
1936	9,462,000	.20
1937	8,179,000	1.50

	Mintage	Value
Y77 eagle		
1936	inc. above	$ .30
1937	inc. above	.20
1938	17,001,000	.20
1939	22,000,000	.20
Y83 (aluminum-bronze)		
1939	1,000,000	.30
1940	9,632,000	.20
1941	16,340,000	.20
1942	25,200,000	.20
1943	13,922,000	1.50

10 CENTESIMI
Victor Emanuel II

Y9 (copper) 30mm

1862M		.75
1862 no mint mark (Parigi)		.50
1863 same as above		.50
1866H		.50
1866M		.50
1866N		.50
1866OM		.50
1866T		.50
1866 no mint mark (Parigi)		2.50
1867H		.50
1867N		.50
1867OM		.50
1867T		.75

Humbert I
Y25

1893BI	28,000,000	.50
1893R	8,547,000	.60
1894BI	32,000,000	.50
1894R	5,909,780	.75

Victor Emanuel III
Y40 (bronze)

1908	extremely rare	——

Y41 50th Anniversary

1911	2,000,000	1.00

Y43 bee, 22.5mm

1919	986,000	1.25
1920	37,975,000	.25
1921	66,510,000	.25
1922	45,217,487	.25
1923	31,259,000	.25
1924	35,312,000	.25
1925	22,370,000	.25
1926	25,190,000	.25
1927	22,673,000	.25
1928	15,680,000	.25

	Mintage	Value
1929	19,593,000	$ .25
1930	17,115,000	.25
1931	10,750,000	.25
1932	5,678,000	.25
1933	10,250,000	.25
1934	18,300,000	.25
1935	10,500,000	.25
1936	8,770,000	.25
1937	12,712,000	.25
Y78 shield		
1936	inc. above	.25
1937	inc. above	.25
1938	13,251,000	.25
1939	24,750,000	.25
Y84 (aluminum-bronze)		
1939	750,000	1.00
1940	23,355,000	.25
1941	27,050,000	.25
1942	18,100,000	.25
1943	25,400,000	.25

20 CENTESIMI
(silver) 16mm

Victor Emanuel II
Y10 shield and crown

1863T	461	25.00

Y15 20 centesimi reverse

1863M		.50
1863T		.75
1867T		3.50

Humbert I
Y26 (nickel) 20mm

1894KB	75,000,000	.25
1894R	13,901,000	.60
1895R	11,099,000	.60

Victor Emanuel III
Y44 21.5mm

1908	14,315,000	.20
1909	19,280,000	.20
1910	21,887,000	.20
1911	13,671,000	.20
1912	21,040,000	.20
1913	20,727,000	.20
1914	14,307,666	.20
1919	3,474,725	.60
1920	27,283,800	.20
1921	50,372,000	.20
1922	17,134,309	.20

	Mintage	Value
Y46 new design		
1918	43,097,000	$ .20
1919	33,342,000	.20
1920	923,000	1.00
Y79 new design		
1936	117,050	2.00
Y85 (steel)		
1939 XVII	463,000	.50
1939 XVIII	inc above	.50
1940	35,350,000	.20
1941	107,300,000	.20
1942	99,900,000	.20
1943	57,003,000	.20

25 CENTESIMI

Victor Emanuel III

	Mintage	Value
Y45 (nickel) 21.5mm		
1902	5,974,242	.65
1903	7,693,758	.65

50 CENTESIMI

Victor Emanuel II

	Mintage	Value
Y11 (silver) 18mm		
1861 FIRENZE shield rev		5.00
1861M		1.50
1861T		7.50
1862N		1.00
1862T		5.00
1863M		1.50
1863T		3.00
Y16 50 Centesimi reverse		
1863M		.60
1863N		1.25
1863T		.75
1866M		1.50
1867M		.60
1867N		1.25
1867T		7.50

Humbert I

	Mintage	Value
Y27		
1889		5.00
1892		5.00

Victor Emanuel III

	Mintage	Value
Y47 (nickel) 24mm		
1919	3,700,000	.60
1920	29,750,378	.35
1921	16,849,622	.35
1924	599,000	2.00
1925	24,884,000	.35

	Mintage	Value
Y80 new design		
1936	118,050	$2.00
Y86 (steel)		
1939 XVII	372,000	.40
1939 XVIII	inc. above	.40
1940	19,005,000	.25
1941	58,100,000	.25
1942	26,450,000	.25
1943	3,681,000	1.50

1 LIRA

Victor Emanuel II

	Value
Y12 (silver) 23mm	
1861 FIRENZE shield reverse	8.00
1861T	12.50
1862N	2.50
1862T	7.50
1863M	1.00
1863T	2.00
1867M	1.25
1867T	4.00
Y17 1 Lira reverse	
1863M	1.25
1863T	5.00

Humbert I

	Mintage	Value
Y28		
1883	5,420	20.00
1884		1.50
1886	5,000,000	1.00
1887	17,400,000	1.00
1892		15.00
1899	1,298,544	1.25
1900	817,445	1.50

Victor Emanuel III

	Mintage	Value
Y51		
1901		1.25
1902	4,083,605	1.00
1905	700,069	3.00
1906	4,665,071	1.00
1907	8,471,824	1.00
Y54 new design		
1908	2,112,088	2.50
1909	3,474,800	2.50
1910	5,524,672	1.25
1912	5,864,646	1.25
1913	16,176,910	1.00
Y58 new design		
1915	5,229,214	1.00
1916	1,834,892	2.00

	Mintage	Value
1917	9,744,014	$1.00
Y49 (nickel) 26.5mm		
1922	82,226,500	.60
1923	20,175,276	.75
1924	29,288,000	.60
1928	19,995,500	1.50
Y81 new design		
1936	119,050	2.50
Y87 (steel)		
1939 XVII		50
1939 XVIII		.50
1940	25,997,000	.40
1941	8,550,000	.40
1942	5,700,000	.40
1943	11,500,000	2.00

Republic (1946 to date)

	Mintage	Value
Y95 (aluminum) 21.5mm		
1946	104,000	2.00
1947	12,000	2.00
1948	9,900,000	.20
1949	12,300,000	.20
1950	1,942,000	.25
Y99 new design, 17mm		
1951	3,760,000	.10
1952	2,720,000	.10
1953	2,800,000	.10
1954	49,840,000	.10
1955	32,640,000	.10
1956	1,840,050	.15
1957	7,440,000	.10
1958	5,280,000	.10
1959	1,680,000	.15

2 LIRE
(silver) 27mm

Victor Emanuel II

		Value
Y13 shield and crown		
1861T		25.00
1862N		6.00
1863N		1.50
1863T		2.50
Y16 2 Lire reverse		
1863N		1.75
1863T		2.50

Humbert I

		Value
Y29		
1881		2.00
1882		2.00
1883		2.00
1884		2.00

	Mintage	Value
1885	348,773	$3.00
1886	2,111,202	2.50
1887	7,500,000	2.00
1897	797,816	2.50
1898	1,369,602	2.50
1899	609,665	3.00

Victor Emanuel III

	Mintage	Value
Y52		
1901		15.00
1902	549,288	2.50
1903	53,622	25.00
1904	157,071	15.00
1905	1,643,037	2.00
1906	969,567	2.25
1907	1,245,450	2.00
Y55 new design		
1908	2,282,365	2.00
1910	718,670	2.00
1911	534,810	5.00
1912	2,166,202	2.00
Y56 (1861-1911)		
1911	1,000,000	3.50
Y59 new design		
1914	10,390,042	2.00
1915	7,947,783	2.00
1916	10,923,056	2.00
1917	6,122,657	2.00
Y50 (nickel) 29mm		
1923	33,260,000	1.00
1924	45,050,500	1.00
1925	14,627,921	1.25
1926	5,101,353	3.00
1927	1,631,500	5.00
Y82 new design		
1936	120,050	1.50
Y88 (steel)		
1939 XVII		.75
1939 XVIII		.75
1940	13,483,000	.60
1941	1,865,000	1.00
1942	2,450,000	3.00
1943	600,000	2.50

Republic

	Mintage	Value
Y96 (aluminum) 24mm		
1946	123,000	1.00
1947	12,000	1.50
1948	7,650,000	.20
1949	900,000	.40
1950	2,790,000	.20

	Mintage	Value
Y100 18.5mm		
1953...............4,125,000		$ .10
1954............26,825,000		.10
1955.............2,750,000		.15
1956.............1,500,050		.50
1957.............6,312,500		.10
1958...............125,000		1.50
1959.............2,000,000		.15

5 LIRE

Victor Emanuel II

Y14 (silver) 37mm

1861 FIRENZE......21,472		75.00
1861T....................		40.00
1862N....................		20.00
1862T....................		17.50
1864N....................		17.50
1865N....................		15.00
1865T....................		15.00
1866N....................		75.00
1869M....................		3.50
1870M....................		3.50
1870R....................		6.00
1871M....................		3.50
1871R....................		7.50
1872M....................		3.50
1872R....................		25.00
1873M....................		3.50
1873R....................		40.00
1874M....................		3.50
1875M....................		3.50
1875R....................		4.00
1876R....................		3.50
1877R....................		3.50
1878R....................		4.00

Humbert I

Y30

1878R....................		20.00
1879R....................		6.00

Victor Emanuel III

Y53

1901..................114		——

Y57 (1861-1911)

1911...............200,000		50.00

Y60 horses

1914...............272,515		150.00

Y61 eagle, 23mm

1926.............5,405,000		1.50
1927............92,887,460		.75
1928.............9,907,540		1.25

	Mintage	Value
1929............33,803,000		$1.00
1930............19,525,500		1.00
Y89 new design		
1936.............1,106,050		2.00
1937............inc. above		2.50

Republic

Y97 (aluminum) 26.5mm

1946................81,000		2.00
1947................16,500		2.00
1948............41,985,000		.25
1949...........121,425,000		.25
1950............47,665,000		.25

Y101 fish, 20mm

1951............40,260,000		.10
1952............57,400,000		.10
1953...........196,200,000		.10
1954...........450,450,000		.10
1955...........159,000,000		.10
1956...............400,000		1.00

10 LIRE
(silver) 27mm

Victor Emanuel III

Y62 horses

1926.............1,747,500		4.00
1927............44,800,720		1.50
1928.............6,651,780		2.50
1929.............6,800,000		2.00
1930.............3,667,500		3.50

Y90 woman

1936...............618,500		4.50

Republic

Y98 (aluminum) 29mm

1946...............101,000		2.00
1947................12,000		2.00
1948............28,425,000		.25
1949............54,150,000		.25
1950............31,050,000		.25

Y102 plow, 23mm

1951............96,736,000		.15
1952...........105,150,000		.15
1953...........151,500,000		.15
1954............96,300,000		.15
1955...........274,950,000		.15
1956............76,650,000		.15

20 LIRE

Victor Emanuel III

Y63 (silver) 35.5mm

1927 V...........3,518,102		75.00

	Mintage	Value		Mintage	Value
1927 VI	inc. above	$20.00	1961	11,100,000	$ .35
1928	2,486,898	20.00	1962	17,600,000	.35

Y64 king, helmeted

1928	3,536,250	15.00

100 LIRE

Republic

Y91 horses

Y104 (steel) 28mm

1936	10,000	70.00

	Mintage	Value
1955	8,600,000	.60
1956	99,800,000	.60

Republic

1957	90,600,000	.60

Y102a (aluminum-bronze)

1958	25,640,000	.60
1957	60,075,000	.20	1959	19,500,000	.60
1958	80,550,000	.20	1960	20,700,000	.60
1959	4,005,000	.25	1961	11,860,000	.60
			1962	23,000,000	.60

50 LIRE

500 LIRE

Republic

Republic

Y103 (steel) 25mm

Y105 (silver) 29.5mm

1954	17,600,000	.35
1955	88,100,000	.35
1956	69,400,000	.35
1957	8,925,000	.35
1958	825,000	.75
1959	8,800,000	.35
1960	2,025,000	.40

1958	24,240,000	1.75
1959	19,360,000	1.75
1960	24,080,000	1.75
1961	30,480,000	1.75

Y106

1961	inc. above	1.75

KIAO CHAU
(Deutsch Kiautschou Gebeit)

Former German territory on the east coast of China; now a district of China. Coinage obsolete.

100 Cents = 1 Dollar

5 CENTS			10 CENTS		
Y1 (copper-nickel) 18.5mm			**Y2** (copper-nickel) 21.5mm		
1909	100,178	17.50	1909	150,464	17.50

LATVIA
(Latvija)

On the Baltic Sea between Lithuania and Estonia. Was a Russian province until 1918. It was an independent republic until 1940 when it was incorporated into the U.S.S.R. Coinage obsolete; coins of U.S.S.R. now circulating.

100 Santimu = 1 Lats

1 SANTIMS			1926	5,000,000	1.50
			1928	5,000,000	1.50
Y1 (bronze) 17mm			1932	5,000,000	1.50
1922	5,000,000	1.50	1935	5,000,000	1.50
1924	4,990,000	1.50			

	Mintage	Value
Y10 design changed		
1937	2,700,000	$3.00
1938	1,900,000	3.00
1939	unknown	3.00

2 SANTIMI
	Mintage	Value
Y2 (bronze) 19mm		
1922	10,000,000	1.50
1926	5,000,000	1.50
1928	5,000,000	1.50
1932	5,000,000	1.50
Y11 design changed		
1937	44,600	10.00
Y11a larger, 19.5mm		
1939	unknown	3.00

5 SANTIMI
	Mintage	Value
Y3 (bronze) 21mm		
1922	15,000,000	1.50

10 SANTIMU
	Mintage	Value
Y4 (nickel) 19mm		
1922	15,000,000	1.00

20 SANTIMU
	Mintage	Value
Y5 (nickel) 21mm		
1922	15,000,000	$1.50

50 SANTIMU
	Mintage	Value
Y6 (nickel) 25mm		
1922	9,000,000	2.50

1 LATS
	Mintage	Value
Y7 (silver) 23mm		
1924	10,000,000	3.00

2 LATI
	Mintage	Value
Y8 (silver) 27mm		
1925	6,385,531	4.00
1926	1,114,469	5.00

5 LATI
	Mintage	Value
Y9 (silver) 37mm		
1929	1,000,000	8.50
1931	2,000,000	7.50
1932	600,000	10.00

LIECHTENSTEIN

A principality between Austria and Switzerland. Used Austrian monetary system until the end of World War I. The Swiss monetary system was adopted in 1920.

100 Heller = 1 Krone 1892-1923
100 Rappen = 1 Frank 1924 on

Austrian System
1 KRONE
	Mintage	Value
Y2 (silver) 23mm		
1900	50,000	4.00
1904	75,009	4.00
1910	50,009	4.00
1915	75,010	4.00

2 KRONEN
	Mintage	Value
Y3 (silver) 27mm		
1912	50,004	6.00
1915	37,504	6.00

5 KRONEN
	Mintage	Value
Y4 (silver) 37mm		
1900	5,000	45.00
1904	15,003	35.00
1910	10,003	35.00
1915	10,004	35.00

Swiss System
½ FRANK
	Mintage	Value
Y7 (silver) 18mm		
1924	30,000	5.00

1 FRANK
	Mintage	Value
Y8 (silver) 23mm		
1924	60,000	7.50

2 FRANKEN
	Mintage	Value
Y9 (silver) 27mm		
1924	50,000	10.00

5 FRANKEN
	Mintage	Value
Y10 (silver) 37mm		
1924	15,000	50.00

(Lietuva, Lietuvos)

Became an independent nation in 1918. Was occupied by, and annexed to, the U.S.S.R. in 1940. Coinage obsolete; coins of U.S.S.R. now circulating.

100 Centu = 1 Litas

	Mintage	Value
1 CENTAS		
Y1 (aluminum-bronze) 16mm		
1925.............5,000,000		$2.50
Y9 (bronze)		
1936...........10,190,000		1.50
2 CENTAI		
Y10 (bronze) 18.5mm		
1936.............4,951,000		2.50
5 CENTAI		
Y2 (aluminum-bronze) 19mm		
1925...........12,000,000		1.50
Y10 (bronze)		
1936.............4,800,000		2.00
10 CENTU		
Y3 (aluminum-bronze) 21mm		
1925...........12,000,000		1.75
20 CENTU		
Y4 (aluminum-bronze) 23mm		
1925.............8,000,000		2.00

	Mintage	Value
50 CENTU		
Y5 (aluminum-bronze) 25mm		
1925.............5,000,000		$3.00
1 LITAS		
Y6 (silver) 19mm		
1925.............5,985,000		3.00
2 LITU		
Y7 (silver) 23mm		
1925.............3,000,000		5.00
5 LITAI		
Y8 (silver) 30mm		
1925.............1,000,000		17.50
Y12 new design, 27mm		
1936.............2,750,000		8.50
10 LITU		
Y13 (silver) 32mm		
1936..............876,000		22.50
Y14 Smetona		
1938..............160,000		27.50

LUXEMBURG
(Luxembourg, Letzeburg)

A small independent nation in western Europe between Belgium, Germany and France.

100 Centimes = 1 Franc

2½ CENTIMES		
William III of Netherlands (1849-1890)		
Y1 (bronze) 21mm		
1854...............640,000		.50
1870...............209,880		.50
Adolphe (1890-1905)		
1901...............800,000		.35
William IV (1905-1912)		
1908...............400,000		.35

5 CENTIMES		
William III of Netherlands		
Y2 (bronze) 25mm		
1854...............680,000		1.00
1855...............600,000		1.00
1860...............200,000		1.25
1870...............303,900		1.25
Adolphe		
Y5 (copper-nickel) 18mm		
1901.............2,000,000		.30

	Mintage	Value
William IV		
Y8		
1908 1,500,000		$ .50
Marie Adelaide (1912-1919)		
Y9 (zinc)		
1915 1,200,000		.35
Y12 (iron) new design		
1918		.75
Charlotte (1919 to date)		
1921		.75
1922 400,000		.75
Y18 (copper-nickel)		
1924 3,000,000		.25
Y25 (bronze) 19mm		
1930 5,000,000		.25

10 CENTIMES

William III of Netherlands

Y3 (bronze) 30mm

	Mintage	Value
1854 500,000		1.00
1855 1,200,000		1.00
1860 900,000		1.00
1865 1,000,000		1.00
1870 1,313,050		1.00

Adolphe

Y6 (copper-nickel) 20mm

1901 4,000,000		.35

Marie Adelaide

Y10 (zinc)

1915 1,400,000		.50

Y13 (iron) 20.5mm

1918		1.00

Charlotte

1921		1.00
1923 350,000		1.00
Y19 (copper-nickel) 21mm		
1924 3,500,000		.50
Y26 (bronze) 22mm		
1930 5,000,000		.30

25 CENTIMES

Marie Adelaide

Y11 (zinc) 24mm

1916 800,000		.75

Y14 (iron) 23mm

1919		1.25

Charlotte

1920		1.25
1922 600,000		1.25

	Mintage	Value
Y22 (copper-nickel) 25mm		
1927 2,500,000		$ .50
Y27 (bronze)		
1930 1,000,000		.35
Y27a (copper-nickel)		
1938 2,000,000		.40
Y30 (bronze) 19mm		
1946 4,000,000		.15
1947 4,000,000		.15
Y30a (aluminum)		
1954 7,000,000		.10
1957 3,020,000		.10
1960 3,020,000		.10

50 CENTIMES

Charlotte

Y28 (nickel) 20.5mm

1930 2,000,000		.40

1 FRANC

Charlotte

Y20 (nickel) 23mm

1924 1,000,000		.50
1928 2,000,000		.50
1935 1,000,000		.50

Y29 (copper-nickel) 24mm

1939 5,000,000		.50

Y31 new design, 23mm

1946 4,000,000		.35
1947 2,000,000		.35

Y32 21mm

1952 5,000,000		.20

Y32a

1953 2,000,000		.20
1955 1,003,424		.25
1957 2,000,000		.20
1960 2,000,000		.20
1962 2,000,000		.20

2 FRANCS

Charlotte

Y21 (nickel) 27mm

1924 1,000,000		1.00

5 FRANCS

Charlotte

Y23 (silver) 28mm

1929 2,000,000		2.50

Y36 (copper-nickel) 25.5mm

1949 2,000,000		.50

Y37 new design, 24mm

1962 2,000,000		.50

	Mintage	Value
10 FRANCS		
Charlotte		
Y24 (silver) 31mm		
1929............1,000,000		$5.00
20 FRANCS		
Charlotte		
Y33 (silver) 27mm		
1946..............100,000		2.50

	Mintage	Value
50 FRANCS		
Y34 (silver) 31mm		
1946..............100,000		$3.50
100 FRANCS		
Charlotte		
Y35 (silver) 37mm		
1946..............100,000		8.50

MACAO
(Macau)

A Portuguese province at the mouth of the Canton River in China.

100 Avos = 1 Pataca

5 AVOS		
Y1 (bronze) 17mm		
1952............1,032,150		.25
10 AVOS		
Y2 (bronze) 22mm		
1952............6,825,150		.35
50 AVOS		
Y3 (copper-nickel) 20mm		
1952............2,560,150		.50

1 PATACA		
Y4 (silver) 19mm		
1952..............521,600		1.00
5 PATACAS		
Y5 (silver) 31mm		
1952..............500,100		4.00

MADAGASGAR

A large island off the southeast coast of Africa. In 1960 it gained independence from France and became the Malagasy Republic.

100 Centimes = 1 Franc

"Free French" Issue		
50 CENTIMES		
Y1 (bronze) 20mm		
1943............4,000,000		1.50
1 FRANC		
Y2 (bronze) 25mm		
1943............5,000,000		2.00
Postwar Issues		
1 FRANC		
Y3 (aluminum) 23mm		
1948...........10,000,000		.50

2 FRANCS		
Y4 (aluminum) 27mm		
1948...........10,000,000		.65
5 FRANCS		
Y5 (aluminum) 31mm		
1953...........30,000,000		.75
10 FRANCS		
Y6 (aluminum-bronze) 20mm		
1953...........25,000,000		.75
20 FRANCS		
Y7 (aluminum-bronze) 23mm		
1953...........15,000,000		1.00

A French possession in the Caribbean Sea. Coins of France now circulating.

100 Centimes = 1 Franc

	Mintage	Value			Mintage	Value
50 CENTIMES				**1 FRANC**		
Y1 (copper-nickel) 22mm				**Y2** (copper-nickel) 25mm		
1897...............600,000		$2.50		1897...............300,000		$3.50
1922...............500,000		2.50		1922...............350,000		3.50

MONACO

A small principality on the Mediterranean Sea, bounded by France.

100 Centimes = 1 Franc

50 CENTIMES		
Louis II (1922-1949)		
Y2 (aluminum-bronze) 18.5mm		
1924...............150,000		1.25
Y5		
1926...............100,000		1.25

1 FRANC		
Louis II		
Y3 (aluminum-bronze) 23.5mm		
1924...............150,000		1.25
Y6		
1926...............100,000		1.25
Y8 not dated		
(1943)..........1,589,135		.50
Y8a (aluminum) not dated		
(1943)..........2,500,000		.50
Rainier III (1949 to date)		
Y18 (nickel)		
1960...............500,000		.85

2 FRANCS		
Louis II		
Y4 (aluminum-bronze) 27.5mm		
1924...............75,000		2.50
Y7		
1926...............75,000		2.50
Y9 not dated		
(1943)..........1,082,687		.75
Y9a (aluminum) not dated		
(1943)..........1,250,000		.75

5 FRANCS		
Louis II		
Y10 (aluminum) 32mm		
1945............1,000,000		1.00

Rainier III		
Y19 (silver) 29mm		
1960...............125,000		2.00

10 FRANCS		
Louis II		
Y11 (copper-nickel) 26mm		
1946............1,000,000		.75
Rainier III		
Y13 (aluminum-bronze) 20mm		
1950...............500,000		.25
1951...............500,000		.25

20 FRANCS		
Louis II		
Y12		
1947............1,000,000		1.50
Rainier III		
Y14 (aluminum-bronze) 23mm		
1950...............500,000		.40
1951...............500,000		.40

50 FRANCS		
Rainer III		
Y15 (aluminum-bronze) 27mm		
1950...............500,000		.50

100 FRANCS		
Rainier III		
Y16 (copper-nickel) 31mm		
1950...............500,000		1.50
Y17 new design, 23.5mm		
1956...............500,000		1.00

(ЦРНА ГОРА)

A former kingdom north of Albania, now a part of Yugoslavia. Coinage obsolete.

100 Para = 1 Perper

(Nicholas I 1860-1918)

1 PARA

	Mintage	Value
Y1 (bronze) 17mm		
1906	200,000	$1.50
1908	500,000	1.50
Y11		
1913	100,000	2.00
1914	200,000	1.50

2 PARE

	Mintage	Value
Y2 (bronze) 19mm		
1906	600,000	1.25
1908	250,000	1.25
Y12		
1913	500,000	1.00
1914	400,000	1.00

10 PARA

	Mintage	Value
Y3 (nickel) 19mm		
1906	750,000	1.00
1908	250,000	1.25
Y13		
1913	200,000	1.50
1914	800,000	1.00

20 PARA

	Mintage	Value
Y4 (nickel) 21mm		
1906	600,000	$1.50
1908	400,000	1.50
Y14		
1913	200,000	1.75
1914	800,000	1.25

1 PERPER

	Mintage	Value
Y5 (silver) 23mm		
1909	500,000	3.00
1912	520,000	3.00
1914	500,000	3.00

2 PERPERA

	Mintage	Value
Y6 (silver) 27mm		
1910	300,000	5.00
Y16		
1914	200,000	5.00

5 PERPERA

	Mintage	Value
Y7 (silver) 36mm		
1909	60,000	35.00
Y17		
1912	40,002	40.00
1914	20,000	45.00

A Portuguese province in East Africa.

100 Centavos = 1 Escudo

	Mintage	Value
10 CENTAVOS		
Y1 (bronze) 22.5mm		
1936	2,000,000	$ .35
Y11 16mm		
1942	2,000,000	.25
Y24 new design		
1960	3,750,150	.10
1961	10,249,850	.10
20 CENTAVOS		
Y2 (bronze) 25mm		
1936	2,000,000	.50
Y12 20.5mm		
1941	2,000,000	.40
Y15		
1949	12,500,000	.20
1950	18,500,000	.20
Y25 new design		
1961	12,500,000	.15
50 CENTAVOS		
Y3 (copper-nickel) 23mm		
1936	2,500,000	.60
Y13 (bronze)		
1945	2,500,000	.60
Y16 (nickel-bronze)		
1950	4,000,000	.30
1951	4,000,000	.30
Y18 (bronze) 20mm		
1953	5,010,050	.20
1957	24,989,950	.20
1 ESCUDO		
Y4 (copper-nickel) 27mm		
1936	2,000,000	.90
Y14 (bronze)		
1945	2,000,000	.90
Y17 (nickel-bronze)		
1950	4,000,000	.60
1951	4,000,000	.60

	Mintage	Value
Y19 (bronze) 26mm		
1953	2,013,150	$ .30
1957	2,986,850	.30
2.50 ESCUDOS		
Y5 (silver) 20mm		
1935	1,200,000	1.00
Y8 new design		
1938	1,000,000	1.00
1942	1,200,000	.90
1950	4,000,000	.65
1951	4,000,000	.65
Y20 (copper-nickel)		
1953	6,008,150	.40
1954	6,111,200	.40
1955	3,380,650	.40
5 ESCUDOS		
Y6 (silver) 22mm		
1935	1,000,000	1.50
Y9 new design		
1938	500,000	1.75
1949	8,000,000	1.00
Y21 (silver)		
1960	8,000,000	.75
10 ESCUDOS		
Y7 (silver) 31mm		
1936	496,926	3.50
Y10 new design		
1938	250,000	3.50
Y22 24mm		
1952	1,503,150	1.25
1954	1,335,150	1.25
1955	1,161,700	1.25
1960	2,000,000	1.25
20 ESCUDOS		
Y23 (silver) 30mm		
1952	1,004,400	3.00
1955	995,600	3.00
1960	2,000,000	3.00

(Nederlanden)

A country in northwestern Europe, bordering on the North Sea. All coins bear name of country except Y1 and Y2. During World War II some Netherlands coinage was minted in the U. S., and is identified by the mint marks P, D, or S and acorn. Some were minted for the colonies and will be found listed therein.

100 Cents = 1 Guilder

	Mintage	Value
½ CENT		
William III (1849-1890)		
Y1 (copper) 14.25mm		
1850	2,000,400	$ .50
1851	2,051,400	.50
1852	2,027,560	.50
1853	2,000,000	.50
1854	3,000,000	.50
1855	998,800	1.00
1857	4,154,800	.40
1859	4,052,000	.40
1861	1,446,000	.50
1862	2,026,000	.50
1863	2,428,000	.50
1864	2,016,000	.50
1865	2,006,000	.50
1867	2,008,000	.50
1869	2,014,000	.50
1870	2,004,000	.50
1873	2,026,000	.50
1875	2,026,000	.50
1876	2,020,000	.50
1877	1,400,000	.50
Y3 new type, 12.5mm		
1878	4,000,000	.25
1883	800,000	.75
1884	17,200,000	.25
1885	7,800,000	.25
1886	2,200,000	.30
Wilhelmina (1890-1948)		
Y17 (bronze)		
1891	5,000,000	.20
1894	5,000,000	.20
1898	2,000,000	.25
1900	3,000,000	.25
1901	6,000,000	.20
1903	10,000,000	.15
1906	10,000,000	.15
Y35 design changed		
1909	5,000,000	.15
1911	5,000,000	.15
1912	5,000,000	.15
1914	5,000,000	.15
1915	2,500,000	.20
1916	4,000,000	.15

	Mintage	Value
1917	5,000,000	$ .15
1921	1,500,000	.35
1922	2,500,000	.20
1928	4,000,000	.15
1930	6,000,000	.15
1934	5,000,000	.15
1936	5,000,000	.15
1937	1,600,000	.30
1938	8,400,000	.15
1940	6,000,000	.15
1 CENT		
William III		
Y2 (copper) 20.5mm		
1860	2,032,000	.50
1861	2,050,000	.50
1862	2,026,000	.50
1863	10,246,000	.30
1864	2,026,000	.50
1870	4,010,000	.40
1873	3,026,000	.50
1875	3,015,000	.50
1876	13,047,000	.30
1877	11,026,000	.30
Y4 new type, 18.5mm		
1877	6,100,000	.30
1878	53,900,000	.25
1880	20,000,000	.25
1881	10,000,000	.25
1882	5,000,000	.30
1883	15,000,000	.25
1884	10,000,000	.25
Wilhelmina		
Y18 (bronze)		
1892	5,000,000	.25
1896	3,000,000	.25
1897	2,500,000	.35
1898	5,000,000	.25
1899	5,100,000	.25
1900	12,400,000	.20
1901	10,000,000	.20
1901 type of 1902	10,000,000	.20
1902	10,000,000	.20
1904	10,000,000	.20
1905	10,000,000	.20

	Mintage	Value
1906	9,000,000	$ .20
1907	6,000,000	.20

Y36 design changed

	Mintage	Value
1913	5,000,000	.25
1914	9,000,000	.20
1915	10,800,000	.20
1916	21,700,000	.20
1917	20,000,000	.20
1918	10,000,000	.20
1919	6,000,000	.25
1920	11,400,000	.20
1921	12,600,000	.20
1922	20,000,000	.20
1924	1,400,000	1.00
1925	18,600,000	.15
1926	10,000,000	.15
1927	10,000,000	.15
1928	10,000,000	.15
1929	20,000,000	.15
1930	10,000,000	.15
1931	3,400,000	.35
1937	10,000,000	.15
1938	16,600,000	.15
1939	22,000,000	.15
1940	24,600,000	.15
1941	66,600,000	.10

German Occupation

Y48 new design (zinc) 15.5mm

	Mintage	Value
1941	31,800,000	.15
1942	241,200,000	.10
1943	71,000,000	.15
1944	29,600,000	.15

(U. S. Mintage 1942 and 1943 — See Curacao and Surinam.)

Netherlands Mintage

Y53 new design (bronze) 15.5mm

	Mintage	Value
1948	93,000,000	.10

Juliana
Y57

	Mintage	Value
1950	91,000,000	.10
1951	45,800,000	.10
1952	68,000,000	.10
1953	54,000,000	.10
1954	54,000,000	.10
1955	52,000,000	.10
1956	34,800,000	.10
1957	48,000,000	.10
1958	34,000,000	.10
1959	36,000,000	.10
1960	40,000,000	.10
1961	52,000,000	.10

	Mintage	Value
1962	57,000,000	$ .10

(For pre-World War II type 1 cent dated 1957 and later see Surinam.)

2½ CENTS
William III

Y5 (copper) 22mm

	Mintage	Value
1877	4,000,000	.25
1880	4,000,000	.25
1881	4,000,000	.25
1883	400,000	1.00
1884	3,600,000	.25
1886	2,000,000	.30

Wilhelmina

Y19 (bronze)

	Mintage	Value
1890	2,000,000	.30
1894	1,000,000	.50
1898	1,600,000	.40
1903	4,000,000	.25
1904	4,000,000	.25
1905	4,000,000	.25
1906	8,000,000	.25

Y37 new design

	Mintage	Value
1912	2,000,000	.30
1913	4,000,000	.25
1914	2,000,000	.30
1915	3,000,000	.25
1916	8,000,000	.25
1918	4,000,000	.25
1919	2,000,000	.30
1929	8,000,000	.25
1941	19,800,000	.20

German Occupation

Y49 new design (zinc) 19mm

	Mintage	Value
1941	27,600,000	.30
1942	200,000	2.50

5 CENTS
William III

Y6 (silver) 11.5mm

	Mintage	Value
1850	3,037,000	.60
1853	11,170	12.50
1855	514,809	1.00
1859	400,000	1.00
1862	400,000	1.00
1863	640,000	1.00
1868	200,000	1.25
1869	500,000	1.00
1876	200,000	1.25
1879	200,000	1.25
1887	100,000	1.75

	Mintage	Value
Wilhelmina		
Y33 (copper-nickel) 18mm		
1907	6,000,000	$ .25
1908	4,000,000	.25
1909	4,000,000	.25
Y34 diamond-shaped, 16.5mm		
1913	6,000,000	.35
1914	7,400,000	.30
1923	10,000,000	.25
1929	8,000,000	.30
1932	2,000,000	.50
1933	1,400,000	.75
1934	2,600,000	.50
1936	2,600,000	.50
1938	4,200,000	.40
1939	4,600,000	.40
1940	7,200,000	.30
German Occupation		
Y50 square (zinc) 18mm		
1941	32,200,000	.20
1942	11,800,000	.25
1943	7,000,000	.30
Pre-war type minted in U. S. for Curacao and Surinam. (No mint mark.)		
Y34a		
1943	8,595,000	.25
Netherlands Mintage		
Y54 (bronze) 19.5mm		
1948	22,000,000	.15
Juliana		
Y58		
1950	20,000,000	.10
1951	16,200,000	.10
1952	14,400,000	.10
1953	12,000,000	.10
1954	14,000,000	.10
1955	11,400,000	.10
1956	7,400,000	.10
1957	16,000,000	.10
1958	5,000,000	.15
1959	4,000,000	.15
1960	11,000,000	.10
1961	12,000,000	.10
1962	15,000,000	.10

10 CENTS

	Mintage	Value
William III		
Y7 (silver) 13.5mm		
1849	6,204,155	.60
1850	7,270,000	.60
1853	1,103,527	.75

	Mintage	Value
1855	744,500	$1.00
1856	1,000,000	.75
1859	1,000,000	.75
1862	800,000	1.00
1863	1,240,000	.75
1868	200,000	2.50
1869	1,000,000	.75
1871	1,000,000	.75
1873	1,000,000	.75
1874	1,000,000	.75
1876	1,000,000	.75
1877	1,000,000	.75
1878	1,000,000	.75
1879	1,000,000	.75
1880	1,000,000	.75
1881	2,000,000	.50
1882	2,000,000	.50
1884	1,000,000	.75
1885	2,000,000	.50
1887	1,600,000	.60
1889	2,800,000	.40
1890	2,600,000	.40
Wilhelmina		
Y20 child's head		
1892	2,000,000	.35
1893	2,000,000	.35
1894	1,500,000	.40
1895	1,000,000	.50
1896	2,000,000	.35
1897	7,850,000	.25
Y23 woman's head		
1898	2,000,000	.35
1901	2,000,000	.35
Y23a large head		
1903	6,000,000	.30
Y23b small head		
1904	3,000,000	.35
1905	2,000,000	.35
1906	4,000,000	.30
Y39 design changed		
1910	2,250,000	.30
1911	4,000,000	.30
1912	4,000,000	.30
1913	5,000,000	.30
1914	9,000,000	.30
1915	5,000,000	.30
1916	5,000,000	.30
1917	10,000,000	.25
1918	20,000,000	.25
1919	10,000,000	.25
1921	5,000,000	.30
1925	5,000,000	.30

	Mintage	Value
Y43 new design		
1926	2,700,000	$ .30
1927	2,300,000	.30
1928	10,000,000	.20
1930	5,000,000	.25
1934	2,000,000	.30
1935	8,000,000	.20
1936	15,000,000	.20
1937	18,600,000	.20
1938	21,400,000	.20
1939	20,000,000	.20
1941	43,000,000	.15

German Occupation

Y51 new design (zinc) 20.5mm

	Mintage	Value
1941	34,600,000	.20
1942	27,800,000	.20
1943	13,600,000	.25

U. S. Mintage

(1941 and 1942 PDS see Curacao and Surinam.)

Y43 for Netherlands

	Mintage	Value
1943P	120,000,000	.45
1944P	inc. above	.15
1944D	17,000,000	2.50
1944S	64,040,000	1.25
1945P	90,560,000	2.50
1945D	8,400,000	2.50

Netherlands Mintage

Y55 (nickel) 13.5mm

	Mintage	Value
1948	69,200,000	.15

Juliana
Y59

	Mintage	Value
1950	56,600,000	.15
1951	42,400,000	.15
1952	11,800,000	.15
1954	8,200,000	.15
1955	18,200,000	.15
1956	12,000,000	.15
1957	18,600,000	.15
1958	34,000,000	.15
1959	44,000,000	.15
1960	12,000,000	.15
1961	25,000,000	.15
1962	30,000,000	.15

25 CENTS

William III

Y8 (silver) 19mm

	Mintage	Value
1849		10.00
1850	2,207,140	.50

	Mintage	Value
1853	7,974	$25.00
1887	100,000	2.50
1889	200,000	1.50
1890	600,000	.75

Wilhelmina

Y21 child's head

	Mintage	Value
1892	800,000	.75
1893	800,000	.75
1894	1,000,000	.60
1895	1,200,000	.60
1896	600,000	1.00
1897	3,100,000	.50

Y24 woman's head

	Mintage	Value
1898	400,000	1.50
1901	1,600,000	.50
1902	1,200,000	.50
1903	1,200,000	.50
1904	1,600,000	.50
1905	1,200,000	.50
1906	2,000,000	.50

Y40 design changed

	Mintage	Value
1910	880,000	.75
1911	1,600,000	.60
1912	1,600,000	.60
1913	1,200,000	.60
1914	5,600,000	.50
1915	2,000,000	.50
1916	2,000,000	.50
1917	4,000,000	.50
1918	6,000,000	.50
1919	4,000,000	.50
1925	2,000,000	.50

Y44 design changed

	Mintage	Value
1926	2,000,000	.50
1928	8,000,000	.30
1939	4,000,000	.30
1940	9,000,000	.30
1941	40,000,000	.30

German Occupation

Y52 new design (zinc) 26mm

	Mintage	Value
1941	34,600,000	.30
1942	27,800,000	.30
1943	13,600,000	.35

U. S. Mintage

(1941 and 1942 see Curacao and Surinam.)

Y44 for Netherlands

	Mintage	Value
1943P	40,000,000	.50
1944P	inc. above	.25
1945P	92,000,000	5.00

Mintage	Value

Netherlands Mintage

Y56 new design (nickel)

	Mintage	Value
1948	27,400,000	$ .25

Juliana

Y60

	Mintage	Value
1950	43,000,000	.25
1951	21,200,000	.25
1952	8,400,000	.25
1953	3,600,000	.30
1954	6,400,000	.25
1955	10,000,000	.25
1956	8,000,000	.25
1957	8,000,000	.25
1958	7,000,000	.25
1959	8,000,000	.25
1960	9,000,000	.25
1961	6,000,000	.25
1962	12,000,000	.25

½ GUILDER

William III

Y9 (silver) 22mm

	Mintage	Value
1853	1,711	50.00
1857	3,606,444	1.00
1858	7,604,462	.75
1859	3,000,510	1.00
1860	6,602,687	.75
1861	6,001,252	.75
1862	4,001,577	1.00
1863	5,152,084	.75
1864	4,001,385	1.00
1866	1,402,446	1.25
1868	4,004,161	1.00

Wilhelmina

Y25

	Mintage	Value
1898	2,000,000	1.00

Y25a design changed

	Mintage	Value
1904	1,000,000	1.00
1905	4,000,000	.75
1906	1,000,000	1.00
1907	3,300,000	.75
1908	4,000,000	.75
1909	3,000,000	.75

Y41 design changed

	Mintage	Value
1910	4,000,000	1.00
1912	4,000,000	1.00
1913	8,000,000	1.00
1919	8,000,000	1.00

Y45 design changed

	Mintage	Value
1921	5,000,000	.75
1922	11,240,000	.50

	Mintage	Value
1928	5,000,000	$ .75
1929	9,500,000	.60
1930	18,500,000	.50

1 GUILDER

William III

Y10 (silver) 28mm

	Mintage	Value
1851	2,125,148	1.50
1853	652,035	2.50
1854	4,511,054	1.00
1855	5,133,283	1.00
1856	4,954,661	1.00
1857	2,125,200	1.00
1858	4,199,241	1.00
1859	2,717,216	1.00
1860	4,035,791	1.00
1861	5,078,886	1.00
1863	7,986,113	1.00
1864	3,600,143	1.00
1865	6,401,755	1.00
1866	1,002,450	1.50

Wilhelmina

Y22 child's head

	Mintage	Value
1892	3,500,000	1.00
1896	100,000	10.00
1897	2,500,000	1.25

Y26 woman's head

	Mintage	Value
1898	2,000,000	1.25
1901	2,000,000	1.25

Y26a design changed

	Mintage	Value
1904	2,000,000	1.00
1905	1,000,000	1.25
1906	500,000	2.00
1907	5,100,000	1.00
1908	4,700,000	1.00
1909	2,000,000	1.00

Y42 design changed

	Mintage	Value
1910	1,000,000	1.25
1911	2,000,000	1.25
1912	3,000,000	1.25
1913	8,000,000	1.00
1914	15,785,000	1.00
1915	14,215,000	1.00
1916	5,000,000	1.00
1917	2,300,000	1.25

Y46 design changed

	Mintage	Value
1922	9,550,000	.75
1923	8,050,000	.75
1924	8,000,000	.75
1928	6,150,000	.90
1929	32,350,000	.75
1930	13,500,000	.75

	Mintage	Value		Mintage	Value
1931	38,100,000	$ .75	1864	2,033,644	$3.50
1938	5,000,000	.90	1865	2,287,612	3.50
1939	14,200,000	.75	1866	3,562,608	3.50
1940	21,300,000	.75	1867	4,948,886	3.50
(1943D see Netherlands East Indies.)			1868	4,040,021	3.50
			1869	5,046,192	3.50
Y46 Netherlands			1870	6,639,847	3.50
1944P	105,125,000	.75	1871	6,875,035	3.50
1945P	25,375,000	5.00	1872	13,416,378	3.50
			1873	5,515,073	3.50
Juliana			1874	12,795,726	3.50

Juliana		
Y61 25mm		
1954	6,600,000	1.00
1955	37,500,000	.90
1956	38,900,000	.90
1957	27,000,000	.90
1958	30,000,000	.90

Wilhelmina		
Y27		
1898	100,000	17.50
Y47 design changed		
1929	4,400,000	2.25
1930	11,600,000	2.25
1931	4,400,000	2.50
1932	6,320,000	2.50
1933	3,560,000	2.50
1937	4,000,000	2.50
1938	2,000,000	2.50
1939	3,760,000	2.50
1940	4,640,000	2.50
(1943D see Netherlands East Indies.)		

2½ GULDEN

William III		
Y11 (silver) 38mm		
1850	5,008,210	3.50
1851	3,647,493	3.50
1852	4,546,764	3.50
1853	234,128	7.50
1854	4,334,526	3.50
1855	2,082,046	3.50
1856	909,345	4.00
1857	3,353,072	3.50
1858	8,357,486	3.50
1859	4,306,594	3.50
1860	847,104	4.00
1861	876,003	4.00
1862	3,304,118	3.50
1863	50,652	15.00

Juliana		
Y62		
1959	7,200,000	2.00
1960	12,800,000	2.00
1961	10,000,000	2.00
1962	5,000,000	2.00

NETHERLANDS ANTILLES
(Nederlandse Antillen)

Islands in the West Indies, north of Venezuela. Part of the Kingdom of the Netherlands.

100 Cents = 1 Guilder

1 CENT		
Y1 (bronze) 17mm		
1952	1,000,000	.10
1954	1,000,000	.10
1957	1,000,000	.10
1959	1,000,000	.10
1961	1,000,000	.10

2½ CENTS		
Y5 (bronze) 22mm		
1956	400,000	.15
1959	1,000,000	.15

5 CENTS		
Y6 (copper-nickel) square 16.5mm		
1957	500,000	.20

	Mintage	Value
1/10 GUILDER		
Y2 (silver) 13mm		
1954	200,000	$ .25
1956	250,000	.25
1957	250,000	.25
1959	250,000	.25
1960	400,000	.25

	Mintage	Value
¼ GUILDER		
Y3 (silver) 17mm		
1954	200,000	$ .50
1956	200,000	.50
1957	200,000	.50
1960	240,000	.50
1962	300,000	.50
1 GUILDER		
Y4 (silver) 26.5mm		
1952	1,000,000	1.25

NETHERLANDS EAST INDIES
(Nederlandsch Indie)

Consists of the islands of Sumatra, Java, the Lesser Sundas, Madura, two thirds of Borneo, Celebes, the Moluccas, western New Guinea, and many smaller islands. Became independent country of Indonesia in 1950. During World War II coins were minted in the United States with P, D, S and palm tree mint marks. Coinage obsolete.

100 Cents = 1 Guilder

½ CENT		
William III (1849-1890)		
Y1 (copper) 15.5mm		
1856	10,800,000	.50
1857	36,800,000	.40
1858	53,588,017	.40
1859	219,600,000	.30
1860	107,123,913	.30
Wilhelmina (1890-1948)		
Y7		
1902	20,000,000	.25
1908	10,600,000	.25
1909	4,400,000	.40
Y18 new design		
1914	50,000,000	.25
1916	10,000,000	.25
1921	4,000,000	.40
1932	10,000,000	.25
1933 mint mark —		
sea horse	15,000,000	.25
1933 mint mark —		
grapes	5,000,000	.40
1934	30,000,000	.25
1935	14,000,000	.25
1936	12,000,000	.25
1937	8,400,000	.30
1938	3,600,000	.40
1939	2,000,000	.50

1945P	400,000,000	.20
1 CENT		
William III		
Y2 (copper) 22mm		
1855	100,000	5.00
1856	67,900,000	.40
1857	162,000,000	.25
1858	119,430,741	.25
1859	40,800,000	.40
1860	14,455,000	.50
Wilhelmina		
Y8		
1896	60,400,000	.35
1897	69,600,000	.35
1898	36,600,000	.35
1899	18,400,000	.40
1901	15,000,000	.40
1902	10,000,000	.50
1907	7,500,000	.50
1908	12,500,000	.40
1909	7,500,000	.50
1912	25,000,000	.35
Y19 new design		
1914	85,000,000	.30
1916	16,440,000	.50
1919	20,000,000	.50
1920	120,000,000	.30

	Mintage	Value
1926	10,000,000	$ .50
1929	50,000,000	.30

Y21 hole in center

	Mintage	Value
1936	52,000,000	.30
1937	120,400,000	.25
1938	150,000,000	.25
1939	81,400,000	.25
1942P	100,000,000	.25
1945P	335,000,000	.25
1945D	133,800,000	.25
1945S	102,568,000	1.75

2½ CENTS

William III

Y3 (copper) 29.5mm

1856	2,480,000	.75
1857	36,560,000	.40
1858	40,989,886	.40

Wilhelmina

Y9

1896	1,120,000	1.00
1897	18,105,230	.50
1898	7,600,000	.75
1899	10,400,000	.50
1902	6,000,000	.75
1907	3,000,000	.90
1908	5,940,000	.75
1909	3,060,000	.90
1913	4,000,000	.90

Y20 new design

1914	22,000,000	.50
1915	6,000,000	.75
1920	48,000,000	.50
1945P	200,000,000	.40

1/20 GUILDER

William III

Y4 (silver) 11.5mm

1854		10.00
1855	491,960	1.00

5 CENTS

Wilhelmina

Y17 (copper-nickel) 21mm

1913	60,000,000	.50
1921	40,000,000	.50
1922	20,000,000	.50

1/10 GUILDER

William III

Y5 (silver) 13.5mm

1854	3,550,000	.90
1855	6,452,000	.75

	Mintage	Value
1856	3,000,000	$ .90
1857	11,000,000	.60
1858	14,000,000	.60
1882	7,500,000	.75
1884	3,550,000	.90
1885	825,000	1.25

Wilhelmina

Y10

1891	5,000,000	.30
1893	5,000,000	.30
1896	3,075,000	.30
1898	2,500,000	.40
1900	6,850,000	.30
1901	5,000,000	.30

Y12 design changed

1903	5,000,000	.35
1904	5,000,000	.35
1905	5,000,000	.35
1906	7,500,000	.35
1907	14,000,000	.35
1908	3,000,000	.40
1909	10,000,000	.35

Y14 design changed

1910	15,000,000	.25
1911	10,000,000	.25
1912	25,000,000	.25
1913	15,000,000	.25
1914	25,000,000	.25
1915	15,000,000	.25
1918	30,000,000	.25
1919	20,000,000	.25
1920	85,000,000	.25
1928	30,000,000	.25
1930	15,000,000	.25
1937	20,000,000	.25
1938	30,000,000	.25
1939	5,400,000	.30
1940	10,000,000	.25
1941P	41,850,000	.20
1941S	58,150,000	2.00
1942S	75,000,000	.20
1945P	100,720,000	2.50
1945S	19,280,000	2.50

¼ GUILDER

William III

Y6 (silver) 17.2mm

1854	11,460,000	1.00
1855	4,540,608	1.00
1857	2,400,000	1.00
1858	4,800,000	1.00
1882	2,200,000	1.00

	Mintage	Value		Mintage	Value
1883	800,000	$2.00	1937	8,000,000	$ .50
1885	1,750,000	1.25	1938	12,000,000	.35
			1939	10,400,000	.35
Wilhelmina			1941P	34,947,000	.35
Y11			1941S	5,053,000	4.00
1890	1,140,000	.75	1942S	32,000,000	.35
1891	860,000	1.00	1945S	56,000,000	4.00
1893	2,000,000	.60			
1896	1,230,000	.75	*Netherlands Type*		
1898	3,000,000	.50	1 GUILDER		
1900	2,800,000	.50	(silver) 26.5mm		
1901	2,000,000	.50	1943D	20,000,000	1.00
Y13 design changed					
1903	2,000,000	.60	2½ GULDEN		
1904	2,000,000	.60	(silver) 31.5mm		
1905	2,000,000	.60	1943D	2,000,000	5.00
1906	4,000,000	.60			
1907	4,400,000	.60	*Japanese Occupation,*		
1908	2,000,000	.60	*Dates in Japanese Calendar*		
1909	4,000,000	60	1 SEN		
Y15 design changed			**Y22** (aluminum) 16mm		
1910	6,000,000	.50	(1943) 2603		——
1911	4,000,000	.50	(1944) 2604		——
1912	10,000,000	.35			
1913	6,000,000	.50	5 SEN		
1914	10,000,000	.35	**Y23** (aluminum) 18mm		
1915	6,000,000	.50	(1943) 2603		——
1917	12,000,000	.35	(1944) 2604		——
1919	6,000,000	.50			
1920	20,000,000	.35	10 SEN		
1921	24,000,000	.35	**Y24** (zinc) 21.5mm		
1929	5,000,000	.50	(1943) 2603		20.00
1930	7,000,000	.50	(1944) 2604		13.50

NEW CALEDONIA
(Nouvelle Caledonie)

A French island in the South Pacific.

100 Centimes = 1 Franc

50 CENTIMES
Y1 (aluminum) 18mm

	Mintage	Value
1949	1,000,000	.20

1 FRANC
Y2 (aluminum) 23mm

	Mintage	Value
1949	4,000,000	.30

2 FRANCS
Y3 (aluminum) 27mm

	Mintage	Value
1949	3,000,000	.40

5 FRANCS
Y4 (aluminum) 32mm

	Mintage	Value
1952	4,000,000	.75

(Norge)

The western portion of the Scandinavian peninsula. Until 1905 was united with Sweden and the king ruled both countries. Copper coins from 1863 to 1870 do not have name of country on them and are inscribed: "Skilling Skillemynt" or "Skilling." Silver coins of 50 Øre, 1 and 2 Krone to 1904 are inscribed "NORGES SVER...." or "NORGES O. SVER....". Copper coins 1876 to 1907 and 10 and 25 Øre silver coins 1874 to 1904 have lion holding ax, but do not bear name of country. The 1942 (London) coinage was made in large quantities but all were melted except 7,000 pieces each.

120 Skilling = 1 Speciedaler (1863-1873)
100 Øre = 1 Krone (1874 to date)

	Mintage	Value
Skilling-Speciedaler System		
½ **SKILLING**		
Charles XV (1859-1872)		
Y1 (copper) 21mm		
1863 480,000		$1.00
Y2 new design, 18mm		
1867 3,600,000		.50
1 **SKILLING**		
Charles XV		
Y3 (copper) 21mm		
1870 1,200,000		.30
2 **SKILLING**		
Charles XV		
Y8 (silver) 15mm		
1870 900,000		.50
1871 1,114,000		.50
3 **SKILLING**		
Charles XV		
Y9 (silver) 17mm		
1868 600,000		1.50
1869 600,000		1.00
Oscar II (1872-1905)		
Y18		
1872 1,000,000		1.00
1873 600,000		1.25
4 **SKILLING**		
Charles XV		
Y10 (silver) 18mm		
1871 55,000		2.50

	Mintage	Value
12 **SKILLING**		
Charles XV		
Y4 (silver) 20mm		
1861 2,500		$25.00
1862 2,500		25.00
Y11 larger head		
1865 50,000		3.00
Oscar II		
Y19		
1873 500,000		2.50
24 **SKILLING**		
Charles XV		
Y5 (silver) 25mm		
1861 1,250		30.00
1862 1,250		30.00
Y12 larger head		
1865 15,000		5.00
½ **SPECIEDALER**		
Charles XV		
Y6 (silver) 30.5mm		
1861 . . . . .about 30,000		20.00
1862 . . . . .about 60,000		15.00
Y13 larger head, 31mm		
1865 790		25.00
Oscar II		
Y20		
1873 2,000		75.00
1 **SPECIEDALER**		
Charles XV		
Y7 (silver) 39mm		
1861 40,000		40.00
1862 60,000		40.00

	Mintage	Value
Y14 larger head		
1864	127,647	$35.00
1865	85,200	35.00
1867	70,668	75.00
1868	73,540	35.00
1869	55,900	35.00

Øre-Kroner System
1 ØRE

Oscar II

Y15 (bronze) 16mm

	Mintage	Value
1876	7,000,000	.25
1877	3,100,000	1.25
1878	1,900,000	1.25
1884	1,710,000	.35
1885	2,290,000	.30
1889	3,000,000	.25
1891	3,000,000	.25
1893	3,000,000	.25
1897	3,000,000	.25
1899	4,500,000	.25
1902	4,500,000	.25

Haakon VII (1905-1957)

Y32

	Mintage	Value
1906	3,000,000	.25
1907	2,550,000	.25

Y35 new design

	Mintage	Value
1908	1,450,000	.25
1910	2,480,000	.25
1911	3,270,000	.25
1912	2,850,000	.25
1913	2,840,000	.25
1914	4,710,000	.25
1915	1,850,000	.35

Y57 (iron)

	Mintage	Value
1918	6,000,000	.25
1919	12,900,000	.25
1920	4,450,000	.25
1921	2,270,000	1.00

Y35 (bronze)

	Mintage	Value
1921	1,270,000	1.00
1922	3,645,000	.25
1923	1,000,000	.40
1925	3,000,000	.25
1926	870,000	1.00
1927	2,130,000	.30
1928	3,000,000	.25
1929	4,990,000	.25
1930	2,010,000	.30
1931	4,500,000	.25

	Mintage	Value
1932	2,000,000	$ .30
1933	2,000,000	.30
1934	1,500,000	.35
1935	5,360,000	.20
1936	6,900,000	.20
1937	5,810,000	.20
1938	4,950,000	.20
1939	2,500,000	.25
1940	7,890,000	.20
1941	12,380,000	.20

German Occupation

Y60 (iron)

	Mintage	Value
1941	13,140,000	.20
1942	42,600,000	.20
1943	37,230,000	.20
1944	inc. above	.20
1945	1,700,000	.35

Prewar type

Y35 (bronze)

	Mintage	Value
1946	6,600,000	.20
1947	inc. above	.20
1948	9,590,000	.15
1949	2,970,000	.20
1950	5,730,000	.15
1951	6,290,000	.15
1952	8,130,000	.15

Y69 new design

	Mintage	Value
1952	inc. above	.15
1953	8,130,000	.10
1954	9,210,000	.10
1955	7,920,000	.10
1956	11,705,000	.10
1957	15,750,000	.10

Olav V (1957 to date)

Y76 squirrel

	Mintage	Value
1958	2,820,000	.15
1959	9,120,000	.10
1960	7,890,200	.10
1961	5,670,700	.10
1962	12,180,000	.10

2 ØRE

Oscar II

Y16 (bronze) 21mm

	Mintage	Value
1876	1,500,000	.25
1877	2,250,000	.25
1884	1,000,000	.75
1889	1,000,000	.25

	Mintage	Value
1891	1,000,000	$ .25
1893	1,000,000	.25
1897	1,000,000	.25
1899	1,000,000	.25
1902	1,005,000	.25

Haakon VII

Y33

	Mintage	Value
1906	500,000	.40
1907	1,000,000	.25

Y36 new design

1909	500,000	.35
1910	500,000	.35
1911	195,000	1.50
1912	805,000	.30
1913	2,010,000	.25
1914	2,365,000	.20
1915	625,000	.30

Y58 (iron)

1917	720,000	.35
1918	1,280,000	.25
1919	3,350,000	.25
1920	2,635,000	.25

Y36 (bronze)

1921	1,592,500	.25
1922	1,882,500	.25
1923	1,585,000	.25
1928	2,250,000	.20
1929	750,000	.30
1931	1,000,000	.25
1932	1,000,000	.25
1933	750,000	.30
1934	500,000	.35
1935	2,190,000	.20
1936	4,435,000	.20
1937	3,955,000	.20
1938	3,530,000	.20
1939	3,400,000	.20
1940	2,800,000	.20

German Occupation

Y61 (iron)

1943	6,300,000	.20
1944	inc. above	.20
1945	2,500,000	.25

Y36 (bronze)

1946	1,575,000	.20
1947	5,500,000	.20
1948	inc. above	.20
1949	1,455,000	.20
1950	5,790,000	.15
1951	4,600,000	.15
1952	4,995,000	.15

Y70 new design

	Mintage	Value
1952	inc. above	$ .15
1953	5,715,000	.10
1954	3,645,000	.10
1955	4,485,000	.10
1956	6,990,000	.10
1957	6,900,000	.10

Olav V

Y77 chicken

1958	2,700,000	.10

Y77a

1959	4,515,000	.10
1960	3,735,200	.25
1961	4,777,100	.10
1962	6,205,000	.10

5 ØRE

Oscar II

Y17 (bronze) 26mm

1875	1,000,000	.40
1876	1,000,000	.40
1878	500,000	.60
1896	1,000,000	.40
1899	700,000	.45
1902	705,000	.45

Haakon VII

Y34 H VII and shield

1907	200,000	1.00

Y37 new design

1908	600,000	.35
1911	480,000	.50
1912	520,000	.50
1913	1,000,000	.25
1914	472,000	.50
1915	528,000	.50
1916	133,000	2.00

Y59 (iron)

1917	300,000	.75
1918	756,000	1.50
1919	2,208,000	.60
1920	2,885,000	.60

Y37 (bronze)

1921	683,000	.50
1922	1,816,000	.25
1923	936,000	.30
1928	296,000	.75
1929	1,004,000	.25
1930	820,000	.30
1931	580,000	.35
1932	500,000	.35
1933	300,000	.40

	Mintage	Value
1935	640,000	$ .30
1936	616,000	.75
1937	1,496,000	.25
1938	1,388,000	.25
1939	1,360,000	.25
1940	2,600,000	.25
1941	3,500,000	.20

German Occupation
Y62 (iron)

	Mintage	Value
1941	6,560,000	.25
1942	10,200,000	.25
1943	10,448,000	.25
1944	inc. above	.25
1945	432,000	2.50

Y37 (bronze)

	Mintage	Value
1951	1,216,000	.25
1952	5,944,000	.15

Y71 new design

	Mintage	Value
1952	inc. above	.15
1953	7,184,000	.15
1954	4,456,000	.15
1955	5,864,000	.15
1956	3,764,000	.15
1957	2,200,000	.15

Olav V
Y78 moose

	Mintage	Value
1958	2,040,000	.15
1959	3,200,000	.15
1960	5,315,200	.15
1961	4,758,000	.15
1962	7,761,000	.15

10 ØRE
(silver) 15mm
Oscar II
Y21 3 Skilling

	Mintage	Value
1874	2,000,000	.60
1875	1,000,000	.60

Y25 monogram

	Mintage	Value
1875	3,000,000	.50
1876	3,000,000	.50
1877	288,000	.75
1878	912,000	.50
1880	600,000	.50
1882	100,000	1.25
1883	100,000	1.25
1888	750,000	.50
1889	500,000	.50
1890	1,000,000	.40
1892	2,000,000	.40
1894	1,500,000	.40

	Mintage	Value
1897	1,500,000	$ .40
1898	2,000,000	.40
1899	2,500,000	.40
1901	2,021,158	.40
1903	1,500,725	.40

Haakon VII
Y48

	Mintage	Value
1909	2,000,000	.25
1911	1,650,000	.25
1912	2,350,000	.25
1913	2,000,000	.25
1914	1,900,000	.25
1915	2,100,000	.25
1916	1,500,000	.60
1917	5,550,000	.25
1918	2,100,000	.25
1919	7,800,000	.25

Y38 (copper-nickel)

	Mintage	Value
1920	2,310,000	.25
1921	6,690,000	.25
1922	4,050,000	.25
1923	7,050,000	.25

Y43 center hole

	Mintage	Value
1924	10,800,000	.25
1925	8,981,000	.25
1926	11,800,000	.25
1927	1,250,000	.25
1937	5,000,000	.50
1938	3,350,000	.20
1939	1,600,000	.25
1940	4,950,000	.20
1941	10,000,000	.20

Y66 London

	Mintage	Value
1942	7,000	5.00

German Occupation
Y63 new design (zinc)

	Mintage	Value
1941	15,250,000	.20
1942	64,300,000	.15
1943	inc. above	.15
1944	3,400,000	.15
1945	5,750,000	.25

Prewar Type
Y43 (copper-nickel) holed

	Mintage	Value
1945	1,600,000	.20
1946	5,450,000	.15
1947	5,300,000	.15
1948	3,450,000	.15
1949	11,550,000	.15
1951	7,600,000	.15

	Mintage	Value
Y72 design changed — no center hole		
1951............inc. above	$ .15
1952............14,950,000	.15
1953.............7,700,000	.15
1954.............9,600,000	.15
1955.............9,200,000	.15
1956............11,200,000	.15
1957............22,900,000	.15

Olav V
Y79 bee

| 1958.............1,425,000 | .20 |

Y79a

1959.............2,500,000	.30
1960............12,765,200	.15
1961............11,110,700	.15
1962............16,210,000	.15

25 ØRE
Oscar II
Y-A25 (silver) 17mm

| 1876.............3,200,000 | 1.00 |

Y26

1896..............400,000	.50
1898..............400,000	.50
1899..............600,000	.35
1900..............400,000	.50
1901..............606,941	.35
1902..............611,741	.35
1904..............600,000	.35

Haakon VII
Y49

1909..............600,000	.40
1911..............400,000	.40
1912..............200,000	.50
1913..............400,000	.40
1914..............212,000	.50
1915.............1,220,000	.40
1916..............368,000	.40
1917..............400,000	.40
1918..............800,000	.40
1919.............1,600,000	.30

Y39 (copper-nickel)

1921.............4,400,000	.30
1922.............3,700,000	.30
1923.............5,360,000	.30

Y44 new design with hole in center

1924.............4,740,000	.20
1927.............6,200,000	.20
1929..............800,000	.75

	Mintage	Value
1939.............1,600,000	$ .20
1940.............1,160,000	.20
Y67 London		
1942................7,000	5.00

German Occupation
Y64 new design (zinc)

1943............14,000,000	.20
1944.............2,800,000	.25
1945.............3,540,000	.25

Prewar Type
Y44 (copper-nickel)

1946.............1,840,000	.20
1947.............2,600,000	.20
1949.............2,600,000	.20
1950.............2,800,000	.20

Y73 new design — no center hole

1952.............4,060,000	.20
1953.............2,320,000	.20
1954.............3,140,000	.20
1955.............1,860,000	.20
1956.............2,920,000	.20
1957.............4,560,000	.20

Olav V
Y80 bird

1958.............1,280,000	.20
1959.............2,500,000	.20
1960.............3,548,200	.20
1961.............5,072,700	.20
1962.............6,030,000	.20

50 ØRE
(silver) 22mm
Oscar II
Y23 15 Skilling

| 1874..............400,000 | 2.00 |
| 1875..............400,000 | 2.00 |

Y27 design changed

1877..............800,000	.90
1880..............120,000	2.00
1885..............100,000	2.00
1887..............200,000	1.50
1888..............100,000	2.00
1889..............200,000	1.50
1891..............400,000	1.00
1893..............600,000	.90
1895..............400,000	2.00
1896..............300,000	1.00
1897..............200,000	2.00
1898..............300,000	1.00

	Mintage	Value
1899	200,000	$2.00
1900	300,000	1.00
1901	404,400	1.00
1902	301,286	1.00
1904	100,580	1.00

Haakon VII

Y50

	Mintage	Value
1909	200,000	1.25
1911	200,000	1.25
1912	200,000	1.25
1913	200,000	1.25
1914	800,000	.60
1915	300,000	1.00
1916	700,000	.60
1918	3,000,000	.50
1919	1,210,000	.50

Y41 new design (copper-nickel)

	Mintage	Value
1920	1,152,000	.60
1921	7,400,000	.50
1922	3,000,000	.60
1923	4,540,000	.50

Y45 design changed — hole in center

	Mintage	Value
1926	2,000,000	.40
1927	2,000,000	.40
1928	2,800,000	.40
1929	600,000	.75
1939	900,000	.60
1940	2,200,000	.40
1941	2,440,000	.40

Y68 London

	Mintage	Value
1942	7,000	5.00

German Occupation

Y65 new design (zinc)

	Mintage	Value
1941	7,600,000	.35
1942	9,400,000	.60
1943	1,530,000	.60
1944	1,480,000	.40
1945	290,000	2.00

Prewar Type

Y45 (copper-nickel)

	Mintage	Value
1945	1,350,000	.40
1946	1,350,000	.40
1947	2,900,000	.35
1948	5,370,000	.35
1949	1,040,000	.40

Y74 design changed — no center hole

	Mintage	Value
1953	2,370,000	.35
1954	230,000	1.00

	Mintage	Value
1955	1,930,000	$ .35
1956	710,000	.40
1957	1,760,000	.35

Olav V

Y81 dog

	Mintage	Value
1958	1,560,000	.35
1959	340,000	.45
1960	1,584,200	.35
1961	2,424,700	.35
1962	3,064,000	.35

1 KRONE

Oscar II

Y24 30 Skilling

	Mintage	Value
1875	600,000	3.00

Y28 new design

	Mintage	Value
1877	1,000,000	1.50
1878	100,000	2.50
1879	100,000	2.50
1881	100,000	2.50
1882	100,000	2.50
1885	100,000	2.50
1887	100,000	3.00
1888	75,000	3.00
1889	200,000	2.00
1890	200,000	2.00
1892	150,000	2.00
1893	100,000	5.00
1894	100,000	2.50
1895	100,000	2.50
1897	250,000	2.00
1898	150,000	2.00
1900	250,000	2.00
1901	151,847	2.00
1904	100,148	2.50

Haakon VII

Y51

	Mintage	Value
1908	350,000	1.00
1910	100,000	3.00
1912	140,000	2.00
1913	290,000	1.00
1914	602,000	1.00
1915	498,000	1.00
1916	300,000	1.00
1917	700,000	1.00

Y46 new design — hole in center (copper-nickel)

	Mintage	Value
1925	4,200,000	.70
1926	6,470,000	.70
1927	1,000,000	.75
1936	610,000	.90

	Mintage	Value		Mintage	Value
1937	1,090,000	$ .75	1888	25,000	$7.50
1938	810,000	.80	1890	100,000	3.50
1939	2,310,000	.65	1892	50,000	4.00
1940	4,010,000	.65	1893	75,000	4.00
1946	5,490,000	.65	1894	75,000	4.00
1947	810,000	.75	1897	50,000	4.00
1949	7,671,000	.65	1898	50,000	4.00
1950	10,080,000	.65	1900	125,000	3.50
1951	8,580,000	.65	1902	153,020	3.50
			1904	75,681	4.00

Y75 design changed — no center hole

1951	inc. above	.65
1953	1,465,000	.65
1954	3,045,000	.65
1955	1,970,000	.65
1956	3,960,000	.65
1957	3,300,000	.65

Haakon VII

Y47 Independence commem.

1906	100,000	6.00

Y47a same, smaller shield

1907	54,000	8.50

Olav V

Y82 horse

1958	4,670,000	.65
1959	4,200,000	.65
1960	2,440,200	.65
1961	3,933,700	.65
1962	6,015,000	.65

Y52 same, crossed rifles

1907	27,000	37.50

Y53 regular issue

1908	200,000	3.00
1910	150,000	3.00
1912	150,000	3.00
1913	150,000	3.00
1914	345,000	3.00
1915	250,000	3.00
1916	204,000	3.00
1917	420,000	3.00

2 KRONER

Oscar II

Y29 (silver) 31mm

1878	300,000	3.50
1885	25,000	12.50
1887	25,000	10.00

Y54 Constitution Centennial

1914	225,000	6.00

POLAND

(Krolestwo Polskie) 1917-18
(Rzeczpospolita Polska) 1923 to 1956
(Polska Rzeczpospolita Ludowa) 1957 to date

In central Europe on the Baltic Sea. Occupied by Germany during World War II. Some Russian coins prior to 1865 were minted at Warsaw (See Russia). 1923 bronze coins were struck in both brown and yellow metal. Zinc coins dated 1923 or 1939 were struck during 1939-1945 under German occupation. *Mint marks:* Coins minted at Warsaw until 1939 have ◂K in eagle's right talon. Coins minted in other countries are without this mint mark. Some mints, such as Birmingham, use their standard mint marks (H).

World War I Occupation Coinage (Baltic States, Poland, and Northwest Russia) coined at Berlin (A) and Hamburg (J).

100 Fenigow = 1 Mark (1917-1918)

100 Groszy = 1 Zloty (1923 to date)

	Mintage	Value
1 KOPEK		
Y1 (iron) 20mm		
1916A	11,942,046	$ .60
1916J	7,682,000	.60
2 KOPEKS		
Y2 (iron) 23mm		
1916A	6,872,574	.90
1916J	8,017,000	.90
3 KOPEKS		
Y3 (iron) 27mm		
1916A	8,670,000	1.25
1916J	7,903,000	1.25

REGENCY

(Germany and Austria)
1917-1918

	Mintage	Value
1 FENIG		
Y4 (iron) 15mm		
1918	51,484,000	5.00
5 FENIGOW		
Y5 (iron) 18mm		
1917	18,700,000	.50
1918	22,690,000	.50
10 FENIGOW		
Y6 (iron) 21mm		
1917	33,000,000	.60
1918	14,990,000	.60
20 FENIGOW		
Y7 (iron) 23mm		
1917	1,900,000	2.00
1918	19,259,800	.75

REPUBLIC (1923-1939)

	Mintage	Value
1 GROSZ		
Y8 (bronze) 14.5mm		
1923	20,000,000	.25
1925	38,102,178	.25
1925 21.V.1925 — commem	inc above	10.00
1927 regular	13,342,076	.25
1928	25,901,839	.25
1930	20,865,000	.25
1931	13,456,690	.25
1932	10,215,000	.25
1933	10,785,000	.25
1934	5,900,000	.40
1935	4,660,000	.50

	Mintage	Value
1936	12,600,000	$ .25
1937	17,370,000	.25
1938		.25
1939		.25

German Occupation

	Mintage	Value
Y34 (zinc)		
1939		.25
2 GROSZE		
Y9 (bronze) 17.5mm		
1923	20,429,000	.25
1925	39,014,596	.25
1926 27/X-26 and IM	inc. above	15.00
1927 regular	11,179,954	.25
1928	26,235,749	.25
1930	18,600,000	.25
1931	12,609,264	.25
1932	9,980,000	.30
1933	2,270,000	.60
1934	9,350,000	.30
1935	5,800,000	.40
1936	12,800,000	.25
1937	17,365,000	.25
1938		.25
1939		.25
5 GROSZY		
Y10 (bronze) 20mm		
1923	32,150,000	.30
1923 12/IV-24 — commem	inc. above	20.00
1925 regular	44,976,857	.30
1928	18,485,093	.30
1929 commemorative		20.00
1930 regular	10,845,000	.40
1931	8,601,481	.50
1934	420,000	1.25
1935	7,300,000	.50
1936	5,950,000	.50
1937	9,050,000	.50
1938		.50
1939		.50
Y35 (zinc, holed) 16mm		
1939		2.00
10 GROSZY		
Y11 (nickel) 17.5mm		
1923	122,200,000	.20
Y36 (zinc)		
1923		.15

	Mintage	Value
20 GROSZY		
Y12 (nickel) 20mm		
1923...........142,626,000		$ .30
Y37 (zinc)		
1923.....................		.20
50 GROSZY		
Y13 (nickel) 23mm		
1923...........101,200,000		.45
Y38 (iron)		
1938....................		1.00
1 ZLOTY		
Y15 (silver) 23mm		
1924...........16,073,339		1.50
1925...........24,000,000		1.50
Y14 (nickel) 25mm		
1929...........30,000,000		.75
2 ZLOTE		
Y16 (silver) 27mm		
1924 torches both sides of date (Paris) 8,178,641		2.00
1924H no torches (Birmingham)......		3.00
1924 no torches — (Philadelphia) 4,400,000		15.00
1925 dot after date — (London)....10,800,000		2.00
1925 no dot — (Philadelphia) 1,600,000		15.00
Y20 new design, 22mm		
1932............8,200,000		.75
1933...........16,125,000		.75
1934...........10,675,000		.75
Y27 Pilsudski		
1934...........inc. above		2.00
1936............2,925,000		2.00
Y30 ship		
1936...........inc. above		3.00
5 ZLOTYCH		
Y18 (silver) 33mm		
1928 (Warsaw)....9,070,000		7.00
1928 (London) — no mint mark........5,490,000		7.00
1930............3,587,200		10.00
1931............2,422,000		15.00
1932..............593,000		10.00
Y19 1830-1930, commem.		
1930............1,000,000		8.00

	Mintage	Value
Y21 new design, 28mm		
1932 (Warsaw)...inc. above		$2.50
1932 (London)— no mint mark........3,000,000		2.50
1933 (Warsaw)...11,660,000		2.50
1934............6,760,000		2.50
Y28		
1934 Pilsudski — no S in shield.......inc. above		2.50
1935 no S in shield........1,800,000		2.50
1936............1,000,000		3.00
1938....................		3.00
Y25		
1934 Pilsudski — S in shield.........300,000		4.50
Y31 ship		
1936............1,630,000		5.00
10 ZLOTYCH		
Y22 (silver) 34mm		
1932 (Warsaw)....3,075,000		5.00
1932 (London) no mint mark........6,000,000		5.00
1933 (Warsaw)....2,825,000		5.00
Y23 Jan III Sobieski		
1933...............300,000		10.00
Y24 Romauld Traugutt		
1933...............300,000		10.00
Y26 Pilsudski — S in shield		
1934...............300,000		10.00
Y29 Pilsudski — no S in shield		
1934............1,620,000		5.00
1935...........inc. above		5.00
1936............2,130,000		5.00
1937............1,008,500		6.00
1938....................		6.00
1939....................		8.00
Post World War II People's Republic		
1 GROSZ		
Y39 (aluminum) 14.5mm		
1949....................		.15
2 GROSZE		
Y40 (aluminum) 17mm		
1949....................		.20

	Mintage	Value
5 GROSZY		
Y41 (bronze) 20mm		
1949		$ .60
Y41a (aluminum)		
1949		.50
Y-A46		
1958		.20
1962		.20
10 GROSZY		
Y42 (copper-nickel) 17.5mm		
1949		.50
Y42a (aluminum)		
1949		.25
Y-AA47		
1961		.15
20 GROSZY		
Y43 (copper-nickel) 20mm		
1949		.75
Y43a (aluminum)		
1949		.35
Y-A47		
1957		.50
50 GROSZY		
Y44 (copper-nickel) 23mm		
1949		1.25

	Mintage	Value
Y44a (aluminum)		
1949		$ .75
Y48		
1957		.60
1 ZLOTY		
Y45 (copper-nickel) 25mm		
1949		1.50
Y45a (aluminum)		
1949		1.00
Y49		
1957		1.50
2 ZLOTE		
Y46 (aluminum) 27mm		
1958		1.25
5 ZLOTYCH		
Y47 (aluminum) 29mm		
1959		1.25
10 ZLOTYCH		
Y50 (copper-nickel) 30mm		
1959 Kosciuszko		3.50
Y51		
1959 Kopernik		3.50

PORTUGAL
(Portuguesa)

On the western part of the Iberian peninsula facing the Atlantic Ocean. Was a kingdom until 1910 when a republic was established. All coins were minted at Lisbon except 10 and 20 Reis 1891-1892 (Paris).

1000 Reis = 1 Milreis

100 Centavos = 1 Escudo

MONARCHY
III (3 REIS)
Louis I (1861-1889)

Y1 (copper) 23.5mm

1868	100,000	.75
1874	280,000	.75
1875	1,200,000	1.00

V (5 REIS)
Louis I

Y2 (copper) 27mm

1867	737,000	.40
1868	840,000	.50
1871	240,000	.75

1872	700,000	.60
1873	600,000	1.00
1874	1,080,000	.35
1875	2,200,000	.35
1876	320,000	1.00
1877	620,000	1.00
1878	inc. above	1.50
1879	332,000	.60
1882	inc. below	10.00

Y5 head, 21mm

1882	5,200,000	.25
1883	4,700,000	.25
1884	1,730,000	.25
1885	3,200,000	.25
1886	4,170,000	.25

	Mintage	Value
Charles I (1889-1908)		
Y15 5 REIS		
1890............430,000		$ .75
1891............inc. above		.60
1892............1,510,000		.25
1893............3,280,000		.25
1897............1,120,000		.25
1898............790,000		.30
1899............1,220,000		.25
1900............1,110,000		.25
1901............1,070,000		.50
1904............720,000		.30
1905............1,340,000		.25
1906............5,670,000		.20
Manuel II (1908-1910)		
Y28 (bronze)		
1910............1,000,000		.50
X (10 REIS)		
Louis I		
Y3 (copper) 32mm		
1867............300,000		1.00
1868............450,000		1.25
1870............inc. w/1871		3.00
1871............360,000		1.25
1873............2,000,000		.60
1874............220,000		7.50
1878....................		10.00
Y6 head, 25.5mm		
1882............14,795,000		.30
1883............inc. above		.30
1884............10,190,000		.30
1885............8,100,000		.30
1886............3,915,000		.45
Charles I		
Y16 10 REIS		
1891 (Lisbon).....3,445,224		.35
1891A (Paris).......894,776		.60
1892 (Lisbon)....10,299,776		.30
1892A (Paris).....5,768,613		.30
XX (20 REIS)		
Louis I		
Y4 (copper) 37.5mm		
1867............745,000		1.50
1870....................		3.00
1871............310,000		1.50
1872............50,000		10.00
1873............2,500,000		1.00
1874............1,575,000		1.00

	Mintage	Value
Y7 head, 30mm		
1882............inc. w/1883		$1.00
1883............17,235,000		.50
1884............17,200,000		.50
1885............18,492,000		.50
1886............4,572,500		.60
Charles I		
Y17 20 REIS		
1891 (Lisbon).....3,281,885		.50
1891A (Paris).....6,015,615		.50
1892 (Lisbon)....15,410,623		.75
1892A (Paris).......657,766		1.50
	50 REIS	
Louis I		
Y8 (silver) 15mm		
1862............17,200		1.50
1863............215,000		.60
1864............50,000		1.25
1868....................		5.00
1874............60,000		1.25
1875............inc. above		1.75
1876............100,000		.75
1877............100,000		.75
1879............80,000		1.00
1880............320,000		.50
1886............100,000		.90
1887............inc. above		1.50
1888............inc. w/1889		5.00
1889............1,000,000		.40
Charles I		
Y20		
1893............620,000		2.00
Y18 (copper-nickel) 18mm		
1900............8,000,000		.30
	100 REIS	
Louis I		
Y9 (silver) 19mm		
1864............160,000		4.00
1865............100,000		1.50
1866............10,000		6.00
1869............10,000		5.00
1871............60,000		2.00
1872............60,000		2.00
1873............inc. w/1874		7.50
1874............170,000		1.50
1875............130,000		1.00
1876............220,000		1.25
1877............120,000		1.25
1878............590,000		1.00
1879............inc. above		1.00

	Mintage	Value
1880	440,000	$1.00
1881	inc. above	7.50
1886	750,000	.75
1888	500,000	.75
1889	1,500,000	.60

Charles I

Y21

	Mintage	Value
1890	700,000	1.50
1891	271,000	2.00
1893	1,050,000	1.25
1894	inc. above	2.50
1898	930,000	1.25

Y19 (copper-nickel) 23mm

	Mintage	Value
1900	16,000,000	.35

Manuel II

Y29 (silver) 19mm

	Mintage	Value
1909	inc. w/1910	.50
1910	6,362,831	.40

200 REIS

Louis I

Y10 (silver) 24mm

	Mintage	Value
1862	693,740	2.00
1863	420,500	2.00
1865	50,000	3.50
1866	10,000	5.00
1867	10,000	5.00
1868	5,000	7.50
1871	75,000	5.00
1872	70,000	7.50
1875	70,000	3.50
1876	80,000	5.00
1877	30,000	5.00
1878	20,000	5.00
1879	5,050	7.50
1880	150,000	2.50
1886	340,000	2.00
1887	3,160,000	1.25
1888	700,000	2.00

Charles I

Y22

	Mintage	Value
1891	2,365,000	1.25
1892	2,450,000	1.25
1893	1,220,000	1.25
1901	205,000	2.50
1903	200,000	2.50

Y25 400th Anniv. India

	Mintage	Value
1898	250,000	2.50

Manuel II

Y30

	Mintage	Value
1909	7,650,000	$1.00

500 REIS

Louis I

Y11 (silver) 30mm

	Mintage	Value
1863	215,000	4.00
1864	30,000	5.00
1865	406,000	3.00
1866	378,000	3.00
1867	458,000	3.00
1868	388,000	3.00
1870	314,000	3.00
1871	228,000	3.50
1872	576,000	5.00
1875	140,000	3.00
1876	280,000	6.00
1877	55,000	3.50
1879	787,980	3.00
1886	300,000	3.00
1887	432,000	3.00
1888	2,740,000	2.50
1889	960,000	2.50

Charles I

Y23

	Mintage	Value
1891	12,476,000	2.00
1892	4,716,000	2.00
1893	2,494,000	2.50
1894	254,000	10.00
1895	216,000	6.00
1896	5,120,000	2.00
1898	1,320,000	3.00
1899	3,100,000	2.50
1900	200,000	7.50
1901	1,050,000	2.50
1903	920,000	3.00
1906	inc. above	4.00
1907	384,000	3.00
1908	1,840,000	3.00

Y26 400th Anniv. India

	Mintage	Value
1898	inc. above	5.00

Manuel II

Y31

	Mintage	Value
1908	2,500,000	1.75
1909	1,513,167	1.75

Y32 Peninsular War

	Mintage	Value
1910	200,000	6.00

	Mintage	Value
Y34 Pombal		
1910 400,000		$8.00

1000 REIS
(silver) 37mm
Charles I

Y27 400th Anniv. India

1898 300,000		10.00

Y24 regular

1899 1,500,000		8.00
1900 . . . . .inc. above		30.00

Manuel II

Y33 Peninsular War

1910 200,000		10.00

REPUBLIC
(Escudo Coinage System)
1 CENTAVO

Y36 (bronze) 19mm

1917 2,550,000		.50
1918 22,996,000		.20
1920 12,535,000		.20
1921 4,949,000		.50
1922 . . . . .inc. above		10.00

2 CENTAVOS

Y35 (iron) 22mm

1918 170,000		7.50

Y37 (bronze)

1918 4,295,000		.25
1920 10,102,500		.25
1921 678,750		.75

4 CENTAVOS

Y42 (copper-nickel) 25mm

1917 4,960,750		.50
1919 10,066,673		.40

5 CENTAVOS

Y38 (bronze) 25mm

1920 114,000		1.00
1921 5,916,000		.30
1922 . . . . .inc. above		2.00

Y39

1924 6,480,000		.20
1925 7,260,000		.20

Y52

1927 26,320,000		.20

10 CENTAVOS

Y48 (silver) 19.5mm

1915 3,418,400		.50

	Mintage	Value
Y43 (copper-nickel) 19mm		
1920 1,120,000		$ .30
1921 1,285,000		.30

Y40 (bronze) 22mm

1924 1,210,000		.30
1925 9,090,000		.20
1926 26,250,000		.20

Y53

1930		1.00
1938 2,000,000		.25
1940 3,383,620		.25

Y60 X CENTAVOS, 17.5mm

1942 1,035,000		.25
1943 18,765,000		.10
1944 5,090,000		.10
1945 8,090,000		.10
1946 7,740,000		.10
1947 9,282,600		.10
1948 5,900,000		.10
1949 15,240,000		.10
1950 8,860,000		.10
1951 5,040,000		.10
1952 4,960,000		.10
1953 7,547,800		.10
1954 2,452,000		.10
1955 10,000,000		.10
1956 3,336,000		.10
1957 6,654,400		.10
1958 7,320,000		.10
1959 7,140,000		.10
1960 15,055,000		.10
1961 5,020,000		.10
1962 14,980,000		.10

20 CENTAVOS

Y49 (silver) 24mm

1913 539,775		1.25
1916 706,225		1.25

Y44 (copper-nickel) 23.5mm

1920 1,567,500		.45
1921 3,030,000		.30
1922 580,000		5.00

Y41 (bronze) 24.5mm

1924 6,220,000		.25
1925 10,560,000		.25

Y61 XX CENTAVOS, 20.5mm

1942 . . . . .inc. w/1943		.40
1943 10,170,000		.15
1944 7,290,000		.15
1945 7,552,505		.15
1948 2,750,000		.20
1949 12,250,000		.15

	Mintage	Value
1951	3,185,000	$ .15
1952	1,815,000	.25
1953	9,426,200	.15
1955	5,573,800	.15
1956	3,550,000	.15
1957	1,450,000	.25
1958	7,470,000	.15
1959	4,780,000	.15
1960	4,790,000	.15
1961	5,180,000	.15
1962	2,500,000	.15

50 CENTAVOS

Y50 (silver) 30.5mm

	Mintage	Value
1912	1,695,000	1.75
1913	4,443,298	1.50
1914	4,991,790	1.50
1916	5,079,935	1.50

Y45 (aluminum-bronze) 23mm

	Mintage	Value
1924	810,000	1.25
1925		12.50
1926	14,340,000	.35

Y54 (copper-nickel)

	Mintage	Value
1927	3,330,000	.25
1928	6,823,140	.20
1929	9,778,860	.20
1930	1,116,000	.30
1931	7,127,200	.20
1935	902,100	1.50
1938	922,700	.50
1940	2,000,000	.25
1944	2,973,685	.20
1945	5,699,940	.20
1946	4,334,107	.20
1947	6,998,268	.20
1951	4,609,516	.20
1952	2,421,480	.20
1953	2,369,004	.20
1955	3,056,700	.20
1956	3,003,000	.20
1957	3,940,300	.20
1958	2,687,000	.20
1959	4,027,000	.20
1960	2,592,000	.20
1961	3,324,000	.20
1962	6,678,136	.20

1 ESCUDO

(silver) 37mm

Y47 Birth of Republic

	Mintage	Value
1910	1,000,000	10.00

Y51 regular

	Mintage	Value
1915	1,817,587	6.50
1916	1,405,394	6.50

Y46 (aluminum-bronze) 26mm

	Mintage	Value
1924	2,709,000	$ .60
1926	2,346,000	.60

Y55 (copper-nickel) 27mm

	Mintage	Value
1927	1,917,000	.50
1928	7,462,355	.35
1929	1,616,645	.50
1930	1,911,000	.50
1931	2,038,700	.50
1935		2.50
1939	304,300	1.00
1940	1,259,359	.50
1944	993,000	.75
1945	inc. above	.75
1946	2,507,141	.35
1951	2,500,000	.35
1952	2,500,000	.35
1957	1,656,400	.35
1958	1,446,700	.35
1959	1,908,300	.35
1961	2,505,000	.35
1962	2,757,000	.35

2.50 ESCUDOS

Y57 (silver) 20.5mm

	Mintage	Value
1932	2,592,000	.75
1933	2,457,124	.75
1937	1,000,000	.75
1940	2,762,906	.60
1942	3,846,945	.50
1943	8,301,888	.50
1944	9,133,667	.50
1945	6,316,170	.50
1946	3,208,180	.50
1947	2,609,535	.50
1948	1,814,465	.60
1951	4,000,000	.50

5 ESCUDOS

Y58 (silver) 25mm

	Mintage	Value
1932	800,000	1.00
1933	6,717,267	.75
1934	1,012,152	.75
1937	1,500,000	.75
1940	578,160	.90
1942	2,051,247	.75
1943	1,353,742	.75
1946	404,000	1.00
1947	2,419,590	.75
1948	2,017,874	.75
1951	965,836	.75

Y64 new design

	Mintage	Value
1960	800,000	1.00

	Mintage	Value
10 ESCUDOS		
(silver) 30.5mm		
Y56 Ourique		
1928. 200,000		$6.00
Y59 regular		
1932. 3,220,000		1.75
1933. 1,780,000		1.75
1934. 400,000		2.00
1937. 500,000		2.00
1940. 1,199,529		1.75
1942. 186,190		3.00
1948. 507,452		2.00
Y63 new design		
1954. 5,764,350		1.50

	Mintage	Value
1955. 4,055,650		$1.50
Y65 new design		
1960. 200,000		2.50
20 ESCUDOS		
(silver) 34mm		
Y62 Commemorative		
1953. 1,000,000		4.00
Y66 new design		
1960. 200,000		4.50

The 50 Centavos and 1 Escudo dated 1935, though valid in Portugal, were minted for use solely in the Azores.

PORTUGUESE GUINEA
(Guine)

A Portuguese province on the west coast of Africa.

100 Centavos = 1 Escudo

5 CENTAVOS
Y1 (bronze) 19mm
1933. 100,000		.50

10 CENTAVOS
Y2 (bronze) 22mm
1933. 250,000		.75

20 CENTAVOS
Y3 (bronze) 24.5mm
1933. 350,000		1.25

50 CENTAVOS
Y4 (nickel-bronze) 23mm
1933. 600,000		1.25

Y6 (bronze)
1946. 2,000,000		.50

Y8 21mm
1952. 3,019,910		.25

1 ESCUDO
Y5 (nickel-bronze) 27mm
1933. 800,000		1.50

Y7 (bronze)
1946. 2,000,000		.75

2.50 ESCUDOS
Y9 (copper-nickel) 20mm
1952. 3,017,880		.50

10 ESCUDOS
Y10 (silver) 24mm
1952. 1,200,000		1.50

20 ESCUDOS
Y11 (silver) 30mm
1952. 750,000		3.00

The 50 Centavos and 1 Escudo of 1946 commemorate the 500th anniversary of the discovery of Portuguese Guinea.

(India Portugueza, Estado Da India)

Three small areas on the west coast of India. Had been a Portuguese possession for several hundred years until seized by India in 1962.

60 Reis = 1 Tanga
16 Tangas = 1 Rupia
100 Centavos = 1 Escudo (1958)

	Mintage	Value
3 REIS		
Louis I (1861-1889)		
Y1 (copper) 16mm		
1871.....................		$1.00
5 REIS		
Louis I		
Y2 (copper) 18mm		
1871.....................		1.00
10 REIS		
Louis I		
Y3 (copper) 20mm		
1871.....................		1.50
1/12 TANGA		
Charles I (1889-1908)		
Y15 (bronze) 18mm		
1901..............960,000		1.00
1903..............960,000		1.00
1/8 TANGA		
Louis I		
Y7 (copper) 21mm		
1881.....................		1.25
1884.....................		1.25
1886.....................		1.25
Charles I		
Y16 (bronze)		
1901..............960,000		1.00
1903..............960,000		1.00
1/4 TANGA		
Louis 1		
Y4 (copper) 28mm		
1871.....................		2.00
Y8 25.5mm		
1881.....................		1.50
1884.....................		1.50
1886.....................		1.50
1888.....................		1.50

	Mintage	Value
Charles I		
Y17 (bronze) 25mm		
1901..............800,000		$ .50
1903..............800,000		.50
½ TANGA		
Louis I		
Y5 (copper) 32mm		
1871.....................		3.00
Charles I		
Y18 (bronze) 30mm		
1901..............800,000		.75
1903..............800,000		.75
1 TANGA		
Louis I		
Y6 (copper) 37mm		
1871.....................		4.00
New Government (1926-1962)		
Y21 (bronze) 22.5mm		
1934..............100,000		1.00
Y26 25mm		
1947............1,000,000		.75
Y30 20mm		
1952............9,600,000		.50
2 TANGAS		
New Government		
Y22 (copper-nickel) 19mm		
1934..............150,000		1.50
4 TANGAS		
New Government		
Y23 (copper-nickel) 22.5mm		
1934..............100,000		1.75
1/8 RUPIA		
Louis I		
Y11 (silver) 15.5mm		
1881.....................		1.50

	Mintage	Value
¼ RUPIA		
Louis I		
Y12 (silver) 19.5mm		
1881.		$2.00
New Government		
Y27 (copper-nickel) 19mm		
1947. 800,000		1.00
Y31 design changed		
1952. 4,000,000		.60
½ RUPIA		
Louis I		
Y13 (silver) 24.5mm		
1881.		2.00
1882.		2.00
New Government		
Y24 26mm		
1936. 100,000		2.50
Y28 (copper-nickel) 24mm		
1947. 600,000		1.50
Y32 design changed		
1952. 2,000,000		1.00
1 RUPIA		
Louis I		
Y14 (silver) 31mm		
1881.		3.00
1882.		3.00
Charles I		
Y19 30mm		
1903. 50,000		7.50
1904. 250,000		4.50
1905. 25,000		12.50

	Mintage	Value
Republic (1910-1926)		
Y20 30.5mm		
1912. 100,000		$7.50
New Government		
Y25		
1935. 300,000		5.00
Y29 30mm		
1947. 900,000		2.50
Y33 (copper-nickel)		
1952. 1,132,000		2.00
Escudo Coinage System		
10 CENTAVOS		
Y34 (bronze) 18mm		
1958. 5,000,000		.35
30 CENTAVOS		
Y35 (bronze) 22mm		
1958. 5,000,000		.50
60 CENTAVOS		
Y36 (copper-nickel) 20mm		
1958. 5,000,000		.60
1 ESCUDO		
Y37 (copper-nickel) 24mm		
1958. 6,000,000		.90
3 ESCUDOS		
Y38 (copper-nickel) 27mm		
1958. 5,000,000		1.25
6 ESCUDOS		
Y39 (copper-nickel) 31mm		
1958. 4,000,000		2.00

PUERTO RICO

An island in the Caribbean and a Spanish possession until 1898. Now a self-governing commonwealth of the United States. United States coinage now circulating.

100 Centavos = 1 Peso

	Mintage	Value
5 CENTAVOS		
Y1 (silver) 16mm		
1896...............600,000		$7.50
10 CENTAVOS		
Y2 (silver) 18mm		
1896...............700,000		20.00
20 CENTAVOS		
Y3 (silver) 23mm		
1895.............3,350,006		10.00
40 CENTAVOS		
Y4 (silver) 27mm		
1896..............752,002		$35.00
1 PESO		
Y5 (silver) 37mm		
1895.............8,500,021		45.00

REUNION

A French overseas territory in the Indian Ocean east of Madagascar.

100 Centimes = 1 Franc

	Value
50 CENTIMES	
Y1 (copper-nickel) 22mm	
1896.............1,000,000	2.50
1 FRANC	
Y2 (copper-nickel) 25mm	
1896...............500,000	4.00
Y8 (aluminum) 22mm	
1948.............3,000,000	.25
2 FRANCS	
Y9 (aluminum) 27mm	
1948.............2,000,000	.35
5 FRANCS	
Y10 (aluminum) 31mm	
1955.............3,000,000	.50
10 FRANCS	
Y11 (aluminum-bronze) 20mm	
1955.............2,200,000	.65
20 FRANCS	
Y12 (aluminum-bronze) 24mm	
1955.............1,840,000	.85
50 FRANCS	
Y13 (nickel) 23.5mm	
1962.............1,000,000	1.50

In eastern Europe bordering on the U.S.S.R. Became a People's Republic in 1948. Romanian coins were minted at various European mints.

100 Bani = 1 Leu

	Mintage	Value
1 BAN		
Carol I (1866-1914)		
Y1 (copper) 15mm		
1867.		$1.00
Y29 new design		
1900. 20,006,826		.50
2 BANI		
Carol I		
Y2 (copper) 20mm		
1867.		1.00
Y11 new design		
1879.		1.00
1880.		1.00
1881.		1.00
Y17 w/o ROMANIA reverse		
1882.		1.00
1883.		1.00
1884.		1.00
1885.		1.00
Y30 new design		
1900. 20,000,000		.50
5 BANI		
Carol I		
Y3 (copper) 25mm		
1867. 25,000,000		.75
Y18 w/o ROMANIA reverse		
1882. 5,000,000		.75
1883. 3,000,000		.75
1884. 8,400,000		.75
1885. 3,600,000		.75
Y31 (copper-nickel) 19mm		
1900. 20,000,000		.30
Y34 holed		
1905. 2,000,000		.50
1906. 48,000,000		.25
1907. 24,000,000		.25
10 BANI		
Carol I		
Y4 (copper) 30mm		
1867. 25,000,000		1.00
Y32 (copper-nickel) 22mm		
1900. 15,000,000		.40

	Mintage	Value
Y35 holed		
1905. 10,820,000	$	.30
1906. 24,180,000		.30
1907. 17,000,000		.30
20 BANI		
Carol I		
Y33 (copper-nickel) 25mm		
1900. 2,500,000		.60
Y36 holed		
1905. 2,500,000		.60
1906. 5,500,000		.50
25 BANI		
Ferdinand I (1914-1927)		
Y47 (aluminum) 19mm		
1921. 40,000,000		.50
50 BANI		
Carol I		
Y8 (silver) 18mm		
1873. 4,810,000		1.00
1876. 2,116,980		1.25
Y13 new design, DOMNUL		
1881. 1,000,000		1.50
Y19 REGE		
1884. 1,000,000		1.50
1885. 200,000		2.00
Y24 new design		
1894. 600,000		1.25
1900. 3,838,000		.75
1901. 194,205		2.00
Y44 new design		
1910. 3,600,000		1.00
1911. 3,000,000		1.00
1912. 1,800,000		1.00
1914. 1,600,000		1.00
Ferdinand I		
Y48 (aluminum) 21mm		
1921. 20,000,000		.50
Mihai I (1927-1930 & 1940-1947)		
Y88 (brass) 16mm		
1947. 13,266,000		.25

	Mintage	Value
1 LEU		
Carol I		
Y6 (silver) 23mm		
1870	400,000	$2.50
Y9 new design		
1873	4,443,393	1.50
1874	4,511,607	1.50
1876	225,000	2.50
Y14 new design, DOMNUL		
1881	1,800,000	1.50
Y20 REGE		
1884	1,000,000	1.50
Y25 new design		
1894	1,500,000	1.25
1900	798,800	1.50
1901	369,614	2.00
Y37 40th Anniversary		
1906	2,500,000	2.50
Y45 new design		
1910	4,600,000	2.00
1911	2,573,065	2.00
1912	3,540,000	2.00
1914	4,282,935	2.00
Ferdinand I		
Y49 (copper-nickel) 21mm		
1924	200,006,255	.30
Carol II (1930-1940)		
Y57 (brass) 20mm		
1938	27,900,000	.25
Y57a 18mm		
1939		.25
1940		.25
1941		.25
Mihai I		
Y89		
1947	88,341,000	.30
2 LEI		
Carol I		
Y10 (silver) 27mm		
1872	262,000	4.00
1873	1,745,500	2.00
1874	425,000	3.00
1875	3,092,500	2.00
1876	653,255	2.50
Y15 new design, DOMNUL		
1881	1,150,000	3.00

	Mintage	Value
Y26 REGE		
1894	600,000	$2.50
1900	87,279	4.00
1901	12,476	10.00
Y46 new design		
1910	1,800,000	2.50
1911	1,000,000	2.50
1912	1,500,000	2.50
1914	2,452,000	2.50
Ferdinand I		
Y50 (copper-nickel) 25mm		
1924	100,008,298	.60
Mihai I		
Y73 (zinc) 19mm		
1941	25,400,000	.25
1942	51,400,000	.25
1943	16,600,000	.25
1944	4,942,000	.35
1945	1,150,000	.50
Y90 (bronze) 21mm		
1947	40,000,000	.75
5 LEI		
Carol I		
Y16 DOMNUL (silver) 37mm		
1880	1,800,000	12.50
1881	4,000,000	12.50
Y27 REGE		
1881	2,400,000	12.50
Y23 w/o ROMANIA reverse		
1881	1,100,000	12.50
1882	inc. above	12.50
1883	2,300,000	10.00
1884	300,000	12.50
1885	40,000	20.00
1901	82,460	35.00
Y38 40th Anniversary		
1906	200,000	20.00
Mihai I		
Y55 (brass) 21mm		
1930	60,002,278	1.00
Y74 (zinc) 22mm		
1942	6,800,000	.40
1943	101,000,000	.40
1944	16,600,000	.40
1945	15,500,000	.40

	Mintage	Value
Y91 (aluminum) 23mm		
1947............56,026,000		$ .60

10 LEI

Carol II

Y58 (brass) 22mm

| 1930............60,000,000 | | .50 |

20 LEI

Mihai I

Y56 (nickel-brass) 27mm

| 1930............52,000,000 | | 2.00 |

Carol II

Y59 (brass)

| 1930............33,005,037 | | .90 |

Mihai I

Y75 (zinc) 25mm

1942............30,500,000		.50
1943............26,925,000		.50
1944............7,500,000		.50
1945............10,713,000		.50

50 LEI

Carol II

Y60 (nickel) 24mm

1937............10,860,000		1.25
1938............8,000,000		1.25
1939....................		1.25
1940....................		1.25

100 LEI

Carol II

Y62 (silver) 31mm

| 1932............18,400,000 | | 4.00 |

Y61 (nickel) 27mm

1936............3,000,000		1.50
1937............17,230,446		1.50
1938............3,250,000		1.50
1939....................		1.50
1940....................		1.50

Mihai I

Y76 (nickel-clad steel)

1943............40,590,000		1.50
1944............14,500,000		1.50
1945............6,789,000		2.00

200 LEI

Mihai I

Y77 (silver) 24mm

| 1942............21,120,000 | | 2.00 |

	Mintage	Value
1943............5,880,000		$2.00
Y81 (brass) 28mm		
1945............1,399,000		3.00

250 LEI

Carol II

Y63 (silver) 30mm

| 1935............5,625,000 | | 6.00 |

Y64 new design, 31mm

| 1939.................... | | 6.00 |
| 1940.................... | | 6.00 |

Mihai I

Y78 NIHIL SINE DEO
on rim

| 1941............8,559,600 | | 5.00 |

Y78a TOTOL PENTRU TARA
on rim

| 1941.................... | | 47.50 |

500 LEI

Mihai I

Y79 (silver) 38mm

1941............418,000		30.00
1942............289,000		30.00
1943............86,000		40.00

Y80 new design, 33mm

| 1944............9,732,000 | | 5.00 |

Y82 (brass) 30mm

| 1945............3,422,000 | | 2.50 |

Y83 (aluminum) 24mm

| 1946............5,823,000 | | 1.25 |

2000 LEI

Mihai I

Y84 (brass) 24mm

| 1946............24,619,000 | | 2.00 |

10,000 LEI

Mihai I

Y85 (brass) 27mm

| 1947............11,850,000 | | 2.50 |

25,000 LEI

Mihai I

Y86 (silver) 32mm

| 1946............2,372,600 | | 6.00 |

100,000 LEI

Mihai I

Y87 (silver) 38mm

| 1946............2,002,000 | | 25.00 |

	Mintage	Value
PEOPLE'S REPUBLIC 1948		

1 BAN

Y96 (aluminum-bronze) 14mm
1952.................... $ .25

3 BANI

Y97 (aluminum-bronze) 17mm
1952.................... .30

5 BANI

Y98 (aluminum-bronze) 20mm
1952.................... .40
1953.................... .40
1954.................... .40
1955.................... .40
1956.................... .40
1957.................... .40

10 BANI

Y99 (copper-nickel) 16mm
1952.................... .40
1953.................... .40

Y99a
1955.................... .40

15 BANI

Y103 (copper-nickel) 19mm
1960.................... .30

25 BANI

Y100 (copper-nickel) 21mm
1952.................... .75
1953.................... .75

Y100a
1954.................... $ .65
1955.................... .65

Y104
1960.................... .35

50 BANI

Y101 (copper-nickel) 25mm
1955.................... 1.00

1 LEU

Y92 (aluminum-bronze) 16mm
1949.................... .35

Y92a (aluminum)
1951.................... .35

2 LEI

Y93 (aluminum-bronze) 18mm
1950.................... .40

Y93a (aluminum)
1951.................... .40

5 LEI

Y94 (aluminum) 24mm
1948.................... .60
1951.................... .60

20 LEI

Y95 (aluminum)
1951.................... ——

(There is serious doubt that this coin exists.)

RUSSIA

(РОССИИСКА)

The largest country in the world in area, occupying eastern Europe and northern Asia.

Mint marks:

СПБ — St. Petersburg
EM — Ekaterinburg
BM — Warsaw
MW — Warsaw
MWB — Warsaw
Star — Paris (on rim)
2 Stars — Brussels (on rim)

From 1886 25, 50 Kopek and 1 Rouble coins had mint marks and mintmasters' initials on rim of coin.

100 Kopeks = 1 Rouble

¼ KOPEK		
Alexander II (1855-1881)		

Y1 (copper) 13mm
1855EM..........6,442,400   1.25
1855BM..........200,000   2.00

1856EM..........6,000,000   1.25
1857EM..........6,000,000   1.25
1858EM..........6,969,600   1.25
1859EM..........3,833,600   1.25
1860EM..................   5.00

	Mintage	Value
1860BM		$5.00
1861EM	192,000	2.00
1861BM	400,000	1.50
1862EM	992,000	1.25
1863EM	300,000	2.50
1864EM	403,200	1.25
1865EM	121,600	2.50
1866EM	326,400	2.50
1867EM	832,000	5.00

Y7 design altered

	Mintage	Value
1867EM	inc. above	10.00
1867CПБ		4.00
1868EM	700,000	1.00
1868CПБ	60,003	2.50
1869EM	615,000	1.00
1869CПБ	92,003	5.00
1870EM	435,000	1.00
1870CПБ	20,005	7.50
1871EM	155,000	2.50
1872EM	540,000	1.00
1873EM	822,500	1.00
1874EM	340,000	1.25
1875EM	300,000	5.00
1876EM		7.50
1876CПБ	800,005	1.00
1877CПБ	720,003	1.00
1878CПБ	1,100,003	1.00
1879CПБ	280,005	2.50
1880CПБ	180,010	3.50
1881CПБ	60,005	1.00

Alexander III (1881-1894)
Y29

	Mintage	Value
1881CПБ	200,009	2.00
1882CПБ	60,009	2.00
1883CПБ	240,008	1.00
1884CПБ	140,004	2.00
1885CПБ	480,011	1.00
1886CПБ	1,060,007	1.00
1887CПБ	1,000,004	1.00
1888CПБ	200,008	1.00
1889CПБ	181,002	2.00
1890CПБ	inc. above	1.00
1891CПБ	400,008	1.00
1892CПБ	918,006	1.00
1893CПБ	740,008	1.00

Nicholas II (1894-1917)
Y47

	Mintage	Value
1894CПБ		5.00
1895CПБ	62,007	2.50
1896CПБ	5,000,001	.75
1897CПБ	4,000,000	.75
1898CПБ	8,000,000	.75

	Mintage	Value
1899CПБ	8,000,000	$ .75
1900CПБ	4,000,000	.75
1909CПБ	2,200,008	.75
1910CПБ	8,000,009	.75

No mint mark

	Mintage	Value
1915	500,000	1.00
1916	1,200,000	1.00

½ KOPEK

Alexander II

Y2 (copper) 16mm

	Mintage	Value
1855EM	20,510,566	.50
1855BM	6,380,228	.50
1856EM	6,000,000	.50
1856BM	4,452,554	.50
1857EM	6,000,000	.50
1857BM	1,908,584	.50
1858EM	11,147,200	.50
1858BM	311,720	.50
1859EM	5,871,200	.50
1859BM	3,718,922	.50
1860EM	2,838,400	.50
1860BM	1,861,224	.50
1861EM	2,276,800	.50
1861BM	1,564,368	.50
1862EM	3,072,000	.50
1862BM	1,035,632	.60
1863EM	1,011,220	.50
1863BM	2,400,000	.70
1864EM	566,400	.50
1865EM	560,000	7.50
1866EM	332,800	1.25
1867EM	390,000	5.00

Y8 design altered

	Mintage	Value
1867EM	inc. above	5.00
1867CПБ		3.50
1868EM	1,190,000	.50
1868CПБ	60,003	2.00
1869EM	592,500	.60
1869CПБ	145,003	2.00
1870EM	510,000	.60
1870CПБ	25,005	5.00
1871EM	222,500	1.00
1872EM	365,000	.60
1873EM	962,600	1.00
1874EM	300,000	1.00
1875EM	321,100	3.50
1876EM	inc. above	5.00
1876CПБ	770,005	.60
1877CПБ	1,290,003	.30
1878CПБ	1,120,003	.30
1879CПБ	740,005	.50

Mintage	Value		Mintage	Value
1880СПБ.........1,260,010	$ .30	1861BM.........1,800,000	$1.00
1881СПБ..........420,005	.50	1862EM.........10,164,800	.50
		1862BM.........2,099,831	.50
Alexander III		1863EM.........6,544,000	.50
Y30		1863BM.........2,854,491	.50
1881СПБ..........440,011	1.50	1864EM.........4,400,000	.50
1882СПБ..........350,009	.40	1864BM.........1,045,678	.50
1883СПБ..........540,008	.50	1865EM.........14,230,400	.50
1884СПБ..........550,004	.60	1866EM.........12,304,000	1.00
1885СПБ..........680,011	.40	1867EM..........5,851,200	3.00
1886СПБ..........560,007	.50		
1887СПБ..........600,004	.60	**Y9** design altered	
1888СПБ..........610,008	.75	1867EM.........inc. above	5.00
1889СПБ.........4,650,002	.50	1867СПБ..................	3.00
1890СПБ.........2,040,006	.40	1868EM.........10,230,000	.50
1892СПБ.........2,271,006	.25	1868СПБ..........750,003	.75
1893СПБ.........3,900,008	.25	1869EM.........10,230,000	.75
		1869СПБ..........739,003	.75
Nicholas II		1870EM.........9,875,000	.50
Y48		1870СПБ........1,143,005	1.00
1894СПБ.......inc. above	3.00	1871EM.........2,880,300	1.00
1895СПБ........2,992,009	.40	1872EM.........5,712,500	.50
1896СПБ........1,340,001	.40	1873EM.........5,212,575	.75
1897СПБ.......60,000,000	.25	1874EM.........5,012,500	.40
1898СПБ.......76,000,000	.25	1875EM.........6,437,500	.40
1899СПБ.......76,000,000	.25	1876EM.........1,755,000	.40
1900СПБ.......36,000,000	.25	1876СПБ.........2,930,005	.40
1908СПБ........8,000,000	.25	1877СПБ.........7,065,003	.40
1909СПБ.......49,500,010	.25	1878СПБ.........8,241,003	.40
1910СПБ.......24,000,009	.25	1879СПБ.........9,045,005	.40
1911СПБ.......35,800,011	.25	1880СПБ.........7,730,010	.40
1912СПБ.......28,000,008	.25	1881СПБ.........8,415,013	.40
1913СПБ.......50,000,008	.25		
1914СПБ.......14,000,014	.25	*Alexander III*	
		Y31	
No mint mark		1882СПБ.........5,685,008	.35
1915............12,000,000	.25	1883СПБ.........7,830,008	.35
1916.............9,400,000	.25	1884СПБ.........2,500,004	.35
		1885СПБ.........3,400,111	.35
1 KOPEK		1886СПБ.........3,210,007	.35
Alexander II		1887СПБ.........6,000,004	.35
Y3 (copper) 22mm		1888СПБ.........6,000,008	.35
1855EM.........24,593,533	.50	1889СПБ.........9,000,002	.35
1855BM.........3,533,707	1.00	1890СПБ.........6,905,006	.35
1856EM.........10,641,600	.50	1891СПБ.......10,875,008	.35
1856BM.........3,316,293	.75	1892СПБ.........5,640,006	.35
1857EM.........5,659,200	.50	1893СПБ.......13,395,008	.30
1858EM.........13,731,200	.50	1894СПБ.......15,490,007	.25
1858BM.........1,525,162	.50		
1859EM.........11,059,200	.50	*Nicholas II*	
1859BM.........3,019,037	.50	**Y49**	
1860EM.........8,305,600	.50	1895СПБ.......18,200,007	.25
1860BM.........3,765,802	.50	1896СПБ.......22,960,001	.25
1861EM.........10,129,600	.75	1897СПБ.......30,000,000	.25
		1898СПБ.......50,000,000	.25

	Mintage	Value
1899СПБ	50,000,000	$ .25
1900СПБ	30,000,000	.25
1901СПБ	30,000,000	.25
1902СПБ	20,000,004	.25
1903СПБ	74,400,010	.25
1904СПБ	30,600,010	.25
1905СПБ	23,000,000	.25
1906СПБ	20,000,010	.25
1907СПБ	20,000,009	.25
1908СПБ	40,000,000	.25
1909СПБ	27,500,011	.25
1910СПБ	36,500,009	.25
1911СПБ	38,150,011	.25
1912СПБ	31,850,009	.25
1913СПБ	61,500,008	.25
1914СПБ	32,500,014	.25

No mint mark

	Mintage	Value
1915	58,000,000	.25
1916	46,500,000	.25

2 KOPEKS

Alexander II

Y4 (copper) 24mm

	Mintage	Value
1855EM	8,586,601	.60
1855BM	1,162,395	.75
1856EM	9,167,200	.60
1856BM	1,190,081	1.00
1857EM	3,359,400	.60
1858EM	10,028,000	.60
1858BM	879,598	.60
1859EM	14,772,000	.60
1859BM	1,565,742	.75
1860EM	19,239,200	.60
1860BM	1,604,660	.75
1861EM	18,547,200	.75
1861BM	900,000	1.00
1862EM	16,889,200	.75
1862BM	966,092	1.00
1863EM	21,703,200	.50
1863BM	1,733,908	.75
1864EM	14,175,200	.50
1865EM	26,920,800	.50
1866EM	21,889,600	1.00
1867EM	8,970,400	1.00

Y10 design altered

	Mintage	Value
1867EM	150,000	3.00
1867СПБ		3.00
1868EM	18,200,000	.50
1868СПБ	658,753	.60
1869EM	22,173,850	.50
1869СПБ	642,503	.60
1870EM	21,883,750	.50
1870СПБ	231,005	2.50

	Mintage	Value
1871EM	7,057,500	$1.00
1872EM	12,733,750	.40
1873EM	7,363,750	.75
1874EM	8,551,250	.40
1875EM	10,451,250	.40
1876EM	2,905,000	.40
1876СПБ	3,240,005	.40
1877СПБ	5,010,003	.40
1878СПБ	8,092,503	.40
1879СПБ	7,380,005	.40
1880СПБ	6,525,010	.40
1881СПБ	7,299,013	.50

Alexander III

Y32

	Mintage	Value
1882СПБ	4,477,509	.50
1883СПБ	6,230,008	.50
1884СПБ	2,625,004	.50
1885СПБ	3,070,011	.50
1886СПБ	3,122,507	.50
1887СПБ	1,725,004	.50
1888СПБ	1,822,508	.50
1889СПБ	2,815,002	.50
1890СПБ	2,537,506	.50
1891СПБ	2,787,508	.50
1892СПБ	917,506	.50
1893СПБ	10,295,008	.35
1894СПБ	8,600,007	.30

Nicholas II

Y50

	Mintage	Value
1895СПБ	9,122,507	.30
1896СПБ	14,675,001	.30
1897СПБ	9,500,000	.30
1898СПБ	17,500,001	.30
1899СПБ	17,500,000	.30
1900СПБ	20,500,000	.30
1901СПБ	20,000,000	.30
1902СПБ	10,000,004	.30
1903СПБ	29,200,010	.30
1904СПБ	13,300,010	.30
1905СПБ	15,000,000	.30
1906СПБ	6,250,010	.30
1907СПБ	7,500,009	.30
1908СПБ	19,000,009	.30
1909СПБ	16,250,011	.30
1910СПБ	12,000,009	.30
1911СПБ	17,200,011	.30
1912СПБ	17,050,008	.30
1913СПБ	26,000,000	.30
1914СПБ	20,000,014	.30

No mint mark

	Mintage	Value
1915	33,750,000	.30
1916	31,500,000	.30

	Mintage	Value
3 KOPEKS		

Alexander II

Y5 (copper) 28mm

	Mintage	Value
1855EM	2,835,111	$1.00
1856EM	6,700,000	1.00
1856BM	416,667	1.50
1857EM	4,725,867	1.00
1857BM	21,367	5.00
1858EM	10,662,442	1.00
1858BM	711,966	1.00
1859EM	15,821,334	1.00
1859BM	400,000	1.50
1860EM	14,009,600	1.00
1860BM	400,000	1.50
1861EM	7,738,400	1.00
1861BM	283,712	1.50
1862EM	10,377,200	1.00
1862BM	200,000	1.50
1863EM	3,938,667	1.00
1863BM	400,000	1.50
1864EM	6,121,334	1.00
1865EM	inc. above	2.00
1866EM	6,611,200	1.50
1867EM	1,785,667	1.50

Y11 new design

	Mintage	Value
1867EM	160,000	2.00
1867СПБ		2.50
1868EM	6,058,894	1.00
1868СПБ	909,503	1.00
1869EM	5,525,834	1.00
1869СПБ	723,003	1.00
1870EM	5,017,500	1.00
1870СПБ	79,500	2.50
1871EM	1,585,000	2.50
1872EM	3,017,500	.75
1873EM	4,704,167	1.00
1874EM	4,419,167	.75
1875EM	3,595,000	.75
1876EM	890,000	1.25
1876СПБ	4,863,338	.75
1877СПБ	5,901,669	.75
1878СПБ	6,355,003	.75
1879СПБ	7,355,005	.75
1880СПБ	6,773,343	.75
1881СПБ	6,141,343	.75

Alexander III

Y33

	Mintage	Value
1882СПБ	4,280,009	.75
1883СПБ	1,060,508	.50
1884СПБ	2,975,004	.50
1891СПБ	1,983,341	.50
1892СПБ	648,339	.75

	Mintage	Value
1893СПБ	6,365,008	$ .50
1894СПБ	4,803,341	.35

Nicholas II

Y51

	Mintage	Value
1895СПБ	5,416,673	.35
1896СПБ	7,923,334	.35
1897СПБ	6,666,666	.35
1898СПБ	11,666,666	.35
1899СПБ	11,666,666	.35
1900СПБ	16,666,667	.35
1901СПБ	10,000,000	.35
1902СПБ	3,333,333	.35
1903СПБ	11,400,010	.35
1904СПБ	6,933,643	.35
1905СПБ	3,333,343	.35
1906СПБ	5,666,675	.35
1907СПБ	2,500,009	.35
1908СПБ	12,666,675	.35
1909СПБ	6,733,344	.35
1910СПБ	6,666,675	.35
1911СПБ	9,466,677	.35
1912СПБ	8,533,341	.35
1913СПБ	15,333,341	.35
1914СПБ	8,166,681	.35

No mint mark

	Mintage	Value
1915	19,833,333	.35
1916	25,666,666	.35

5 KOPEKS

Alexander II

Y6 (copper) 37mm

	Mintage	Value
1855EM	740,400	1.25
1856EM	5,145,920	1.00
1856BM	40,000	5.00
1857EM	8,675,000	1.00
1858EM	19,560,640	1.00
1859EM	19,441,360	1.00
1860EM	25,260,160	1.00
1861EM	28,021,760	1.00
1862EM	22,055,040	1.00
1863EM	22,510,720	1.00
1864EM	26,042,240	1.00
1865EM	38,943,440	1.00
1866EM	24,767,000	1.00
1867EM	11,697,280	3.00

Y12 new design, 33mm

	Mintage	Value
1867EM	1,459,000	2.00
1867СПБ		3.00
1868EM	23,018,500	1.00
1868СПБ	821,203	1.25
1869EM	20,277,000	1.00
1869СПБ	942,000	1.25

	Mintage	Value
1870EM	21,158,000	$1.00
1870СПБ	28,005	6.00
1871EM	6,304,150	2.00
1872EM	11,890,000	.75
1873EM	13,052,100	.75
1874EM	12,878,500	.75
1875EM	19,623,900	.75
1876EM	5,329,000	.75
1876СПБ	4,655,000	.75
1877СПБ	7,184,003	.75
1878СПБ	12,542,003	.75
1879СПБ	14,652,005	.75
1880СПБ	6,773,343	.75
1881СПБ	13,824,013	.75

Nicholas II
Y52

	Mintage	Value
1911СПБ	3,800,009	1.50
1912СПБ	2,700,008	1.50

No mint mark

	Mintage	Value
1916	8,000,000	1.50

Mintmasters' Initials: Most silver coins contain these initials which are found on the reverse except for 25 and 50 Kopeks and 1 Rouble from 1886 where they are found on rim.

Mintmasters' initials are enclosed in brackets [ ].

5 KOPEKS

Alexander II
Y13 (silver) 15mm

	Mintage	Value
1855СПБ [H.I.]	640,001	1.00
1856СПБ [ФБ]	680,003	1.00
1857СПБ [ФБ]	80,003	1.50
1858СПБ [ФБ]	40,006	1.50
1859СПБ [none]	120,005	5.00
1859СПБ [ФБ]	inc. above	1.25
1860СПБ [ФБ]	20,001	10.00

Y19

	Mintage	Value
1860СПБ [ФБ]	180,003	1.00
1861СПБ [ФБ]	360,004	2.50
1861СПБ [МИ]	inc. above	5.00
1862СПБ [МИ]	400,009	1.00
1863СПБ [АБ]	200,003	1.00
1864СПБ [НФ]	240,003	1.00
1865СПБ [НФ]	190,003	1.00
1866СПБ [НФ]	200,013	5.00
1866СПБ [H.I.]	inc. above	6.00
1867СПБ [H.I.]	180,025	1.00
1868СПБ [H.I.]	240,003	1.00
1869СПБ [H.I.]	170,003	1.00

	Mintage	Value
1870СПБ [H.I.]	220,005	$1.00
1871СПБ [H.I.]	200,003	1.00
1872СПБ [H.I.]	180,003	1.00
1873СПБ [H.I.]	160,004	1.00
1874СПБ [H.I.]	200,003	1.00
1875СПБ [H.I.]	200,003	1.00
1876СПБ [H.I.]	240,005	1.00
1877СПБ [H.I.]	200,003	1.50
1877СПБ [НФ]	inc. above	2.50
1878СПБ [НФ]	220,006	1.25
1878СПБ [H.I.]	inc. above	5.00
1879СПБ [НФ]	140,005	1.00
1880СПБ [НФ]	240,008	1.00
1881СПБ [НФ]	200,011	1.00

Alexander III
Y34

	Mintage	Value
1882СПБ [НФ]	1,820,207	.40
1883СПБ [ДС]	960,008	.75
1883СПБ [АГ]	inc. above	.75
1884СПБ [АГ]	1,800,026	.40
1885СПБ [АГ]	1,700,011	.40
1886СПБ [АГ]	2,000,107	.40
1887СПБ [АГ]	3,000,004	.40
1888СПБ [АГ]	4,000,047	.40
1889СПБ [АГ]	3,500,002	.40
1890СПБ [АГ]	8,000,006	.40
1891СПБ [АГ]	2,000,008	.40
1892СПБ [АГ]	8,000,006	.40
1893СПБ [АГ]	2,000,008	.40

Nicholas II
Y53

	Mintage	Value
1897СПБ [АГ]	2,029,009	.40
1898СПБ [АГ]	3,980,009	.40
1899СПБ [АГ]	4,605,022	.40
1899СПБ [ЗБ]	inc. above	.40
1900СПБ [ФЗ]	5,205,009	.40
1901СПБ [ФЗ]	5,790,020	.40
1901СПБ [A.P.]	inc. above	.40
1902СПБ [A.P.]	6,000,000	.40
1903СПБ [A.P.]	9,000,005	.40
1904СПБ [A.P.]	very few	20.00
1905СПБ [A.P.]	10,000,019	.40
1906СПБ [ЗБ]	4,000,010	.40
1908СПБ [ЗБ]	400,009	.75
1909СПБ [ЗБ]	3,100,010	.40
1910СПБ [ЗБ]	2,500,009	.40
1911СПБ [ЗБ]	2,700,011	.40
1912СПБ [ЗБ]	3,000,009	.40
1913СПБ [ЗБ]	1,300,017	.40
1913СПБ [B.C.]	inc. above	.40
1914СПБ [B.C.]	4,200,015	.40

	Mintage	Value
No mint mark		
1915 [B.C.]........3,000,000		$ .40

10 KOPEKS

Alexander II

Y14 (silver) 17.5mm

1855СПБ [H.I.]...3,201,101		1.00
1855MW [none].....102,603		2.50
1856СПБ [ФБ]....1,940,003		1.00
1857СПБ [ФБ]...3,110,003		1.00
1858СПБ [ФБ]....2,600,006		1.00
1859СПБ [ФБ]....3,920,005		1.00
1860СПБ [ФБ]......580,001		1.25

Y20

1860СПБ [ФБ]....2,810,003		1.00
1861СПБ [ФБ]....5,660,008		1.00
1861СПБ [МИ]...inc. above		1.50
1861СПБ [none]..19,300,000		.75
1862СПБ [МИ]....5,800,009		.75
1863СПБ [АБ]....5,750,003		.75
1864СПБ [НФ]....3,740,013		.75
1865СПБ [НФ]....3,886,513		.75
1866СПБ [НФ]....2,532,506		.75
1866СПБ [H.I.]...inc. above		.90
1867СПБ [H.I.]...6,445,092		.75
1868СПБ [H.I.]...4,740,003		.75
1869СПБ [H.I.]...3,710,003		.75
1870СПБ [H.I.]...3,310,005		.75
1871СПБ [H.I.]...4,194,693		.75
1872СПБ [H.I.]...2,130,003		.75
1873СПБ [H.I.]...2,620,004		.75
1874СПБ [H.I.]...2,520,003		.75
1875СПБ [H.I.]...3,590,003		.60
1876СПБ [H.I.]...4,900,005		.60
1877СПБ [H.I.]...2,090,003		.60
1877СПБ [НФ]...inc. above		.60
1878СПБ [НФ]...6,920,006		.60
1878СПБ [H.I.]...inc. above		3.00
1879СПБ [НФ]....6,890,005		.60
1880СПБ [НФ]....6,740,008		.60
1881СПБ [НФ]....2,950,011		.60

Alexander III

Y35

1882СПБ [НФ]......920,007		.75
1883СПБ [ДС]....1,520,008		.75
1883СПБ [АГ]....inc. above		.75
1884СПБ [АГ]....1,710,004		.50
1885СПБ [АГ]....1,300,011		.60
1886СПБ [АГ]....2,000,107		.60
1887СПБ [АГ]....4,000,004		.50
1888СПБ [АГ]....2,000,007		.50
1889СПБ [АГ]....5,000,002		.50
1890СПБ [АГ]...3,750,006		.50

	Mintage	Value
1891СПБ [АГ]....3,240,008		$ .50
1893СПБ [АГ]....4,250,008		.50
1894СПБ [АГ]....4,000,007		.40

Nicholas II

Y54

1895СПБ [АГ]....1,000,006		.60
1896СПБ [АГ]....2,010,005		.40
1897СПБ [АГ]....3,150,009		.40
1898СПБ [АГ]....6,610,009		.40
1899СПБ [АГ]...14,000,022		.40
1899СПБ [ЭБ]....inc. above		.40
1900СПБ [ФЗ]...14,000,000		.40
1901СПБ [ФЗ]...15,000,020		.40
1901СПБ [A.P.]..inc. above		.40
1902СПБ [A.P.]..17,000,009		.40
1903СПБ [A.P.]..28,500,005		.40
1904СПБ [A.P.]..20,000,010		.40
1905СПБ [A.P.]..25,000,000		.40
1906СПБ [ЭБ]...17,500,015		.40
1907СПБ [ЭБ]...20,000,009		.40
1908СПБ [ЭБ]....8,210,000		.40
1909СПБ [ЭБ]...25,290,011		.40
1910СПБ [ЭБ]...20,000,009		.40
1911СПБ [ЭБ]...19,180,011		.40
1912СПБ [ЭБ]...20,000,008		.40
1913СПБ [ЭБ]....7,250,017		.40
1913СПБ [B.C.]..inc. above		.40
1914СПБ [B.C.]..51,250,015		.40

No mint mark

1915 [B.C.].......82,500,000		.40
1916 [B.C.]......121,500,000		.40
1916 [none](Osaka)70,001,000		.40
1917 [B.C.]..	....	——

15 KOPEKS

Alexander II

Y21 (silver) 20mm

1860СПБ [ФБ]....4,480,003		.90
1861СПБ [ФБ]...10,120,000		.90
1861СПБ [МИ]...inc. above		1.50
1861СПБ [none]..13,300,000		.90
1862СПБ [МИ]...10,000,009		.90
1863СПБ [АБ]....9,960,003		.90
1864СПБ [НФ]...10,715,008		.90
1865СПБ [НФ]...10,703,063		.90
1866СПБ [НФ]....6,329,306		.90
1866СПБ [H.I.]...inc. above		1.00
1867СПБ [H.I.]...8,720,112		.90
1868СПБ [H.I.]...7,460,003		.90
1869СПБ [H.I.]...8,120,003		.90
1870СПБ [H.I.]...9,380,005		.90
1871СПБ [H.I.]...9,460,003		.90

	Mintage	Value
1872СПБ [Н.I.]	5,880,003	$ .75
1873СПБ [Н.I.]	7,960,004	.75
1874СПБ [Н.I.]	6,960,003	.75
1875СПБ [Н.I.]	7,480,003	.60
1876СПБ [Н.I.]	9,760,005	.60
1877СПБ [Н.I.]	4,360,003	.75
1877СПБ [НФ]	inc. above	.75
1878СПБ [Н.I.]	1,115,506	.75
1878СПБ [НФ]	inc. above	.75
1879СПБ [НФ]	12,504,005	.60
1880СПБ [НФ]	11,655,008	.60
1881СПБ [НФ]	4,900,011	.60

Alexander III
У36

1882СПБ [НФ]	1,470,007	.60
1883СПБ [ДС]	3,600,008	.60
1883СПБ [АГ]	inc. above	.60
1884СПБ [АГ]	2,720,004	.50
1885СПБ [АГ]	1,420,011	.50
1886СПБ [АГ]	2,500,107	.50
1887СПБ [АГ]	3,000,004	.50
1888СПБ [АГ]		.50
1889СПБ [АГ]	2,835,002	.50
1890СПБ [АГ]	3,500,006	.50
1891СПБ [АГ]	4,710,008	.50
1893СПБ [АГ]	6,500,008	.50

Nicholas II
У55

1896СПБ [АГ]	3,160,013	.50
1897СПБ [АГ]	inc. above	.50
1898СПБ [АГ]	3,000,009	.50
1899СПБ [АГ]	12,665,021	.40
1899СПБ [ЭБ]	inc. above	3.50
1900СПБ [ФЗ]	12,665,009	.40
1901СПБ [ФЗ]	6,670,020	.40
1901СПБ [А.Р.]	inc. above	.40
1902СПБ [А.Р.]	28,666,675	.40
1903СПБ [А.Р.]	16,666,671	.40
1904СПБ [А.Р.]	15,600,010	.40
1905СПБ [А.Р.]	24,000,010	.40
1906СПБ [ЭБ]	23,333,343	.40
1907СПБ [ЭБ]	30,000,009	.40
1908СПБ [ЭБ]	29,000,009	.40
1909СПБ [ЭБ]	21,666,667	.40
1911СПБ [ЭБ]	6,313,344	.40
1912СПБ [ЭБ]	13,333,341	.40
1912СПБ [B.C.]	inc. above	3.00
1913СПБ [ЭБ]	5,300,017	.40
1913СПБ [B.C.]	inc. above	.40
1914СПБ [B.C.]	43,366,681	.40

No mint mark

1915 [B.C.]	59,333,333	.40
1916 [B.C.]	96,773,333	$ .40
1916 [none](Osaka)	96,666,000	.40
1917 [B.C.]		—

20 KOPEKS

Alexander II
У15 (silver) 22mm

1855СПБ [Н.I.]	3,090,001	1.00
1856СПБ [ФБ]	3,240,003	1.00
1857СПБ [ФБ]	4,275,003	1.00
1857MW [none]	21,865	6.00
1858СПБ [none]	4,150,006	3.00
1858СПБ [ФБ]	inc. above	1.00
1859СПБ [ФБ]	3,680,005	1.00
1860СПБ [ФБ]	1,070,001	1.00

У22

1860СПБ [ФБ]	14,440,003	1.00
1861СПБ [ФБ]	19,500,008	1.00
1861СПБ [МИ]	inc. above	1.50
1861СПБ [none]	19,000,000	1.00
1862СПБ [МИ]	19,500,009	1.00
1863СПБ [АБ]	19,230,003	1.00
1864СПБ [НФ]	20,060,008	1.00
1865СПБ [НФ]	20,047,913	1.00
1866СПБ [НФ]	10,066,731	1.00
1866СПБ [Н.I.]	inc. above	1.00
1867СПБ [Н.I.]	15,355,071	1.00
1868СПБ [Н.I.]	11,975,003	1.00
1869СПБ [Н.I.]	17,017,298	1.00
1870СПБ [Н.I.]	16,255,005	1.00
1871СПБ [Н.I.]	18,860,003	1.00
1872СПБ [Н.I.]	11,980,003	1.00
1873СПБ [Н.I.]	15,185,004	1.00
1874СПБ [Н.I.]	14,850,003	1.00
1875СПБ [Н.I.]	15,545,003	1.00
1876СПБ [Н.I.]	16,255,005	1.00
1877СПБ [Н.I.]	6,950,003	1.25
1877СПБ [НФ]	inc. above	1.25
1878СПБ [НФ]	25,335,006	1.00
1878СПБ [Н.I.]	inc. above	5.00
1879СПБ [НФ]	23,070,005	1.00
1880СПБ [НФ]	22,605,008	1.00
1881СПБ [НФ]	9,350,011	1.00

Alexander III
У37

1882СПБ [НФ]	3,535,007	1.25
1883СПБ [ДС]	3,755,008	1.25
1883СПБ [АГ]	inc. above	1.25
1884СПБ [АГ]	2,905,004	1.00
1885СПБ [АГ]	1,610,011	1.25
1886СПБ [АГ]	2,625,107	1.00
1887СПБ [АГ]	2,500,004	1.00
1888СПБ [АГ]	3,035,037	1.00

	Mintage	Value
1889СПБ [АГ]....1,963,752		$1.00
1890СПБ [АГ]....3,500,006		1.00
1891СПБ [АГ]....6,105,008		1.00
1893СПБ [АГ]....7,500,008		1.00

Nicholas II

У56

	Mintage	Value
1901СПБ [ФЗ]....7,750,026		.75
1901СПБ [A.P.]..inc. above		5.00
1902СПБ [A.P.]..10,000,014		.75
1903СПБ [A.P.]..inc. above		.75
1904СПБ [A.P.]..13,000,010		.75
1905СПБ [A.P.]..11,000,000		.75
1906СПБ [ЗБ]...15,000,010		.75
1907СПБ [ЗБ]...20,000,009		.75
1908СПБ [ЗБ]....5,000,009		.75
1909СПБ [ЗБ]...18,875,011		.75
1910СПБ [ЗБ]...11,000,009		.75
1911СПБ [ЗБ]....7,100,011		.75
1912СПБ [ЗБ]...15,000,008		.75
1912СПБ [B.C.]..inc. above		7.50
1913СПБ [ЗБ]....4,250,017		.75
1913СПБ [B.C.]..inc. above		.75
1914СПБ [B.C.]..52,750,015		.60

No mint mark

	Mintage	Value
1915 [B.C.]......105,500,000		.60
1916 [B.C.]......131,670,000		.60
1917 [B.C.]...............		——

25 KOPEKS

Alexander II

У16 (silver) 24mm

	Mintage	Value
1855СПБ [H.I.]..10,396,003		2.00
1856СПБ [ФБ]....4,444,003		2.50
1857СПБ [ФБ]....5,420,003		2.50
1857MWB [none]....32,636		10.00
1858СПБ [none]...5,528,006		7.50
1858СПБ [ФБ]...inc. above		2.50

У23

	Mintage	Value
1859СПБ [ФБ]....4,400,005		2.50
1860СПБ [ФБ]....1,052,003		2.50
1861СПБ [ФБ]......116,007		4.00
1861СПБ [МИ]...inc. above		25.00
1862СПБ [МИ]......36,009		12.50
1863СПБ [АБ]......36,003		7.50
1864СПБ [НФ]......68,003		7.50
1865СПБ [НФ]......16,019		7.50
1865СПБ [H.I.]...inc. above		7.50
1866СПБ [НФ]......36,014		7.50
1866СПБ [H.I.]...inc. above		7.50
1867СПБ [H.I.]......48,030		7.50
1868СПБ [H.I.]......40,303		7.50
1869СПБ [H.I.]......20,003		15.00

	Mintage	Value
1870СПБ [H.I.]......44,005		$6.00
1871СПБ [H.I.]......24,003		7.50
1872СПБ [H.I.]......44,003		6.00
1873СПБ [H.I.]......36,004		7.50
1874СПБ [H.I.]......32,003		7.50
1875СПБ [H.I.]......24,003		7.50
1876СПБ [H.I.]......40,005		7.50
1877СПБ [H.I.]...1,776,003		3.00
1877СПБ [none]..inc. above		10.00
1877СПБ [НФ]...inc. above		3.00
1878СПБ [НФ]....1,768,006		3.00
1879СПБ [НФ]......32,005		7.50
1880СПБ [НФ].....72,008		7.50
1881СПБ [НФ].......2,001		12.50

Alexander III

У38

	Mintage	Value
1882СПБ [НФ].......2,007		12.50
1883СПБ [ДС].......2,008		12.50
1883СПБ [АГ]....inc. above		20.00
1884СПБ [АГ].......2,004		12.50
1885СПБ [АГ].......1,011		15.00

No mint mark

У44 23mm

	Mintage	Value
1886 [АГ]............4,058		10.00
1887 [АГ]...........28,004		7.50
1888 [АГ]............4,007		10.00
1889 [АГ]............1,002		15.00
1890 [АГ]............2,006		12.50
1891 [АГ]...........24,008		7.50
1892 [АГ]............4,006		10.00
1893 [АГ]............8,008		10.00
1894 [АГ]................		7.50

Nicholas II

У57

	Mintage	Value
1895 [none].......2,660,026		3.00
1896 [none]......25,932,010		2.00
1900 [none]........584,004		3.50
1901 [none]...............		20.00

½ ROUBLE

Alexander II

У17 (silver) 28.5mm

	Mintage	Value
1855СПБ [H.I.].....714,001		3.00
1856СПБ [ФБ]......450,003		3.00
1857СПБ [ФБ]....1,650,003		2.50
1858СПБ [ФБ]....1,112,006		2.50

У24

	Mintage	Value
1859СПБ [ФБ]....1,392,005		2.00
1860СПБ [ФБ]......192,003		3.00
1861СПБ [ФБ].......64,004		4.00

	Mintage	Value
1861СПБ [МИ]...inc. above		$15.00
1862СПБ [МИ]	24,009	7.50
1863СПБ [АБ]	22,003	7.50
1864СПБ [НФ]	34,003	7.50
1865СПБ [НФ]	24,017	7.50
1866СПБ [НФ]	22,014	10.00
1866СПБ [Н.I.]...inc. above		7.50
1867СПБ [Н.I.]	26,040	7.50
1868СПБ [Н.I.]	30,003	20.00
1869СПБ [Н.I.]	20,003	7.50
1870СПБ [Н.I.]	6,005	10.00
1871СПБ [Н.I.]	20,003	7.50
1872СПБ [Н.I.]	22,003	7.50
1873СПБ [Н.I.]	36,004	7.50
1874СПБ [Н.I.]	16,003	7.50
1875СПБ [Н.I.]	14,003	7.50
1876СПБ [Н.I.]	24,005	7.50
1876СПБ [none]..inc. above		12.50
1877СПБ [Н.I.]...1,034,033		2.00
1877СПБ [НФ]...inc. above		10.00
1878СПБ [НФ]	778,006	2.00
1879СПБ [НФ]	14,005	20.00
1880СПБ [НФ]	42,008	6.00
1881СПБ [НФ]	1,011	25.00

Alexander III
Y39

	Mintage	Value
1882СПБ [НФ]	1,007	25.00
1883СПБ [ДС]	1,008	25.00
1883СПБ [АБ]...inc. above		30.00
1884СПБ [АБ]	1,004	25.00
1885СПБ [АБ]	511	25.00

50 KOPEKS
(silver) 27mm

Alexander III
Y45 no mint marks

	Mintage	Value
1886 [АГ]	2,058	12.50
1887 [АГ]	26,004	7.50
1888 [АГ]	2,007	12.50
1889 [АГ]	1,002	20.00
1890 [АГ]	2,006	12.50
1891 [АГ]	24,008	7.50
1892 [АГ]	2,006	12.50
1893 [АГ]	4,008	10.00
1894 [АГ]		10.00

Nicholas II
Y58

	Mintage	Value
1895 [АГ]	5,400,026	1.25
1896 [АГ]	17,002,010	1.25
1896 ★ on rim [none]	244,562	5.00
1897 ★ on rim [none]	46,755,438	1.25
1898 [АГ]		15.00

	Mintage	Value
1899 [ЗБ]	15,442,021	$1.25
1899 [ФЗ]........inc. above		1.25
1899 [АГ]........inc. above		1.25
1899 ★ on rim [none]	10,000,000	1.25
1900 [ФЗ]	3,360,009	1.25
1901 [А.Р.]	412,020	2.50
1901 [ФЗ]........inc. above		2.50
1902 [А.Р.]	36,004	7.50
1903 [А.Р.]		20.00
1904 [А.Р.]	4,010	10.00
1906 [ЗБ]	10,009	6.00
1907 [ЗБ]	200,009	3.00
1908 [ЗБ]	40,009	7.50
1909 [ЗБ]	50,011	7.50
1910 [ЗБ]	150,009	3.50
1911 [ЗБ]	800,011	2.00
1912 [ЗБ]	7,085,008	1.25
1913 [ЗБ]	6,420,017	1.25
1913 [В.С.]......inc. above		1.25
1914 [В.С.]	1,200,015	1.50

1 ROUBLE

Alexander II
Y18 [silver] 36mm

	Mintage	Value
1855СПБ [Н.I.]...1,068,001		5.00
1856СПБ [Н.I.]...1,388,003		5.00
1857СПБ [Н.I.]	250,003	7.50
1858СПБ [Н.I.]	570,011	7.50

Y28 Memorial

	Mintage	Value
1859	50,118	20.00

Y25 regular

	Mintage	Value
1859СПБ [Н.I.]	14,036	25.00
1860СПБ [Н.I.]	18,003	20.00
1861СПБ [Н.I.]	76,024	15.00
1861СПБ [МИ]...inc. above		25.00
1862СПБ [МИ]	22,009	15.00
1863СПБ [АБ]	5,193	25.00
1864СПБ [НФ]	114,003	7.50
1865СПБ [НФ]	115,062	7.50
1866СПБ [НФ]	110,014	7.50
1866СПБ [Н.I.]...inc. above		7.50
1867СПБ [Н.I.]	425,040	7.50
1868СПБ [Н.I.]	775,003	7.50
1869СПБ [Н.I.]	285,003	7.50
1870СПБ [Н.I.]	386,005	7.50
1871СПБ [Н.I.]	884,003	6.00
1872СПБ [Н.I.]	978,003	6.00
1873СПБ [Н.I.]	673,004	7.50
1874СПБ [Н.I.]	648,003	7.50
1875СПБ [Н.I.]	687,003	7.50
1876СПБ [Н.I.]	778,005	7.50

	Mintage	Value
1877СПБ [Н.I.]...6,923,003		$4.50
1877СПБ [НФ]...inc. above		15.00
1878СПБ [НФ]....8,087,006		4.50
1879СПБ [НФ]....611,005		7.50
1880СПБ [НФ]....521,008		7.50
1881СПБ [НФ]....699,001		7.50

Alexander III

Y40

1882СПБ [НФ].....434,007		7.50
1883СПБ [ДС].....425,008		10.00
1883СПБ [АГ]....inc. above		20.00
1884СПБ [АГ].....355,006		7.50
1885СПБ [АГ].....499,511		7.50

Y43 Coronation

1883...............279,143		17.50

Y46 no mint mark, 33.5mm

1886 [АГ]...........487,592		7.50
1887 [АГ]...........490,504		7.50
1888 [АГ]...........498,017		7.50
1889 [АГ]............1,002		40.00
1890 [АГ]...........90,256		12.50
1891 [АГ].........1,117,018		6.00
1892 [АГ].........2,131,006		6.00
1893 [АГ].........1,848,015		6.00
1894 [АГ].......inc. above		7.50

Nicholas II

Y59

1895 [АГ].........1,240,034		5.00
1896 [АГ].........12,349,010		3.50
1896 ★ on rim (Paris)......12,000,000		3.50
1897 [АГ].........18,515,000		3.50
1897 2 stars on rim (Brussels)...26,000,000		3.50
1898 ★ on rim [none].......5,000,000		3.50
1898 2 stars on rim [none]......14,000,000		3.50
1898 [АГ].........18,724,872		3.50
1899 2 stars on rim 10,000,000		3.50
1899 [ЗБ].........14,502,659		3.50
1899 [ФЗ]........inc. above		3.50
1900 [ФЗ].........3,484,013		3.50
1901 [ФЗ].........2,608,021		3.50
1901 [A.P.].......inc. above		4.00
1902 [A.P.].........140,009		5.00
1903 [A.P.]..........55,519		6.00
1904 [A.P.]..........12,010		10.00

	Mintage	Value
1905 [A.P.]..........20,515		$10.00
1906 [ЗБ]...........45,710		7.50
1907 [ЗБ]..........400,009		6.00
1908 [ЗБ].........130,409		6.00
1909 [ЗБ]..........50,011		7.50
1910 [ЗБ]..........75,009		7.50
1911 [ЗБ]..........200,011		6.00
1912 [ЗБ].........2,061,221		4.00
1913 [ЗБ]..........50,106		10.00
1913 [B.C.].......inc. above		10.00
1914 [B.C.]........506,015		6.00
1915 [B.C.].............600		50.00

Y60 Coronation

1896...............190,845		17.50

Y61 Memorial

1898.....................		50.00

Y68 Defeat of Napoleon

1912...............25,000		45.00

Y69 Memorial (statue)

1912...............25,000		75.00

Y70 300th Anniversary

1913.............1,472,019		7.50

Y71 Battle of Gangut

1914...............30,000		250.00

Union of Soviet Socialist Republics (U.S.S.R.)

(РСФСР 1921-1923)
(СССР 1924 to date)

½ KOPEK

Y75 (bronze) 16mm

1925............45,380,017		2.50
1927.....................		2.50
1928.....................		2.50

1 KOPEK

Y76 (bronze) 21mm

1924............34,705,008		.75
1925...........141,806,011		.75

Y91 (aluminum-bronze) 15mm

1926............87,915,024		.25
1927.....................		.25
1928.....................		.25
1929............95,950,006		.25

	Mintage	Value
1930	85,351,974	$ .25
1931	106,100,000	.25
1932	56,900,000	.25
1933	111,256,800	.25
1934	100,245,000	.25
1935	66,405,000	.25

Y98 new design

	Mintage	Value
1935	inc. above	.25
1936	132,204,363	.20

Y105

		Value
1937		.20
1938		.20
1939		.20
1940		.20
1941		.15
1945		.15
1946		.15

Y112

		Value
1948		.15
1949		.15
1950		.15
1951		.10
1952		.10
1953		.10
1954		.10
1955		.10
1956		.10

Y119

		Value
1957		.10
1958		.10
1959		.10
1960		.10

Y126 new design (copper-zinc)

		Value
1961		.10
1962		.10

2 KOPEKS

Y77 (bronze) 24mm

	Mintage	Value
1924	119,995,815	1.00

Y92 (aluminum-bronze) 18mm

	Mintage	Value
1926	105,052,524	.25
1927		.25
1928		.25
1929	80,000,010	.25
1930	134,185,961	.25
1931	99,522,730	.25
1932	39,572,565	.25
1933	54,873,878	.25
1934	61,574,228	.25
1935	81,121,097	.25

Y99

	Mintage	Value
1936	94,353,537	$ .25

Y106

		Value
1937		.25
1938		.25
1939		.25
1940		.20
1941		.20
1945		.20
1946		.20

Y113

		Value
1948		.20
1949		.20
1950		.20
1951		.15
1952		.15
1953		.15
1954		.15
1955		.15
1956		.15

Y120

		Value
1957		.15
1958		.15
1959		.15
1960		.15

Y127 new design (copper-zinc)

		Value
1961		.15
1962		.15

3 KOPEKS

Y78 (bronze) 28mm

	Mintage	Value
1924	101,282,815	1.50

Y93 (aluminum-bronze) 22mm

	Mintage	Value
1926	19,940,024	.30
1927		.30
1928		.30
1929	50,150,010	.30
1930	74,158,724	.30
1931	121,168,180	.30
1932	37,718,290	.30
1933	44,764,310	.30
1934	44,528,847	.30
1935	58,302,602	.30

Y100 new design

	Mintage	Value
1936	62,757,275	.30

Y107

		Value
1937		.30
1938		.30
1939		.30
1940		.30
1941		.30

	Mintage	Value		Mintage	Value
1943		$ .25	1952		$ .35
1945		.25	1953		.35
1946		.25	1954		.35
			1955		.35
Y114			1956		.35
1948		.25			
1949		.25	**Y122**		
1950		.20	1957		.30
1951		.20	1958		.30
1952		.20	1959		.30
1953		.20	1960		.30
1954		.20			
1955		.20	**Y129** new design (copper-zinc)		
1956		.20	1961		.30
1957		.20	1962		.30
1958		.20			
1959		.20			
1960		.20	**10 KOPEKS**		
			Y80 (silver) 18mm		
Y128 new design (copper-zinc)			1921	950,000	2.00
1961		.20	1922	18,640,138	1.25
1962		.20	1923	33,424,279	1.25
			Y86 new design		
			1924	67,350,886	.35
5 KOPEKS			1925	101,013,313	.35
Y79 (bronze) 32mm			1929	64,900,000	.35
1924	88,510,221	3.00	1930	163,424,218	.35
			1931	8,790,765	.60
Y94 (aluminum-bronze) 25mm					
1926	14,697,024	.45	**Y95** new design (copper-nickel)		
1927		.45	1931	122,511,380	.30
1928		.45	1932	171,641,411	.30
1929	20,220,012	.45	1933	163,124,870	.30
1930	44,490,010	.45	1934	104,058,776	.30
1931	89,540,000	.45			
1932	65,100,000	.45	**Y102** new design		
1933	18,134,578	.45	1935	79,627,697	.30
1934	5,354,007	.50	1936	122,259,899	.30
1935	11,735,000	.45			
			Y109		
Y101			1937		.15
1936	5,241,892	.75	1938		.15
			1939		.15
Y108			1940		.15
1937		.25	1941		.15
1938		.25	1942		.15
1939		.25	1943		.15
1940		.25	1944		.15
1941		.25	1945		.15
1943		.25	1946		.15
1945		.25			
1946		.25	**Y116**		
			1948		.25
Y115			1949		.25
1948		.35	1950		.25
1949		.35	1951		.25
1950		.35	1952		.25
1951		.35	1953		.25

	Mintage	Value
1954		$ .25
1955		.25
Y123		
1956		.25
1957		.25
1958		.25
1959		.25
1960		.25
Y130 new design		
1961		.35
1962		.35

15 KOPEKS

	Mintage	Value
Y81 (silver) 20mm		
1921	933,333	3.00
1922	13,633,474	1.75
1923	28,503,819	1.75
Y87 new design		
1924	72,426,111	.50
1925	112,708,754	.50
1929	46,400,004	.50
1930	79,867,891	.50
1931	5,099,490	.75
Y96 new design (copper-nickel)		
1931	75,859,000	.40
1932	136,045,726	.40
1933	127,590,744	.40
1934	58,367,483	.40
Y103 new design		
1935	51,308,458	.40
1936	52,183,407	.40
Y110		
1937		.20
1938		.20
1939		.20
1940		.20
1941		.20
1942		.20
1943		.20
1944		.20
1945		.20
1946		.20
Y117		
1948		.30
1949		.30
1950		.30
1951		.30
1952		.30
1953		.30
1954		.30
1955		.30
1956		.30

	Mintage	Value
Y124		
1957		$ .35
1958		.35
1959		.35
1960		.35
Y131 new design		
1961		.45
1962		.45

20 KOPEKS

	Mintage	Value
Y82 (silver) 22mm		
1921	825,000	4.00
1922	14,220,140	2.00
1923	27,580,003	2.00
Y88 new design		
1924	93,810,029	.60
1925	134,875,027	.60
1929	67,250,004	.60
1930	125,658,003	.60
1931	9,530,000	1.00
Y97 new design (copper-nickel)		
1931	82,200,000	.60
1932	175,350,000	.60
1933	143,927,491	.60
1934	70,425,000	.60
Y104		
1935	54,760,000	.40
1936	52,968,016	.40
Y111		
1937		.30
1938		.30
1939		.30
1940		.30
1941		.30
1942		.30
1943		.30
1944		.30
1945		.30
1946		.30
Y118		
1948		.50
1949		.50
1950		.50
1951		.50
1952		.50
1953		.50
1954		.50
1955		.50
1956		.50
Y125		
1957		.50

	Mintage	Value
1958		$ .50
1959		.50
1960		.50
Y132 new design		
1961		.50
1962		.50

50 KOPEKS

Y83 (silver) 27mm

	Mintage	Value
1921 [AГ]	1,400,004	5.00
1922 [AГ]	8,224,152	5.00
1922 [ПЛ]	inc. above	5.00

Y89

	Mintage	Value
1924 [ПЛI]	26,559,432	3.00
1924 [T.P.]	40,000,000	3.00
1925 [ПЛI]	43,557,525	3.00

	Mintage	Value
1926 [ПЛI]	24,374,018	$3.00
1927 [ПЛI]		3.00
Y133 new design (copper-nickel) 24mm		
1961		1.00

1 ROUBLE

Y84 (silver) 34mm

	Mintage	Value
1921 [A.Г.]	1,000,041	10.00
1922 [A.Г.]	2,050,456	10.00
1922 [П.Л.]	inc. above	10.00
Y90		
1924 [П.Л.]	12,998,054	7.50
Y134 new design (copper-nickel) 27mm		
1961		1.50

SAARLAND

A mining region occupied by France after World War II. Was returned to Germany in 1957. Coinage obsolete.

100 Centimen = 1 Frank

10 FRANKEN

Y1 (aluminum-bronze) 20mm

	Mintage	Value
1954	11,000,000	1.00

20 FRANKEN

Y2 (aluminum-bronze) 23mm

	Mintage	Value
1954	12,950,000	1.50

50 FRANKEN

Y3 (aluminum-bronze) 27mm

	Mintage	Value
1954	5,300,000	2.00

100 FRANKEN

Y4 (copper-nickel) 23mm

	Mintage	Value
1955	11,000,000	3.50

ST. PIERRE AND MIQUELON

Small islands off the southwest coast of Newfoundland belonging to France. Coinage obsolete.

100 Centimes = 1 Franc

1 FRANC

Y1 (aluminum) 23mm

	Mintage	Value
1948	600,000	.30

2 FRANCS

Y2 (aluminum) 27mm

	Mintage	Value
1948	300,000	.40

ST. THOMAS AND PRINCE ISLANDS
(S. Tome E Principe)

A Portuguese province consisting of islands in the gulf of Guinea off the west coast of Africa.

100 Centavos = 1 Escudo

	Mintage	Value
10 CENTAVOS		
Y1 (nickel-bronze) 19mm		
1929..............500,000		$1.25
Y15 (bronze)		
1962..............500,000		.50
20 CENTAVOS		
Y2 (nickel-bronze) 23mm		
1929..............250,000		1.50
Y16 (bronze)		
1962..............250,000		.60
50 CENTAVOS		
Y3 (nickel-bronze) 30mm		
1929..............400,000		2.50
Y5 22.5mm		
1948...............80,000		1.00
Y10 (copper-nickel)		
1951...............48,000		.75
Y17 (bronze)		
1962..............480,000		.75
1 ESCUDO		
Y4 (copper-nickel) 27mm		
1939..............100,000		1.50
Y6 (nickel-bronze)		
1948...............60,000		1.50

	Mintage	Value
Y11 (copper-nickel)		
1951...............18,000		$1.25
Y18 (bronze)		
1962..............160,000		.85
2.50 ESCUDOS		
Y7 (silver) 20mm		
1939...............80,000		2.00
1948..............120,000		1.50
Y12		
1951...............64,000		1.50
Y19 (copper-nickel)		
1962..............144,000		1.25
5 ESCUDOS		
Y8 (silver) 25mm		
1939...............60,000		2.50
1948..............100,000		2.00
Y13		
1951...............72,000		2.00
Y20		
1962...............88,000		2.00
10 ESCUDOS		
Y9 (silver) 30mm		
1939...............40,000		3.50
Y14		
1951...............40,000		3.50

(Respvblica S. Marini)
(Repubblica Di S. Marino)

A small independent country within the boundaries of Italy. Coinage obsolete; coins of Italy now circulating.

100 Centesimi = 1 Lira

	Mintage	Value
5 CENTESIMI		
Y1 (copper) 25mm		
1864....................		$3.00
1869..................		3.00
1894..............600,000		2.00
Y14 (bronze) 19.5mm		
1935..............400,000		1.00
1936..............400,000		1.00
1937..............400,000		1.00
1938..............200,000		1.00
10 CENTESIMI		
Y2 (copper) 30mm		
1875....................		2.50
1893..................		2.50
1894..............150,000		2.50
Y15 (bronze) 22.5mm		
1935..............300,000		1.50
1936..............300,000		1.50
1937..............300,100		1.50
1938..............400,000		1.50
50 CENTESIMI		
Y3 (silver) 18mm		
1898..............40,000		7.50
1 LIRA		
Y4 (silver) 23mm		
1898..............20,000		12.50
1906..............30,000		7.50
2 LIRE		
Y5 (silver) 27mm		
1898..............10,000		15.00
1906..............15,000		10.00

	Mintage	Value
5 LIRE		
Y6 (silver) 37mm		
1898...............18,000		$60.00
Y9 23mm		
1931..............50,000		3.50
1932..............50,000		3.50
1933..............50,000		3.50
1935..............200,000		3.50
1936..........inc. above		4.00
1937..............100,100		3.50
1938..............120,000		3.50
10 LIRE		
Y10 (silver) 27mm		
1931..............25,000		5.00
1932..............25,000		5.00
1933..............25,000		5.00
1935..............30,000		5.00
1936..........inc. above		7.50
1937..............15,100		5.00
1938..............10,000		8.00
20 LIRE		
Y11 (silver) 35.5mm		
1931..............10,000		25.00
1932..............10,000		25.00
1933..............10,000		25.00
1935 15 gram........10,000		25.00
1936...........inc. above		35.00
Y11a 20 gram		
1935...........inc. above		75.00
1937..............5,100		45.00
1938..............2,500		60.00

(СРБСКИ, СРБИЈА)

In southeastern Europe, now part of Yugoslavia. During World War II was a German occupied puppet state.

100 Para = 1 Dinar

	Mintage	Value
1 PARA		
Michael, Obrenovich III (1860-1868)		
Y1 (copper) 15mm		
1868. 7,500,000		$1.25
2 PARE		
Peter I (1903-1918)		
Y18 (bronze) 20mm		
1904. 12,500,006		.65
5 PARA		
Michael, Obrenovich III		
Y2 (copper) 25mm		
1868. 7,420,000		1.00
Milan, Obrenovich IV (1868-1889)		
Y4		
1879. 6,000,000		1.00
Y6 (copper-nickel) 17mm		
1883. 4,000,000		.75
1884. 3,000,000		.75
Peter I		
Y19		
1904. 8,000,056		.75
1912. 10,000,032		.75
1917. 5,000,000		.75
10 PARA		
Michael, Obrenovich III		
Y3 (copper) 30mm		
1868. 6,590,000		1.75
Milan, Obrenovich IV		
Y5		
1879. 9,000,000		1.50
Y7 (copper-nickel) 20mm		
1883. 5,000,000		1.00
1884. 6,500,000		1.00
Peter I		
Y20		
1912. 7,700,032		1.00
1917. 5,000,000		1.00

	Mintage	Value
20 PARA		
Milan, Obrenovich IV		
Y8 (copper-nickel) 22mm		
1883. 2,500,000		$1.50
1884. 6,000,000		1.50
Peter I		
Y21		
1912. 5,650,035		1.25
1917. 5,000,000		1.25
50 PARA		
Milan, Obrenovich IV		
Y9 (silver) 18mm		
1875. 2,000,000		2.00
1879. 600,000		2.00
Peter I		
Y22		
1904. 1,400,031		1.25
1912. 800,004		1.50
1915. 14,000,000		1.00
1 DINAR		
Milan, Obrenovich IV		
Y10 (silver) 22.5mm		
1875. 3,000,000		3.00
1879. 800,000		3.50
Alexander I (1889-1902)		
Y16		
1897. 4,000,000		2.00
Peter I		
Y23		
1904. 993,642		2.00
1905. 1,006,444		2.00
1912. 8,000,116		1.75
1915. 13,000,015		1.75
2 DINARA		
Milan, Obrenovich IV		
Y11		
1875. 1,000,000		4.00
1879. 750,000		4.00

	Mintage	Value
Alexander I		
Y17		
1897............1,000,000		$3.50
Peter I		
Y24 (silver)		
1904..............387,180		5.00
1905..............762,864		4.00
1912..............800,016		4.00
1915............5,000,000		3.50

5 DINARA
Milan, Obrenovich IV

Y12 (silver) 37mm
1875..............200,000   17.50
1879..............200,000   17.50

Peter I

Y25 100th Anniversary
1904..............200,004   17.50

World War II —
German Formed State
50 PARA
Y26 (zinc) 18mm
1942.................... $1.25

1 DINAR
Y27 (zinc) 20mm
1942....................   .50

2 DINARA
Y28 (zinc) 22mm
1942....................   .50

10 DINARA
Y29 (zinc) 26.5mm
1943....................   1.50

SLOVAKIA
(Slovenska)

Prior to and after World War II was part of Czechoslovakia. Became a German protectorate during World War II. Coinage obsolete. Coins of Czechoslovakia now circulating.

100 Halierov = 1 Koruna

5 HALIEROV
Y-S19b (zinc) 14mm
1942....................   1.00

10 HALIEROV
Y-S20 (bronze) 15mm
1939....................   .40
1940....................   .40
1941....................   .40
1942....................   .40

20 HALIEROV
Y-S21 (bronze) 17mm
1939....................   .60
1940....................   .60
1941....................   .60
Y-S21a (aluminum)
1942....................   .50
1943....................   .50

50 HALIEROV
Y-S22 (copper-nickel) 19mm
1940....................   .75
1941....................   .75
Y-S22b (aluminum)
1943....................   .50
1944....................   .50

1 KORUNA
Y-S23 (copper-nickel) 21mm
1940....................   .75
1941....................   .75
1942....................   .75
1944....................   .75
1945....................   .75

5 KORUN
Y-S24 (nickel) 27mm
1939............5,000,000   1.25

	Mintage	Value		Mintage	Value
10 KORUN			**Y-S27** new design		
Y-S25 (silver) 28mm			1941....................		$7.50
1944....................		$6.00			
20 KORUN			**50 KORUN**		
Y-S26 Tiso (silver) 30mm			**Y-S28** (silver) 34mm		
1939............2,000,000		10.00	1944....................		6.00

SOMALIA

In northeastern Africa. After World War II was administered by the United Nations under Italian trusteeship. Became independent in 1960.

100 Centesimi = 1 Somalo

1 CENTESIMO			**50 CENTESIMI**	
Y1 (bronze) 20mm			**Y4** (silver) 22mm	
1950............4,000,000	.20		1950............1,800,000	.60
5 CENTESIMI			**1 SOMALO**	
Y2 (bronze) 25mm			**Y5** (silver) 27mm	
1950............6,800,000	.30		1950...........11,480,000	1.25
10 CENTESIMI				
Y3 (bronze) 30mm				
1950............7,400,000	.30			

SPAIN
(España)

In southwestern Europe, occupying most of the Iberian peninsula. Coins were often minted in years other than date on coin. The true date is found in tiny numerals in the stars which flank the large date. Dates listed below in parentheses are the true dates. These true dates can be identified with a strong glass, and coin must normally be in fine or better condition, otherwise the incused date would be worn away. Note: 10, 20, and 50 centavos 1880-1885 bearded face to right are issues of the Philippines.

100 Centimos = 1 Peseta

1 CENTIMO		*Alfonso XIII (1886-1931)*	
Provisional Government		**Y96**	
(1868-1870)		1906............7,500,006	.40
Y51 (copper or bronze) 15mm		**Y98** facing left	
1870..........169,890,697	.50	1911............1,461,653	.50

	Mintage	Value
912	2,109,201	$ .50
913	1,429,149	.50

2 CENTIMOS
Provisional Government

Y52 (copper or bronze) 20mm

1870	115,868,832	.50

Alfonso XIII
Y97

1904	10,000,003	.35
1905	5,000,003	.35

Y99 facing left

1911	2,283,547	.45
1912	3,475,207	.45
1913	1,741,276	.50

5 CENTIMOS
Provisional Government

Y53 (copper) 25mm

1870	287,380,761	.30

Alfonso XII (1875-1885)
Y69

1877		.30
1878	}102,326,328	.30
1879		.30

Republic (1931-1938)
Y103 (iron) 20mm

1937		.75

*Nationalist Government
(1937 to date)*
Y110 (aluminum)

1940		.15
1941		.15
1945		.15

10 CENTIMOS
Provisional Government

Y54 (copper) 30mm

1870	170,088,104	.40

Alfonso XII
Y70

1877		.35
1878	}85,880,170	.35
1879		.35

Nationalist Government
Y111 (aluminum) 23mm

1940		.15

	Mintage	Value
1941		$ .15
1945		.15
1953	205,044,225	.15

Y121 (aluminum) 18mm

1959		.10

20 CENTIMOS
Provisional Government

Y55 (silver) 16.5mm

1869	inc. w/1870	17.50
1870	5,091	10.00

25 CENTIMOS
Alfonso XIII

Y100 (copper-nickel) 25mm

1925	8,000,030	.75

Y101 holed

1927	12,000,042	.50

Republic
Y107 (nickel-bronze)

1934	12,272,424	.75

Y104 (bronze) 22mm

1938	45,500,000	.75

Nationalist Government
Y109 (copper-nickel) holed, 25mm

1937		.50

50 CENTIMOS
Provisional Government

Y56 (silver) 19mm

1869	452,726	1.25
1870	539,808	1.25

Alfonso XII
Y-A76

1880	2,787,117	.50
1881	5,647,486	.50
1885 (86)	1,468,399	.50

Alfonso XIII
Y79 baby head

1889	537,260	1.00
1892	3,953,638	.50

Y83 boy head

1894	409,003	1.00
1895	700,201	1.00

Y87 older head

1896	296,929	1.50
1900	2,128,369	.50

	Mintage	Value
Y92 new design		
1904	4,851,497	$ .50
1904 (10)	1,303,015	.75
Y93 older head		
1910	4,526,046	.60
Y102 new design		
1926	4,000,012	1.00
Republic		
Y105 (bronze) 23mm		
1937		.75
Nationalist Government		
Y115 (copper-nickel) holed, 20.5mm arrows down		
1949 (50)	200,000	1.50
1949 (51)	inc. below	1.50
Y116 arrows up		
1949 (51)	9,841,800	.25
1949 (52)	18,566,877	.25
1949 (53)	16,745,694	.25
1949 (54)	22,333,549	.25
1949 (55)	23,037,671	.25
1949 (56)	12,978,707	.25
1949 (57)	4,662,120	.30
1949 (58)	7,127,000	.25
1949 (62)	3,969,232	.30

1 PESETA

Provisional Government

	Mintage	Value
Y58 1869 GOBIERNO PROVISIONAL (silver)		
23.5mm	7,367,146	1.00
1869 ESPAÑA	inc. above	1.00
1870	3,865,169	1.00
1870 (71)	1,034,675	1.25
1870 (73)	4,130,322	1.00

Alfonso XII

	Mintage	Value
Y-B75		
1876	4,426,701	1.00
1881	798,809	1.50
1882	3,505,024	1.00
1883	8,445,839	1.00
1885	3,336,386	1.00
1885 (86)	3,953,787	1.00

Alfonso XIII

	Mintage	Value
Y80 baby head		
1889	760,149	1.50
1891	4,948,243	.75

	Mintage	Value
Y84 boy head		
1893	1,958,066	$1.25
1894	328,952	2.00
1895	715,437	1.50
Y88 older head		
1896	6,411,640	1.00
1899	7,472,306	1.00
1900	18,650,104	.75
1901	8,448,690	1.00
Y94 new design		
1902	2,599,009	1.00
1903	10,601,512	.90
1904	5,294,313	1.00
1905	491,818	1.75

Republic

	Mintage	Value
Y108 23mm		
1933	2,000,000	2.00
Y106 (brass) 22mm		
1937		.75

Nationalist Government

	Mintage	Value
Y112 (aluminum-bronze)		
1944		.25
Y113 Franco		
1947 (47)	40,949,672	.20
1947 (48)	15,000,000	.20
1947 (49)	27,600,000	.20
1947 (50)	4,000,000	.30
1947 (51)	9,185,000	.20
1947 (52)	19,195,000	.20
1947 (53)	34,000,000	.20
1953 (54)	40,271,954	.20
1953 (55)	14,223,267	.20
1953 (56)	11,310,423	.20
1953 (57)	6,312,821	.20
1953 (58)	62,878,928	.20
1953 (59)	42,941,038	.20
1953 (60)	45,160,000	.20
1953 (61)	25,830,308	.20
1953 (62)	66,251,501	.20

2 PESETAS

Provisional Government

	Mintage	Value
Y59 (silver) 27.5mm		
1869	3,269,853	2.00
1870	1,503,972	2.00
1870 (71)	3,962,618	1.75
1870 (73)	7,917,028	1.50
1870 (74)	14,892,832	1.50
1870 (75)	4,996,834	1.75

	Mintage	Value
Alfonso XII		
Y-C76		
1879	5,578,225	$1.25
1881	3,639,219	1.25
1882	20,342,803	1.00
1883	3,318,205	1.25
1884	2,838,932	1.25
Alfonso XIII		
Y81 baby head		
1889	559,343	2.00
1891	93,245	5.00
1892	1,379,216	1.50
Y85 child head		
1894	278,810	3.50
Y95 new design		
1905	3,588,630	2.00

2½ PESETAS

Nationalist Government

Y114 (aluminum-bronze) 25mm

	Mintage	Value
1953 (54)	10,891,750	.50
1953 (55)	11,891,849	.50
1953 (56)	14,988,893	.50
1953 (57)	15,334,680	.50

5 PESETAS

Provisional Government

Y60 (silver) 37mm

	Mintage	Value
1869	inc. w/1870	30.00
1870	5,923,455	5.00

Amadeo I (1871-1873)

Y61

	Mintage	Value
1871	5,936,978	4.50
1871 (72)	7,704,184	4.50
1871 (73)	2,870,046	4.50
1871 (74)	5,074,992	4.50
1871 (75)	3,093,451	4.50

Alfonso XII

Y74

	Mintage	Value
1875	8,547,961	4.00
1876	inc. above	4.00

Y75

	Mintage	Value
1877	6,987,293	4.00
1878	9,147,986	4.00
1879	1,633,850	5.00
1881	698,782	10.00

Y76

	Mintage	Value
1882	1,661,936	5.00

	Mintage	Value
1882 (81) error	inc. above	——
1883	5,507,459	$4.00
1884	5,847,819	4.00
1885	3,144,452	4.50
1885 (86)	1,951,258	5.00
1885 (87)	11,802,513	4.00

Alfonso XIII

Y82 baby head

	Mintage	Value
1888	10,643,899	4.00
1889	4,681,328	4.00
1890	7,275,258	4.00
1891	11,659,556	4.00
1892	8,294,268	4.00

Y86 boy head

	Mintage	Value
1892	inc. above	4.00
1893	3,018,331	4.50
1894	3,871,145	4.50

Y89 older head

	Mintage	Value
1896	4,271,751	4.00
1897	6,732,536	4.00
1898	39,977,378	3.50
1899	13,929,660	4.00

Nationalist Government

Y117 (nickel) 32mm

	Mintage	Value
1949 (49)	612,000	1.50
1949 (50)	21,000,000	.75
1949 (52)	9,000	6.00

Y118 (copper-nickel) 23mm

	Mintage	Value
1957 (58)	33,359,000	.50
1957 (59)	105,180,000	.50
1957 (60)	66,055,000	.50
1957 (61)	30,991,517	.50
1957 (62)	70,963,361	.50

25 PESETAS

Nationalist Government

Y119 (copper-nickel) 27mm

	Mintage	Value
1957 (58)	8,635,000	1.25
1957 (59)	42,185,000	1.00
1957 (61)	24,119,640	1.00
1957 (62)	323,000	2.50

50 PESETAS

Nationalist Government

Y120 (copper-nickel) 30mm

	Mintage	Value
1957 (58)	21,471,500	2.00
1957 (59)	42,261,000	2.00
1957 (60)	17,451,000	2.00
1957 (61)	6,361,500	2.00
1957 (62)	874,283	2.50

A group of islands in the west Pacific, which was a Spanish colony until 1898. Following the Spanish-American War became a colony and later a common-wealth of the United States. In 1946 became an independent nation. The 1880-1885 coins are similar to SPAIN of same period, except that the bust of the king faces right. The 1 Peso 1897 is inscribed: "Islas Filipinas."

100 Centavos = 1 Peso

	Mintage	Value
10 CENTAVOS		
Isabel II (1833-1868)		
Y3 (silver) 18mm		
1864		$3.00
1865		2.50
1866		3.00
1867		2.75
1868		2.25
Alfonso XII (1875-1885)		
Y9		
1880		3.00
1881		2.00
1882		2.00
1883		2.00
1884		2.75
1885		1.25
20 CENTAVOS		
Isabel II		
Y4 (silver) 23.5mm		
1864		3.50
1865		2.50
1866		2.50
1867		2.50
1868		1.75
Alfonso XII		
Y10		
1880		3.00

	Mintage	Value
1881		$2.75
1882		2.00
1883		2.00
1884		2.00
1885		1.50
50 CENTAVOS		
Isabel II		
Y5 (silver) 27mm		
1865		3.75
1866		5.00
1867		4.50
1868		3.25
Alfonso XII		
Y11		
1880		3.75
1881		3.00
1882		3.00
1883		3.00
1884		3.00
1885		2.25
1 PESO		
Alfonso XIII (1886-1898)		
Y13 (silver) 37mm		
1897	6,000,006	9.00

A former Dutch colony on the northeast coast of South America. In 1954 Surinam became an integral part of the Kingdom of the Netherlands, and in 1962 became an independent country. Wartime coins with P mint mark and palm tree were minted at Philadelphia. One cent coins from 1957 to 1961 are the same type as prewar Netherlands coins and are not identified as "Surinam." See Netherlands.

100 Cents = 1 Guilder

	Mintage	Value		Mintage	Value
1 CENT			**10 CENTS**		
			(silver) 13mm		
Type of Netherlands Y36 for			*Type of Netherlands Y43 for*		
Curacao and Surinam			*Curacao and Surinam*		
1942P (bronze) 17mm			1941P.............800,000		$ .40
..........2,500,000		$ .30			
			Surinam		
Surinam			1942P...........1,500,000		.30
1943P (brass).....4,000,000		.20	*Curacao and Surinam*		
1957 (bronze).....1,200,000		.20	1943P...........4,500,000		.25
1959.............1,000,000		.20			
1960..............800,000		.25	**25 CENTS**		
1961.............1,200,000		.20	(silver) 17mm		
			Type of Netherlands Y44 for		
			Curacao and Surinam		
5 CENTS			1941P.............800,000		.50
(German Silver)					
diamond shaped, 16.5mm			*Surinam*		
			1942P.............300,000		.50
Type of Netherlands Y34a for					
Curacao and Surinam			*Curacao and Surinam*		
1943............8,595,000		.20	1943P...........2,500,000		**.30**

SWEDEN
(Sveriges)

On the eastern part of the Scandinavian peninsula in Northern Europe. Until 1905 the King was ruler of Sweden and Norway. Swedish coins were inscribed: SVERIGES O. NORGES..., while coins of Norway were inscribed: NORGES O. SVER.... Some Swedish coins do not have name of country on them; these are inscribed: BRODRAFOLKENS VAL or MEDFOLKET FOR FOSTERLANDET. The ½ öre 1867 bears the inscription: LAND SKALL MED LAG BYGGAS.

100 Öre = 1 Riksdaler Ryksmynt = 1 Krona

½ ÖRE			**1 ÖRE**		
Charles XV (1859-1872)			*Charles XV*		
			Y2 (bronze) 18mm		
Y1 (bronze) 15mm			1860...............46,250		4.50
1867................64,300		3.50	1861..............300,170		.75

	Mintage	Value
1862	78,500	$1.50
1863	449,500	.50
1864	1,847,515	.25
1865	561,000	.40
1866	326,600	.75
1867	955,850	.30
1870	1,078,893	.25
1871	1,063,000	.25
1872	1,896,601	.25

Oscar II (1872-1907)

Y11 (bronze)

	Mintage	Value
1873	1,866,757	.50

Y14 BRODRAFOLKENS VAL, 16mm

	Mintage	Value
1874	2,370,000	.25
1875	2,829,000	.25
1876	1,889,000	.25

Y14a

	Mintage	Value
1877	1,590,000	.25
1878	1,570,000	.25
1879	1,630,000	.25
1880	1,713,463	.25
1881	1,983,580	.25
1882	2,586,570	.25
1883	2,586,510	.25
1884	2,626,192	.25
1885	2,464,335	.25
1886	1,233,605	.25
1888	1,737,932	.25
1889	1,188,766	.25
1890	1,948,794	.25
1891	2,722,756	.25
1892	280,000	1.00
1893	2,144,901	.25
1894	589,598	.50
1895	2,011,826	.25
1896	1,463,310	.25
1897	2,544,224	.25
1898	2,959,498	.25
1899	2,821,400	.25
1900	2,928,700	.25
1901	3,074,700	.25
1902	2,685,400	.25
1903	2,695,600	.25
1904	2,032,700	.25
1905	3,555,600	.25

Y32 SVERIGES VAL

	Mintage	Value
1906	1,783,300	.25
1907	8,250,500	.20

Gustaf V (1907-1950)

Y44 MED FOLKET FOR FOSTERLANDET

	Mintage	Value
1909	4,210,600	$ .20
1910	1,132,600	.25
1911	3,149,900	.20
1912	3,170,000	.20
1913	3,197,300	.20
1914	2,214,050	.20
1915	4,471,300	.20
1916	7,165,500	.20

Y52 (iron)

	Mintage	Value
1917	8,389,500	.35
1918	9,444,300	.35
1919	7,169,500	.35

Y44 (bronze)

	Mintage	Value
1920	5,547,600	.20
1921	7,441,500	.20
1922	1,165,700	.25
1923	4,271,100	.20
1924	2,578,900	.20
1925	4,714,900	.20
1926	6,739,300	.20
1927	3,601,300	.20
1928	2,380,800	.20
1929	6,090,500	.20
1930	5,477,300	.20
1931	5,679,500	.20
1932	3,339,000	.20
1933	3,426,800	.20
1934	6,120,500	.20
1935	4,599,800	.20
1936	6,116,100	.20
1937	7,738,200	.20
1938	6,992,900	.20
1939	6,562,300	.20
1940	4,059,900	.20
1941	11,599,090	.20
1942	3,992,000	.20
1950	22,421,200	.15

Y69 (iron)

	Mintage	Value
1942	10,053,000	.20
1943	10,714,000	.20
1944	8,698,500	.20
1945	9,527,000	.20
1946	6,611,000	.20
1947	14,244,500	.15
1948	15,442,000	.15
1949	11,778,900	.15
1950	14,431,500	.15

	Mintage	Value
Gustaf VI Adolf		
(1950 to present)		
Y72		
1952	3,819,000	$ .15
1953	20,770,800	.10
1954	15,754,000	.10
1955	24,281,700	.10
1956	21,582,000	.10
1957	18,074,000	.10
1958	23,164,500	.10
1959	12,015,000	.10
1960	23,852,500	.10
1961	15,207,500	.10
1962	20,875,000	.10

2 ÖRE

	Mintage	Value
Charles XV		
Y3 (bronze) 24mm		
1860	196,875	1.25
1861	1,626,075	.25
1862	212,750	1.00
1863	1,621,300	.25
1864	600,000	.40
1865	602,865	.40
1866	399,750	.60
1867	428,012	.50
1871	717,638	.30
1872	1,645,666	.25

	Mintage	Value
Oscar II		
Y12 (bronze)		
1873	1,294,350	.75

Y15 BRODRAFOLKENS VAL,
  21mm

	Mintage	Value
1874	1,914,000	.25
1875	2,441,000	.25
1876	1,402,000	.25
1877	1,015,000	.25

Y15a	Mintage	Value
1878	865,000	.35
1879	935,000	.30
1880	824,972	.35
1881	1,243,973	.25
1882	1,777,293	.25
1883	1,482,781	.25
1884	1,315,543	.25
1885	615,282	.40
1886	1,240,795	.25
1888	865,067	.30
1889	589,455	.50
1890	911,553	.30
1891	941,725	.30

	Mintage	Value
1892	687,500	$ .40
1893	557,574	.50
1894	585,512	.50
1895	780,991	.35
1896	907,916	.30
1897	1,299,520	.25
1898	1,527,100	.25
1899	2,172,250	.20
1900	687,750	.40
1901	1,415,200	.25
1902	2,035,550	.20
1904	698,050	.40
1905	1,429,600	.25

Y33 SVERIGES VAL	Mintage	Value
1906	999,250	.30
1907	3,807,350	.20

	Mintage	Value
Gustaf V		
Y45 MED FOLKET FOR		
FOSTERLANDET		
1909	1,584,550	.20
1910	809,400	.25
1912	445,700	.50
1913	805,650	.25
1914	1,118,630	.20
1915	813,650	.25
1916	2,815,450	.15

Y53 (iron)	Mintage	Value
1917	4,576,200	.60
1918	4,981,750	.60
1919	2,923,100	.60

Y45 (bronze)	Mintage	Value
1919	1,277,700	.20
1920	3,464,750	.15
1921	1,645,750	.20
1922	521,600	.40
1923	1,179,900	.20
1924	1,283,000	.20
1925	3,903,350	.15
1926	3,573,950	.15
1927	2,190,250	.15
1928	832,250	.25
1929	2,384,350	.15
1930	2,589,850	.15
1931	2,295,700	.15
1932	1,179,150	.20
1933	1,721,300	.20
1934	1,294,950	.20
1935	3,677,750	.15
1936	2,244,100	.15
1937	2,980,950	.15
1938	3,224,800	.15
1939	4,014,200	.15

	Mintage	Value
1940	3,304,250	$ .15
1941	7,337,198	.15
1942	1,614,000	.20
1950	5,823,000	.10

Y70 (iron)

	Mintage	Value
1942	9,343,950	.10
1943	6,999,300	.10
1944	6,125,900	.10
1945	4,773,400	.10
1946	5,854,000	.10
1947	9,535,250	.10
1948	11,424,500	.10
1949	10,599,750	.10
1950	13,619,500	.10

Gustaf VI Adolf
Y73

	Mintage	Value
1952	3,011,000	.10
1953	14,911,600	.10
1954	10,794,300	.10
1955	12,736,650	.10
1956	14,117,000	.10
1957	9,579,750	.10
1958	9,185,300	.10
1959	11,314,500	.10
1960	12,681,500	.10
1961	10,047,500	.10
1962	9,341,250	.10

5 ÖRE

Charles XV
Y4 (bronze) 29mm

	Mintage	Value
1860	67,700	2.50
1861	342,980	.75
1862	135,720	1.00
1863	633,000	.60
1864	263,600	.90
1865	104,340	1.00
1866	120,399	1.00
1867	740,507	.60
1872	619,960	.60

Oscar II
Y13 (bronze)

	Mintage	Value
1873	783,080	1.25

Y16 BRODRAFOLKENS VAL,
27mm

	Mintage	Value
1874	866,200	.30
1875	1,234,200	.25
1876	608,500	.40
1877	514,000	.50

	Mintage	Value
1878	364,000	$ .75
1879	350,000	.75
1880	403,338	.75
1881	624,966	.40
1882	824,747	.30
1883	578,110	.50
1884	784,140	.40
1885	282,239	1.00
1886	269,417	1.00
1887	250,641	1.00
1888	214,411	1.00
1889	219,946	1.00

Y16a

	Mintage	Value
1890	338,789	1.00
1891	374,001	.90
1892	585,751	.50
1895	528,530	.50
1896	308,647	1.00
1897	569,656	.50
1898	720,940	.40
1899	1,225,160	.25
1900	364,580	.75
1901	441,660	.75
1902	652,460	.40
1903	243,000	1.50
1904	414,240	.75
1905	545,080	.50

Y34 SVERIGES VAL

	Mintage	Value
1906	565,280	.50
1907	1,953,260	.30

Gustaf V
Y46 MED FOLKET FOR
FOSTERLANDET

	Mintage	Value
1909	917,230	.25
1910	30,600	5.00
1911	778,460	.40
1912	547,480	.50
1913	761,780	.40
1914	400,010	.75
1915	1,222,282	.20
1916	955,440	.25

Y54 (iron)

	Mintage	Value
1917	2,953,320	1.00
1918	2,457,840	1.00
1919	2,302,480	1.00

Y46 (bronze)

	Mintage	Value
1919	1,129,380	.20
1920	2,360,920	.15
1921	1,878,500	.20
1922	763,420	.40
1923	505,580	.50
1924	899,500	.25

	Mintage	Value
1925	1,943,500	$ .20
1926	1,742,100	.20
1927	36,380	4.50
1928	986,900	.25
1929	1,168,560	.20
1930	1,716,140	.20
1931	1,130,960	.20
1932	1,165,320	.20
1933	574,340	.50
1934	1,710,260	.20
1935	1,682,020	.20
1936	1,625,700	.20
1937	2,637,260	.15
1938	2,354,240	.15
1939	2,591,500	.15
1940	2,729,850	.15
1941	2,054,540	.15
1942	395,400	.75
1950	12,559,100	.10

Y71 (iron)

	Mintage	Value
1942	4,343,420	.15
1943	5,570,180	.15
1944	4,561,980	.15
1945	3,771,100	.15
1946	2,375,080	.15
1947	6,034,840	.15
1948	6,246,000	.15
1949	7,839,640	.15
1950	5,289,500	.15

Gustaf VI Adolf
Y74

	Mintage	Value
1952	3,065,400	.15
1953	11,770,540	.10
1954	7,211,080	.10
1955	8,524,180	.10
1956	8,517,360	.10
1957	5,807,100	.10
1958	9,966,900	.10
1959	7,973,000	.10
1960	9,582,300	.10
1961	7,718,000	.10
1962	22,305,500	.10

10 ÖRE

Carl XV
Y5 (silver) 20mm

	Mintage	Value
1861	304,566	1.00
1862	274,150	1.25
1863	449,430	1.00
1864	inc. above	1.00
1865	560,210	.60

	Mintage	Value
1867	609,310	$ .60
1869	209,650	1.25
1870	383,700	1.00
1871	1,162,460	.45

Oscar II
Y17

	Mintage	Value
1872	120,000	2.00
1873	635,440	1.00

Y19 BRODRAFOLKENS VAL

	Mintage	Value
1874	2,875,000	1.00
1875	1,503,365	1.00
1876	1,814,364	1.00

Y27 design changed

	Mintage	Value
1880	851,371	.30
1881	762,741	.40
1882	735,187	.50
1883	694,317	.75
1884	1,558,589	.20
1887	1,512,766	.20
1890	921,850	.30
1891	826,500	.40
1892	1,214,601	.20
1894	1,732,963	.20
1896	2,835,552	.15
1897	818,838	.40
1898	2,086,704	.15
1899	2,041,130	.15
1900	1,172,693	.20
1902	1,945,600	.20
1903	1,508,930	.20
1904	3,279,520	.15

Y35 SVERIGES VAL

	Mintage	Value
1907	7,319,640	.25

Gustaf V
Y47

	Mintage	Value
1909	1,610,460	.20
1911	3,180,065	.15
1913	1,580,900	.20
1914	1,571,330	.20
1915	1,546,950	.20
1916	3,034,880	.15
1917	4,996,130	.15
1918	4,114,180	.15
1919	5,737,020	.15

Y55 (nickel)

	Mintage	Value
1920	3,612,250	.20
1921	2,269,950	.20

	Mintage	Value
1923	2,143,560	$ .20
1924	1,600,000	.20
1925	1,472,340	.20

Y47 (silver)

	Mintage	Value
1927	2,509,590	.20
1928	2,901,180	.20
1929	5,505,200	.15
1930	3,222,710	.15
1931	4,272,073	.15
1933	1,948,090	.20
1934	4,059,293	.15
1935	2,426,283	.20
1936	5,097,270	.15
1937	5,116,920	.15
1938	7,428,140	.15
1939	2,020,670	.20
1940	3,017,320	.15
1941	9,106,380	.15
1942	3,691,640	.15

Y55 (nickel)

	Mintage	Value
1940	3,373,700	.15
1941	815,880	.40
1946	4,116,940	.15
1947	4,132,950	.15

Y64 new design (40% silver)

	Mintage	Value
1942	1,600,000	.20
1943	7,661,000	.15
1944	12,276,900	.10
1945	11,702,510	.10
1946	3,575,500	.15
1947	7,293,250	.15
1948	10,418,650	.10
1949	12,044,000	.10
1950	31,823,870	.10

Gustaf VI Adolf

Y75

	Mintage	Value
1952	4,659,700	.10
1953	26,073,240	.10
1954	11,324,050	.10
1955	15,398,520	.10
1956	21,908,280	.10
1957	22,600,400	.10
1958	19,605,400	.10
1959	13,863,000	.10
1960	21,265,000	.10
1961	13,607,000	.10
1962	11,138,000	.10

25 ÖRE

Charles XV

Y6 (silver) 17mm

	Mintage	Value
1862	unknown	$25.00
1864	265,492	2.00
1865	400,052	1.50
1866	237,496	2.50
1867	inc. above	2.50
1871	659,808	1.00

Oscar II

Y20 BRODRAFOLKENS VAL

	Mintage	Value
1874	2,100,000	.35
1875	1,131,060	.50
1876	2,224,614	.35
1877	894,354	.60
1878	859,127	.60

Y28 design changed

	Mintage	Value
1880	1,179,868	.25
1881	1,391,553	.25
1883	1,100,339	.25
1885	1,168,383	.25
1889	421,589	.50
1890	469,417	.50
1896	793,546	.30
1897	1,097,301	.25
1898	1,457,998	.25
1899	1,458,479	.25
1902	1,259,036	.25
1904	692,088	.40
1905	732,000	.30

Y36 SVERIGES VAL

	Mintage	Value
1907	3,222,580	.40

Gustaf V

Y48

	Mintage	Value
1910	2,043,936	.20
1912	1,013,760	.25
1914	3,719,232	.20
1916	1,269,720	.25
1917	1,657,312	.25
1918	2,364,784	.20
1919	3,205,164	.20
1927	1,687,984	.25
1928	836,896	.35
1929	1,124,932	.25

	Mintage	Value
1930	1,089,628	$ .25
1931	1,391,928	.25
1932	1,133,344	.25
1933	964,340	.30
1934	1,403,648	.25
1936	1,852,000	.25
1937	3,258,956	.20
1938	3,678,876	.20
1939	2,136,600	.20
1940	2,301,788	.20
1941	1,995,200	.25

Y56 (nickel)

1921	1,354,656	.35
1940	2,333,040	.30
1941	1,056,680	.30
1946	2,066,048	.20
1947	1,594,200	.25

Y65 new design (40% silver)

1943	9,854,640	.15
1944	9,532,148	.15
1945	5,362,800	.15
1946	2,249,600	.20
1947	5,632,800	.15
1948	3,191,000	.15
1949	5,812,180	.15
1950	12,059,144	.15

Gustaf VI Adolf

Y76

1952	1,820,000	.25
1953	18,471,360	.15
1954	9,491,740	.15
1955	7,340,800	.15
1956	11,253,100	.15
1957	11,313,500	.15
1958	8,068,140	.15
1959	4,772,000	.15
1960	1,000,000	.25
1961	11,754,800	.15
1962	3,770,000	.15

50 ÖRE

Charles XV

Y7 (silver) 22mm

1862	unknown	20.00

	Mintage	Value
Oscar II		
Y21 BRODRAFOLKENS VAL		
1875	1,908,354	$ .60
1877	148,617	2.00
1878	318,588	1.50
1880	188,318	1.50
1881	267,905	1.50
1883	769,959	.75
1898	505,228	1.00
1899	720,070	.75

Y37 SVERIGES VAL

1906	319,452	1.00
1907	803,340	.60

Gustaf V

Y49

1911	472,354	1.00
1912	482,062	1.00
1914	378,448	1.00
1916	536,718	.75
1919	458,296	1.00
1927	671,596	.75
1928	1,135,054	.35
1929	470,990	1.00
1930	547,920	.75
1931	671,457	.75
1933	547,606	.75
1934	613,124	.75
1935	690,792	.75
1936	823,176	.50
1938	441,546	1.00
1939	921,750	.50

Y57 (nickel)

1920	479,500	1.00
1921	214,922	2.00
1924	645,368	.75
1940	1,340,750	.50
1946	1,425,990	.35
1947	1,031,800	.35

Y66 new design (40% silver)

1943	784,700	.50
1944	1,540,296	.35
1945	2,584,800	.35
1946	1,091,000	.35
1947	1,770,500	.35
1948	1,731,400	.35
1949	1,883,100	.35
1950	1,676,810	.35

	Mintage	Value
Gustaf VI Adolf		
Y77		
1952	460,000	$ .90
1953	5,133,380	.35
1954	5,778,850	.35
1955	2,699,700	.35
1956	7,056,670	.35
1957	2,404,700	.35
1958	1,659,800	.35
1961	2,775,000	.35
1962	1,400,000	.35

1 RIKSDALER RIKSMYNT
Charles XV

Y8 (silver) 24mm

	Mintage	Value
1860	124,633	4.50
1861	158,101	4.50
1862		30.00
1864	85,150	8.00
1865	59,465	10.00
1867	106,358	4.50
1871	208,078	4.50

Oscar II

Y18

	Mintage	Value
1873	166,436	15.00

1 KRONA
Oscar II

Y22

	Mintage	Value
1875	3,531,422	1.00
1876	2,510,237	1.00

Y22a

	Mintage	Value
1877	554,263	1.50
1879	77,254	3.00
1880	177,121	2.50
1881	619,147	1.50
1883	205,088	2.00
1884	381,909	2.00
1887	57,988	4.00
1888	62,368	3.00
1889	425,397	1.75

Y29 design changed

	Mintage	Value
1890	593,951	1.25
1897	735,391	1.25
1898	1,858,122	1.00
1901	270,906	2.00
1903	473,386	1.50
1904	563,856	1.25

Y38 design changed

	Mintage	Value
1906	426,939	$1.50
1907	1,058,286	1.00

Gustaf V

Y50

	Mintage	Value
1910	643,065	.90
1912	303,420	1.25
1913	353,051	1.00
1914	383,810	1.00
1915	1,415,956	.65
1916	1,139,245	.65
1918	258,091	1.50
1923	746,277	.75
1924	2,066,156	.65
1925	369,919	1.00
1926	465,467	1.00
1927	401,167	1.00
1928	739,189	.75
1929	1,345,647	.65
1930	1,743,783	.65
1931	1,007,523	.65
1932	1,035,877	.65
1933	1,044,634	.65
1934	585,673	.90
1935	1,604,343	.65
1936	3,222,617	.65
1937	2,666,998	.65
1938	1,911,464	.65
1939	7,589,316	.65
1940	6,917,460	.65
1941	2,183,338	.65
1942	240,000	1.50

Y67 new design (40% silver)

	Mintage	Value
1942	5,644,990	.50
1943	7,919,850	.50
1944	6,942,763	.50
1945	7,630,700	.50
1946	19,247,600	.50
1947	9,129,249	.50
1948	10,430,588	.50
1949	8,228,212	.50
1950	6,310,141	.50

Gustaf VI Adolf

Y78

	Mintage	Value
1952	1,101,625	.60
1953	2,737,033	.50
1954	7,029,850	.50
1955	3,958,504	.50
1956	6,228,365	.50

	Mintage	Value
1957	3,725,005	$ .50
1958	1,438,940	.60
1959	1,187,000	.60
1960	4,085,250	.50
1961	6,615,650	.50
1962	7,479,175	.50

2 RIKSDALER RIKSMYNT
Charles XV

Y9 (silver) 31mm

	Mintage	Value
1862		50.00
1864	38,165	15.00
1871	18,857	17.50

2 KRONOR
(silver) 31mm

Oscar II

Y23 SVERIGES O. NORGES

	Mintage	Value
1876	370,250	2.00
1877	167,976	2.00
1878	193,419	2.00
1880	127,684	4.00

Y23a SVERIGES OCH NORGES

	Mintage	Value
1878	inc. above	20.00
1880	inc. above	3.00

Y30 design changed

	Mintage	Value
1890	71,887	3.50
1892	86,651	3.50
1893	48,827	4.00
1897	179,929	2.50
1898	141,391	2.50
1900	130,837	2.50
1903	64,308	4.00
1904	175,029	2.50

Y31 Silver Jubilee 1872-97

	Mintage	Value
1897	246,000	4.50

Y39 design changed

	Mintage	Value
1906	112,468	2.50
1907	300,573	2.00

Y40 Golden Wedding 1857-1907

	Mintage	Value
1907	251,000	4.00

Gustaf V

Y51

	Mintage	Value
1910	374,725	2.00

	Mintage	Value
1912	156,912	$3.00
1913	304,616	2.50
1914	191,905	3.00
1915	155,965	3.00
1922	201,821	3.00
1924	199,314	3.00
1926	221,577	3.00
1928	160,319	3.00
1929	184,458	3.00
1930	178,387	3.00
1931	210,576	3.00
1934	273,419	2.50
1935	211,059	3.00
1936	491,296	2.00
1937	383,225	2.00
1938	638,970	2.00
1939	1,200,329	1.75
1940	517,740	2.00

Y58 400th Anniversary
Gustaf Vasa

	Mintage	Value
1921	264,943	4.50

Y59 300th Anniversary
Death of Gustaf II

	Mintage	Value
1932	253,770	3.50

Y61 300th Anniversary
Swedish Settlement
in America

	Mintage	Value
1938	255,250	5.00

Y68 new design (40% silver)

	Mintage	Value
1942	200,000	2.50
1943	271,824	2.00
1944	627,200	1.50
1945	969,675	1.50
1946	978,000	1.50
1947	1,465,975	1.00
1948	281,660	1.50
1949	331,715	1.50
1950	3,727,465	1.00

Gustaf VI Adolf

Y79

	Mintage	Value
1952	31,500	3.00
1953	1,293,205	1.00
1954	2,300,000	1.00
1955	1,137,734	1.00
1956	1,708,468	1.00
1957	688,900	1.10
1958	777,330	1.10

	Mintage	Value
1959	908,555	$1.00
1961	533,770	1.10

4 RIKSDALER RIKSMYNT

Charles XV

Y10 (silver) 40mm

	Mintage	Value
1861	206,769	20.00
1862	942,553	20.00
1863	267,868	20.00
1864	534,735	20.00
1865	107,060	20.00
1866	40,984	30.00
1867	64,024	25.00
1868	120,492	20.00
1869	314,227	20.00
1870	161,461	20.00
1871	259,768	20.00

	Mintage	Value

5 KRONOR
(silver) 36mm

Y60 500th Anniversary of the Riksdag

	Mintage	Value
1935	663,815	$7.50

Y81 70th Birthday of Gustaf VI

1952	242,241	6.00

Y80 regular issue, 34mm

1954	1,510,316	2.50
1955	3,568,988	2.50

Y82 150th Anniversary of new Riksdag Constitution

1959	504,150	4.00

Y86 80th Birthday

1962	256,100	3.50

SWITZERLAND
(Helvetia or Helvetica)

An independent republic in central Europe. Coins dated 1850 and 1851 were minted in Paris (A) and Strasbourg (BB). All other coins from 1853 to date were minted at Berne (B), except 5 Francs 1874 at Brussels (B.), and ½ Franc, 1 Franc, and 2 Franc 1894 minted at Paris (A).

100 Centimes = 1 Franc

1 CENTIME
Y18 (bronze) 16.5mm

1850	2,266,858	.75
1851	2,732,592	.75
1853	2,007,500	.75
1855	500,485	1.25
1856	2,500,492	.75
1857	1,586,565	.75
1863	500,855	1.25
1864	501,000	1.25
1866	1,000,000	.75
1868	2,000,000	.50
1870	500,000	1.25
1872	2,080,000	.50
1875	975,000	.60
1876	1,000,000	.50
1877	922,900	.60
1878	981,300	.60
1879	997,900	.60
1880	992,100	.60
1882	1,000,000	.50
1883	1,000,000	.50
1884	1,000,000	.50

1887	1,503,903	.40
1889	500,000	1.00
1890	1,000,000	.40
1891	2,000,000	.40
1892	1,000,000	.40
1894	1,000,000	.40
1895	2,000,000	.40
1897	500,000	.90
1898	1,500,000	.30
1899	1,500,000	.30
1900	2,000,000	.30
1902	950,000	.30
1903	1,000,000	.25
1904	1,000,000	.25
1905	2,000,000	.25
1906	1,000,000	.25
1907	2,000,000	.25
1908	3,000,000	.25
1909	1,000,000	.25
1910	1,500,000	.25
1911	1,500,000	.25
1912	2,000,000	.25
1913	3,000,000	.25

	Mintage	Value		Mintage	Value
1914	3,500,000	$ .25	1883	1,000,000	$ .50
1915	3,000,000	.25	1886	1,000,000	.50
1917	2,000,000	.25	1888	500,000	1.00
1918	3,000,000	.25	1890	1,000,000	.40
1919	3,000,000	.25	1893	2,000,000	.30
1920	1,000,000	.25	1897	486,700	1.25
1921	3,000,000	.20	1898	500,000	1.00
1924	2,000,000	.20	1899	1,000,000	.30
1925	2,500,000	.20	1900	1,000,000	.30
1926	2,000,000	.20	1902	500,000	.50
1927	1,500,000	.25	1903	500,000	.50
1928	2,000,000	.20	1904	500,000	.50
1929	4,000,000	.20	1906	500,000	.50
1930	2,500,000	.20	1907	1,000,000	.25
1931	5,000,000	.20	1908	1,000,000	.25
1932	5,000,000	.20	1909	1,000,000	.25
1933	3,000,000	.20	1910	500,000	.50
1934	3,000,000	.20	1912	1,000,000	.25
1936	2,000,000	.20	1913	1,000,000	.25
1937	2,400,000	.15	1914	1,000,000	.25
1938	5,300,000	.15	1915	1,000,000	.25
1939	10,000	15.00	1918	1,000,000	.25
1940	3,027,000	.15	1919	2,000,000	.20
1941	12,794,000	.10	1920	500,000	.40
			1925	1,250,000	.25
Y18a (zinc)			1926	750,000	.35
1942	17,969,000	.25	1927	500,000	.40
1943	8,647,000	.25	1928	500,000	.40
1944	11,825,000	.25	1929	750,000	.35
1945	2,800,000	.35	1930	1,000,000	.25
1946	12,063,000	.25	1931	1,288,300	.20
			1932	1,500,000	.20
Y54 (bronze)			1933	1,000,000	.20
1948	10,500,000	.10	1934	500,000	.35
1949	11,100,000	.10	1936	500,000	.35
1950	3,610,000	.10	1937	1,200,000	.20
1951	22,624,000	.10	1938	1,369,000	.20
1952	11,520,000	.10	1941	3,448,000	.15
1953	5,947,300	.10			
1954	5,174,600	.10	**Y19a** (zinc)		
1955	5,281,700	.10	1942	8,954,000	.25
1956	4,960,000	.10	1943	4,499,000	.25
1957	15,226,400	.10	1944	8,086,000	.25
1958	20,142,100	.10	1945	3,640,000	.25
1959	5,582,400	.10	1946	1,393,000	.50
1962	5,010,000	.10			
			Y55 (bronze)		
2 CENTIMES			1948	10,197,000	.10
			1951	9,622,300	.10
Y19 (bronze) 20mm			1952	1,915,800	.10
1850	7,293,597	.60	1953	2,006,900	.10
1851	3,715,263	.60	1954	2,539,100	.10
1866	1,000,000	.60	1955	2,493,100	.10
1870	540,000	1.25	1957	8,099,000	.10
1875	983,500	.60	1958	6,077,600	.10
1879	989,800	.60			

	Mintage	Value
5 CENTIMES		
Y20 (billon) 17.5mm		
1850	7,966,251	$ .50
1851	12,049,035	.50
1872	1,211,800	.50
1873	1,622,200	.50
1874	1,700,000	.50
1876	989,500	.60
1877	978,000	.60
Y23 (copper-nickel)		
1879	1,000,000	.50
1880	2,000,000	.50
1881	2,000,000	.50
1882	3,000,000	.40
1883	3,000,000	.40
1884	2,000,000	.40
1885	3,000,000	.35
1887	500,000	1.00
1888	1,500,000	.40
1889	500,000	1.00
1890	1,000,000	.40
1891	1,000,000	.40
1892	1,000,000	.40
1893	2,000,000	.35
1894	2,000,000	.35
1895	2,000,000	.35
1897	500,000	1.00
1898	2,500,000	.35
1899	1,500,000	.35
1900	2,000,000	.25
1901	3,000,000	.25
1902	1,000,000	.30
1903	2,000,000	.25
1904	1,000,000	.30
1905	1,000,000	.30
1906	3,000,000	.25
1907	5,000,000	.25
1908	3,000,000	.25
1909	2,000,000	.25
1910	1,000,000	.30
1911	2,000,000	.25
1912	3,000,000	.25
1913	3,000,000	.25
1914	3,000,000	.25
1915	3,000,000	.25
1917	1,000,000	.30
Y23b (brass)		
1918	6,000,000	.50
Y23 (copper-nickel)		
1919	6,000,000	.25
1920	5,000,000	.25
1921	3,000,000	.25
1922	4,000,000	.25

	Mintage	Value
1925	3,000,000	$ .25
1926	3,000,000	.25
1927	2,000,000	.25
1928	2,000,000	.25
1929	2,000,000	.25
1930	3,000,000	.25
1931	5,036,600	.25
Y23a (nickel)		
1932	6,000,000	.25
1933	3,000,000	.25
1934	4,000,000	.25
1936	1,000,000	.30
1937	2,000,000	.25
1938	1,000,000	.30
1939	10,048,000	.15
Y23 (copper-nickel)		
1940	1,416,000	.25
1941	3,087,000	.20
1942	5,078,000	.20
1943	6,591,000	.15
1944	9,981,000	.15
1945	985,000	.25
1946	6,179,000	.15
1947	5,125,000	.15
1948	4,710,000	.15
1949	4,889,000	.15
1950	920,000	.25
1951	2,141,000	.15
1952	4,690,000	.15
1953	9,131,000	.15
1954	8,037,900	.15
1955	19,943,000	.10
1957	10,147,400	.10
1958	10,217,300	.10
1959	11,085,500	.10
1962	23,840,000	.10
10 CENTIMES		
Y21 (billon) 19.5mm		
1850	8,778,911	.60
1851	4,528,877	.60
1871	844,000	1.00
1873	1,398,100	.75
1875	174,000	3.00
1876	1,962,200	.60
Y24 (copper-nickel)		
1879	1,000,000	.60
1880	2,000,000	.50
1881	3,000,000	.50
1882	3,000,000	.50
1883	2,000,000	.50
1884	3,000,000	.50
1885	3,000,000	.50
1894	1,000,000	.60

	Mintage	Value
1895	2,000,000	$ .50
1897	500,000	1.00
1898	1,000,000	.50
1899	500,000	1.00
1900	1,500,000	.25
1901	1,000,000	.30
1902	1,000,000	.30
1903	1,000,000	.30
1904	1,000,000	.30
1906	1,000,000	.30
1907	2,000,000	.25
1908	2,000,000	.25
1909	2,000,000	.25
1911	1,000,000	.30
1912	1,500,000	.25
1913	2,000,000	.25
1914	2,000,000	.25
1915	1,200,000	.25

Y24b (brass)

	Mintage	Value
1918	6,000,000	.50
1919	6,000,000	.50

Y24 (copper-nickel)

	Mintage	Value
1920	3,500,000	.25
1921	3,000,000	.25
1922	2,000,000	.25
1924	2,000,000	.25
1925	3,000,000	.25
1926	3,000,000	.25
1927	2,000,000	.25
1928	2,000,000	.25
1929	2,000,000	.25
1930	2,000,000	.25
1931	2,244,400	.25

Y24a (nickel)

	Mintage	Value
1932	3,500,000	.25
1933	2,000,000	.25
1934	3,000,000	.20
1936	1,500,000	.20
1937	1,000,000	.25
1938	1,000,000	.25
1939	10,022,000	.15

Y24 (copper-nickel)

	Mintage	Value
1940	2,000,000	.20
1942	2,110,000	.20
1943	3,176,000	.15
1944	6,133,000	.15
1945	993,000	.25
1946	4,010,000	.15
1947	3,152,000	.15
1948	1,000,000	.20
1949	2,268,900	.15
1950	3,200,000	.15
1951	3,430,000	.15

	Mintage	Value
1952	4,451,500	$ .15
1953	6,148,800	.15
1954	3,200,000	.15
1955	11,794,700	.15
1957	10,092,200	.15
1958	10,040,000	.15
1959	13,052,900	.15
1960	4,040,000	.15
1961	7,949,000	.15
1962	34,965,000	.10

20 CENTIMES

Y22 (billon) 21mm

	Mintage	Value
1850	5,392,853	.75
1851	6,159,461	.75
1858	1,547,860	.75
1859	2,775,965	.75

Y25a (nickel)

	Mintage	Value
1881	1,000,000	.75
1883	2,500,000	.60
1884	4,000,000	.50
1885	3,000,000	.50
1887	500,000	1.00
1891	1,000,000	.60
1893	1,000,000	.60
1894	1,000,000	.60
1896	1,000,000	.60
1897	500,000	.90
1898	500,000	.90
1899	500,000	.90
1900	1,000,000	.50
1901	1,000,000	.50
1902	1,000,000	.50
1903	1,000,000	.50
1906	1,000,000	.50
1907	1,000,000	.50
1908	1,500,000	.50
1909	2,000,000	.40
1911	1,000,000	.40
1912	2,000,000	.40
1913	1,500,000	.40
1919	1,500,000	.40
1920	3,100,000	.35
1921	2,500,000	.35
1924	1,100,000	.40
1925	1,500,000	.35
1926	1,500,000	.35
1927	500,000	.75
1929	2,000,000	.30
1930	2,000,000	.30
1931	2,250,000	.30
1932	2,000,000	.30
1933	1,500,000	.30
1934	2,000,000	.30

	Mintage	Value
1936	1,000,000	$ .30
1938	2,805,000	.30

Y25 (copper-nickel)

	Mintage	Value
1939	8,100,000	.25
1943	10,173,000	.20
1944	7,139,000	.20
1945	1,992,000	.20
1947	5,131,000	.20
1950	5,970,000	.20
1951	3,640,000	.20
1952	3,074,800	.20
1953	6,958,000	.20
1954	1,503,900	.20
1955	11,794,700	.15
1956	5,110,800	.15
1957	2,535,000	.15
1958	5,037,200	.15
1959	10,136,300	.15
1960	15,468,900	.15
1961	8,234,250	.15
1962	30,145,000	.15

½ FRANC

Y26 (silver) 18.5mm

	Mintage	Value
1850	1,875,474	.75
1851	2,123,078	.75

Y30 new design

	Mintage	Value
1875	1,000,000	.75
1877	1,000,000	.75
1878	1,000,000	.75
1879	1,000,000	.75
1881	1,000,000	.75
1882	1,000,000	.75
1894	800,000	.75
1898	1,600,000	.60
1899	400,000	1.00
1900	400,000	1.00
1901	200,000	1.50
1903	800,000	.75
1904	400,000	1.00
1905	600,000	.80
1906	1,000,000	.60
1907	1,200,000	.60
1908	800,000	.75
1909	1,000,000	.60
1910	1,000,000	.60
1913	800,000	.75
1914	2,000,000	.60
1916	800,000	.75
1920	5,400,000	.50
1921	6,000,000	.50
1928	1,000,000	.60
1929	2,000,000	.50
1931	1,000,000	.60

	Mintage	Value
1932	1,000,000	$ .60
1934	2,000,000	.50
1936	400,000	.75
1937	1,000,000	.50
1939	1,001,000	.50
1940	2,002,000	.50
1941	200,000	1.25
1942	2,969,000	.40
1943	4,573,000	.30
1944	7,455,000	.30
1945	4,928,000	.30
1946	6,817,000	.30
1947	1,280,000	.35
1948	6,113,000	.30
1950	7,148,000	.30
1951	8,530,000	.30
1952	14,022,800	.25
1953	3,567,200	.30
1955	1,320,000	.35
1956	4,250,300	.30
1957	12,084,800	.25
1958	11,557,500	.25
1959	12,581,000	.25
1960	14,528,000	.25
1961	6,906,000	.25
1962	18,272,000	.25

1 FRANC

Y27 (silver) 23.5mm

	Mintage	Value
1850	2,136,641	1.00
1851	2,861,535	1.00
1857	526	35.00
1860	515,288	2.00
1861	3,002,270	1.00

Y31 new design

	Mintage	Value
1875	1,035,500	.75
1876	2,500,000	.60
1877	2,520,000	.60
1880	944,500	.75
1886	1,000,000	.60
1887	1,000,000	.60
1894	1,200,000	.60
1898	400,000	1.25
1899	400,000	1.25
1900	400,000	1.25
1901	400,000	1.25
1903	1,000,000	.60
1904	400,000	1.25
1905	700,000	1.00
1906	700,000	1.00
1907	800,000	.90
1908	1,200,000	.60
1909	900,000	.60
1910	1,000,000	.60

	Mintage	Value		Mintage	Value
1911	1,200,000	$ .60	1911	400,000	$2.00
1912	1,200,000	.60	1912	400,000	2.00
1913	1,200,000	.60	1913	300,000	2.00
1914	4,200,000	.50	1914	1,000,000	1.00
1916	1,000,000	.60	1916	250,000	2.00
1920	3,300,000	.50	1920	2,300,000	1.00
1921	3,800,000	.50	1921	2,000,000	1.00
1928	1,500,000	.50	1922	400,000	1.25
1931	1,000,000	.60	1928	750,000	1.25
1932	500,000	.90	1931	500,000	1.25
1934	500,000	.90	1932	250,000	1.50
1936	500,000	.90	1936	250,000	1.50
1937	1,000,000	.50	1937	250,000	1.50
1939	2,106,000	.50	1939	1,455,000	.90
1940	2,003,000	.50	1940	2,503,000	.90
1943	3,526,000	.40	1941	1,192,000	.90
1944	6,225,000	.40	1943	2,089,000	.75
1945	7,794,000	.40	1944	6,276,000	.75
1946	2,539,000	.40	1945	1,134,000	.75
1947	624,000	.75	1946	1,629,000	.75
1952	2,853,000	.40	1947	500,000	1.00
1953	786,000	.60	1948	920,000	.90
1955	194,000	2.00	1953	437,950	1.00
1956	2,500,000	.40	1955	1,032,100	.75
1957	6,420,500	.40	1957	2,298,000	.75
1958	3,580,000	.40	1958	650,000	.90
1959	1,859,000	.40	1959	2,905,000	.75
1960	3,523,000	.40	1960	1,980,000	.75
1961	6,549,000	.40	1961	4,653,000	.75
1962	6,220,000	.40			

2 FRANCS

Y28 (silver) 27.5mm

	Mintage	Value
1850	2,500,000	1.50
1857	622	40.00
1860	2,000,760	1.50
1862	1,000,000	2.00
1863	500,000	2.50

Y32 new design

	Mintage	Value
1874	1,000,000	1.00
1875	982,250	1.25
1878	1,500,000	1.00
1879	517,750	2.00
1886	1,000,000	1.00
1894	700,000	1.50
1901	50,000	5.00
1903	300,000	2.00
1904	200,000	2.50
1905	300,000	2.00
1906	400,000	2.00
1907	300,000	2.00
1908	200,000	2.50
1909	300,000	2.00
1910	250,000	2.25

5 FRANCS

Y29 (silver) 37mm

	Mintage	Value
1850	143,134	8.00
1851	356,586	6.00
1873	30,350	15.00
1874B. (Brussels)	1,400,000	5.00
1874B (Berne)	195,650	7.50

Y33 new design

	Mintage	Value
1888	25,000	15.00
1889	225,000	7.50
1890	305,000	6.00
1891	150,000	8.00
1892	190,000	7.50
1894	34,000	12.50
1895	46,000	12.50
1896	2,000	40.00
1900	33,000	12.50
1904	40,000	12.50
1907	277,000	6.00
1908	200,000	7.50
1909	120,000	8.00
1912	11,400	20.00
1916	22,000	15.00

	Mintage	Value
Y34 new design		
1922 2,400,000		$5.00
1923 11,300,000		5.00
Y35		
1924 182,035		7.50
1925 2,830,000		4.00
1926 2,000,000		4.00
1928 23,791		15.00
Y36 31.5mm		
1931 3,520,000		3.00
1932 10,580,000		2.50
1933 5,900,000		2.75
1935 3,000,000		2.75
1937 645,000		3.00
1939 2,197,000		2.75
1940 1,601,000		2.75
1948 416,000		3.00
1949 406,665		3.00
1950 482,000		3.00
1951 1,095,625		2.75
1952 154,850		4.00

	Mintage	Value
1953 3,403,450		$2.75
1954 6,600,000		2.50
Y46 Armament Fund		
1936 200,000		5.00
Y49 Laupen		
1939 31,000		25.00
Y51 Confederation		
1941 100,000		5.00
Y52 St. Jacob		
1944 102,000		10.00
Y53 Confederation		
1948 500,000		5.00
Y56 Red Cross		
1962 400,000		3.50

The 5 Franc 1939 Zurich Exposition Y50 is not considered to be a circulation coin and is not listed here. Technically this medal was valid currency until November 30, 1939.

TIMOR

Portuguese Timor consists of the eastern portion of the island of Timor in the Malay Archipelago.

100 Avos = 1 Pataca

100 Centavos = 1 Escudo

10 AVOS

Y1 (bronze) 20mm

1945 50,000		2.00
1948 500,000		.60
1951 6,250,000		.35

20 AVOS

Y2 (nickel-bronze) 23mm

1945 50,000		2.00

50 AVOS

Y3 (silver) 20.5mm

1945 100,000		2.50
1948 500,000		1.50
1951 6,250,000		1.00

Escudo Coinage System
10 CENTAVOS

Y4 (bronze) 18mm

1958 999,850		.15

30 CENTAVOS

Y5 (bronze) 22mm

1958 1,999,850		.20

60 CENTAVOS

Y6 (copper-nickel) 23mm

1958 999,850		.30

1 ESCUDO

Y7 (copper-nickel) 26.5mm

1958 1,199,850		.40

3 ESCUDOS

Y8 (silver) 20mm

1958 999,850		.75

6 ESCUDOS

Y9 (silver) 25mm

1958 999,850		1.25

A former French possession in West Africa, which became the Republic of Togo in 1960.

100 Centimes = 1 Franc

	Mintage	Value		Mintage	Value
50 CENTIMES			**2 FRANCS**		
Y1 (aluminum-bronze) 17.5mm			**Y3** (aluminum-bronze) 27mm		
1924	3,691,273	$1.00	1924	750,000	$2.00
1925	2,062,937	1.00	1925	580,154	2.00
1926	445,340	2.00	**Y5** (aluminum)		
			1948	5,000,000	1.00
1 FRANC					
Y2 (aluminum-bronze) 22mm			**5 FRANCS**		
1924	3,471,591	1.25	**Y6** (aluminum-bronze) 20mm		
1925	2,768,101	1.25	1956	10,000,000	.50
Y4 (aluminum) 23mm			See French West Africa for integrated coinage, 1957.		
1948	5,000,000	.60			

TONKIN
(Protectorat Du Tonkin)

Formerly part of French Indo China. Now a part of Communist North Vietnam. Coinage obsolete.

	Mintage	Value
1/600 PIASTRE		
Y1 (zinc, with square hole) 25mm		
1905	60,000,000	3.50

TURKEY
(Turkiye)

A republic in Europe and Asia Minor between the Mediterranean and Black Seas. Coins prior to 1934 are inscribed in Arabic.

100 Kurus = 1 Lira

	Mintage	Value		Mintage	Value
10 PARA (1/4 KURUS)			**Y90** scalloped		
Y91 (aluminum-bronze) 17mm			1938	16,400,000	.25
1940	30,800,000	.25	1939	21,600,000	.25
1941	22,400,000	.25	1940	8,800,000	.25
1942	26,800,000	.25	1941	6,700,000	.25
			1942	10,800,000	.25
1 KURUS			1943	4,000,000	.25
Y87 (copper-nickel) 18.5mm			1944	6,100,000	.25
1936	5,300,000	.30	**Y93** (brass) holed, 18mm		
1937	4,500,000	.30	1947	890,000	.25

	Mintage	Value
1948	35,470,000	$ .15
1949	29,530,000	.15
1950	32,800,000	.15
1951	720,000	.25

Y117 14mm

	Mintage	Value
1961	1,180,000	.10
1962	3,620,000	.10

2½ KURUS

Y94 (brass) holed, 21mm

1948	24,720,000	
1949	23,720,000	.15
1950	11,560,000	.15
1951	2,000,000	.20

5 KURUS

Y88 (copper-nickel) 21.5mm

1935	100,000	1.00
1936	2,900,000	.35
1937	4,060,000	.35
1938	13,380,000	.35
1939	12,520,000	.35
1940	4,340,000	.35
1941	300,000	1.00
1942	10,160,000	.35
1943	15,360,000	.35

Y95 (brass) 16mm

1949	4,500,000	.20
1950	45,900,000	.15
1951	29,599,980	.15
1955	15,300,000	.15
1956	21,380,000	.15
1957	3,320,000	.20

Y111 (bronze) 17mm

1958	25,870,000	.10
1959	21,580,000	.10
1960	17,310,000	.10
1961	10,290,000	.10
1962	15,120,000	.10

10 KURUS

Y89 (copper-nickel) 25.5mm

1935	60,000	1.50
1936	3,580,000	.50
1937	3,020,000	.50
1938	6,610,000	.50
1939	4,610,000	.50
1940	6,960,000	.50

Y96 (brass) 18mm

1949	27,000,000	.20
1951	6,200,000	.20
1955	10,090,000	.20
1956	9,910,000	.20

Y112 (bronze) 21mm

	Mintage	Value
1958	14,770,000	$ .15
1959	11,160,000	.15
1960	9,450,000	.15
1961	4,900,000	.15
1962	9,250,000	.15

25 KURUS

Y83 (silver) 19mm

1935	888,000	2.00
1936	10,576,000	1.00
1937	8,536,000	1.00

Y92 (nickel-bronze)

1944	20,000,000	.40
1945	5,328,000	.40
1946	672,000	1.00

Y97 (brass) 22.5mm

1948	18,000,000	.25
1949	21,600,000	.25
1951	2,000,000	.30
1955	9,624,000	.20
1956	14,376,000	.25

Y113 (steel)

1959	21,864,000	.25
1960	14,754,000	.25
1961	7,252,000	.25
1962	10,744,000	.25

50 KURUS

Y84 (silver) 24mm

1935	630,000	2.50
1936	5,082,000	1.75
1937	4,270,000	1.75

Y98 20mm

1947	9,296,000	.60
1948	12,704,000	.60

100 KURUS

Y82 (silver) 29mm

1934	718,000	4.00

1 LIRA

Y85 (silver) 29mm

1935	6,498,000	4.50
1936	784,000	5.00
1937	1,624,000	4.50
1939	376,000	6.00

Y86

1940	253,000	7.50
1941	6,167,147	4.50

Y99 25mm

1947	11,104,000	1.25

	Mintage	Value
1948	16,896,000	$1.25

Y110 (copper-nickel) 27mm

	Mintage	Value
1957	25,000,000	1.00

Y114 (stainless steel)

	Mintage	Value
1959	7,452,000	.60
1960	11,430,000	.60
1961	2,100,000	.60
1962	4,234,000	.60

2½ LIRA
Y115 (stainless steel) 30mm

	Mintage	Value
1960	4,017,600	$1.00
1961	1,238,400	1.00
1962	3,616,800	1.00

10 LIRA
Y116 (silver) 34mm

	Mintage	Value
1960	8,000,000	3.50

VATICAN CITY
(Citta Del Vaticano)

Formed as an independent state within the city of Rome, Italy in 1929. The Jubilee issue of 1933 has dates 1933-1934 on the coins.

100 Centesimi = 1 Lira

5 CENTESIMI
Pope Pius XI (1922-1939)

Y1 (bronze) 19.5mm

	Mintage	Value
1929	10,000	2.00
1930	100,000	.50
1931	100,000	.50
1932	100,000	.50
1934	100,000	.50
1935	44,000	.75
1936	62,000	.60
1937	62,000	.60

Y11

1933-1934	100,000	1.00

Pope Pius XII (1939-1958)
Y22

1939	62,000	.60
1940	62,000	.60
1941	5,000	2.50

Y31 (brass)

1942	5,000	3.00
1943	1,000	7.50
1944	1,000	7.50
1945	1,000	7.50
1946	1,000	7.50

10 CENTESIMI
Pope Pius XI

Y2 (bronze) 22.5mm

1929	10,000	2.00
1930	90,000	.60
1931	90,000	.60

1932	90,000	.60
1934	90,000	.60
1935	90,000	.60
1936	81,000	.60
1937	81,000	.60

Y12

1933-1934	90,000	1.25

Pope Pius XII
Y23

1939	81,000	.50
1940	81,000	.50
1941	7,500	2.50

Y32 (brass)

1942	7,500	3.00
1943	1,000	7.50
1944	1,000	7.50
1945	1,000	7.50
1946	1,000	7.50

20 CENTESIMI
Pope Pius XI

Y3 (nickel) 21.5mm

1929	10,000	2.00
1930	80,000	.90
1931	80,000	.90
1932	80,000	.90
1934	80,000	.90
1935	9,000	4.50
1936	64,000	.90
1937	64,000	.90

	Mintage	Value
Y13		
1933-1934...........80,000		$1.50
Pope Pius XII		
Y24		
1939...............64,000		1.25
Y24a (stainless steel)		
1940...............64,000		.90
1941..............125,000		.60
Y33		
1942..............125,000		.50
1943................1,000		7.50
1944................1,000		7.50
1945................1,000		7.50
1946................1,000		7.50

50 CENTESIMI

Pope Pius XI

Y4 (nickel) 24mm

	Mintage	Value
1929...............10,000		2.50
1930...............80,000		1.00
1931...............80,000		1.00
1932...............80,000		1.00
1934...............80,000		1.00
1935...............14,000		4.00
1936...............52,000		1.25
1937...............52,000		1.25

Y14

1933-1934...........80,000		1.50

Pope Pius XII

Y25

1939...............52,000		1.25

Y25a (stainless steel)

1940...............52,000		.90
1941..............180,000		.50

Y34

1942..............180,000		.50
1943................1,000		10.00
1944................1,000		10.00
1945................1,000		10.00
1946................1,000		10.00

1 LIRA

Pope Pius XI

Y5 (nickel) 26.5mm

1929...............10,000		3.00
1930...............80,000		1.50
1931...............80,000		1.50
1932...............80,000		1.50

	Mintage	Value
1934...............80,000		$1.50
1935...............40,000		1.75
1936...............40,000		1.75
1937..............100,000		1.25
Y15		
1933-1934...........80,000		2.00

Pope Pius XII

Y26

1939...............70,000		1.50

Y26a (stainless steel)

1940...............70,000		1.00
1941..............284,000		.60

Y35

1942..............284,000		.60
1943................1,000		10.00
1944................1,000		10.00
1945................1,000		10.00
1946................1,000		10.00

Y40 (aluminum) 21.5mm

1947..............120,000		.40
1948...............10,000		1.75
1949...............10,000		1.75

Y44 Holy Year

1950...............50,000		.60

Y49 17mm

1951..............400,000		.15
1952..............400,000		.15
1953..............400,000		.15
1955...............10,000		1.50
1956...............20,000		1.00
1957...............30,000		.90
1958...............30,000		.90

Pope John XXIII (1958-1963)

Y58

1959...............25,000		.75
1960...............25,000		.75
1961...............25,000		.75
1962...............25,000		.75

Y67 Ecumenical Council

1962...............50,000		.60

2 LIRE

Pope Pius XI

Y6 (nickel) 29mm

1929...............10,000		4.00
1930...............50,000		1.50
1931...............50,000		1.50

	Mintage	Value		Mintage	Value
1932	50,000	$1.50	1931	50,000	$2.50
1934	50,000	1.50	1932	50,000	2.50
1935	70,000	1.50	1934	30,000	2.50
1936	10,000	3.00	1935	20,000	3.00
1937	70,000	1.25	1936	40,000	2.50
			1937	40,000	2.50

Y16

1933-1934	50,000	2.00			

Y17

			1933-1934	50,000	3.00

Y20 Sede Vacante

			1939	40,000	4.00

Pope Pius XII

Y27

1939	40,000	1.50

Pope Pius XII

Y28

	Mintage	Value
1939	100,000	1.00
1940	100,000	1.00
1941	4,000	7.50

Y27a (stainless steel)

1940	40,000	1.25
1941	270,000	.75

Y36

1942	270,000	.75
1943	1,000	10.00
1944	1,000	10.00
1945	1,000	10.00
1946	1,000	10.00

Y37

1942	4,000	8.50
1943	1,000	15.00
1944	1,000	15.00
1945	1,000	15.00
1946	1,000	15.00

Y41 (aluminum)

1947	65,000	.50
1948	120,000	.50
1949	10,000	1.50

Y42 (aluminum) 26.5mm

1947	50,000	1.00
1948	50,000	1.00
1949	74,000	1.00

Y45 Holy Year

1950	50,000	.75

Y46 Holy Year

1950	50,000	1.00

Y50 18.5mm

1951	400,000	.20
1952	400,000	.20
1953	400,000	.20
1955	20,000	1.00
1956	40,000	.50
1957	30,000	.60
1958	30,000	.60

Y51 20mm

1951	1,500,000	.20
1952	1,500,000	.20
1953	1,500,000	.20
1955	30,000	1.00
1956	60,000	.90
1957	30,000	1.00
1958	30,000	1.00

Pope John XXIII

Y59

1959	25,000	.90
1960	25,000	.90
1961	25,000	.90
1962	25,000	.90

Pope John XXIII

Y60

1959	25,000	1.00
1960	25,000	1.00
1961	25,000	1.00
1962	25,000	1.00

Y68 Ecumenical Council

1962	50,000	.75

Y69 Ecumenical Council

1962	50,000	.90

5 LIRE

Pope Pius XI

Y7 (silver) 23mm

1929	10,000	7.50
1930	50,000	2.50

10 LIRE

Pope Pius XI

Y8 (silver) 27mm

1929	10,000	15.00

	Mintage	Value
1930	50,000	$3.50
1931	50,000	3.50
1932	50,000	3.50
1934	60,000	3.50
1935	50,000	3.50
1936	40,000	3.50
1937	40,000	3.50

Y18

1933-1934	50,000	4.00

Y21 Sede Vacante

1939	30,000	6.00

Pope Pius XII
Y29

1939	10,000	6.00
1940	10,000	6.00
1941	4,000	12.50

Y38

1942	4,000	15.00
1943	1,000	30.00
1944	1,000	30.00
1945	1,000	30.00
1946	1,000	30.00

Y43 (aluminum) 29mm

1947	50,000	1.00
1948	50,000	1.00
1949	60,000	1.00

Y47 Holy Year

1950	60,000	1.00

Y52 23mm

1951	1,130,000	.30
1952	1,130,000	.30
1953	1,130,000	.30
1955	80,000	.60
1956	160,000	.50
1957	36,000	1.00
1958	30,000	1.00

Pope John XXIII
Y61

1959	50,000	1.00
1960	50,000	1.00
1961	50,000	1.00
1962	50,000	1.00

Y70 Ecumenical Council

1962	100,000	.90

	Mintage	Value
20 LIRE		

Pope Pius XII
Y-A52 (aluminum-bronze) 21mm

1957	20,000	$1.25
1958	60,000	1.00

Pope John XXIII
Y62

1959	60,000	1.00
1960	50,000	1.00
1961	50,000	1.00
1962	50,000	1.00

Y71 Ecumenical Council

1962	100,000	1.00

50 LIRE

Pope Pius XII
Y54 (steel) 25mm

1955	180,000	.50
1956	360,000	.35
1957	180,000	.50
1958	60,000	1.00

Pope John XXIII
Y63

1959	100,000	.50
1960	100,000	.50
1961	100,000	.50
1962	100,000	.50

Y72 Ecumenical Council

1962	200,000	1.00

100 LIRE

Pope Pius XII
Y55 (steel) 28mm

1955	1,300,000	.75
1956	100,000	1.25
1957	1,400,000	.75
1958	852,600	.75

Pope John XXIII
Y64

1959	783,000	.75
1960	783,000	.75
1961	783,000	.75
1962	783,000	.75

Y73 Ecumenical Council

1962	1,566,000	1.00

	Mintage	Value
500 LIRE		
(silver) 29mm		
Pope Pius XII		
Y56 20th Year Commemorative		
1958...............20,000		$15.00
Y57 Sede Vacante		
1958...............100,000		6.00

	Mintage	Value
Pope John XXIII		
Y65		
1959...............30,000		$4.50
1960...............30,000		4.50
1961...............30,000		4.50
1962...............30,000		4.50
Y74 Ecumenical Council		
1962...............60,000		5.00

YUGOSLAVIA
(Kraljevina Jugoslavija)

On the east shore of the Adriatic Sea. Formed after World War I by uniting Serbia, Montenegro and several Austro-Hungarian provinces.

100 Para = 1 Dinar

5 PARA
Peter I (1918-1921)
Y1 (zinc) 19mm
1920.............3,825,514   1.00

10 PARA
Peter I
Y2 (zinc) 21mm
1920............58,946,122   .75

25 PARA
Peter I
Y3 (nickel-bronze) 24mm
1920............48,173,138   .75

Peter II (1934-1945)
Y13 (bronze) 20mm
1938....................   1.00

50 PARA
Alexander I (1921-1934)
Y4 (nickel-bronze) 18mm
1925............50,000,000   .50

Peter II
Y14 (aluminum-bronze)
1938...........100,000,000   .30

Federal Republic (1945 to date)
Y21 (zinc)
1945....................   .15

Y25 (aluminum) 17mm
1953....................   .10

1 DINAR
Alexander I
Y5 (nickel-bronze) 23mm
1925...........75,000,140   .75

Peter II
Y15 (aluminum-bronze) 21mm
1938...........100,000,000   .50

Federal Republic
Y22 (zinc) 20mm
1945...........90,000,000   .25

Y26 (aluminum)
1953....................   .15

2 DINARA
Alexander I
Y6 (nickel-bronze) 27mm
1925...........50,004,177   1.00

Peter II
Y16 (aluminum-bronze) 24.5mm
1938...........75,000,000   .75

Y17 small crown
1938............inc. above   2.50

	Mintage	Value
Federal Republic		
Y23 (zinc) 22mm		
1945 70,000,000		$ .35
Y27 (aluminum)		
1953		.20

5 DINARA

	Mintage	Value
Federal Republic		
Y24 (zinc) 26.5mm		
1945 50,000,000		.50
Y28 (aluminum) 24.5mm		
1953		.35

10 DINARA

	Mintage	Value
Alexander I		
Y7 (silver) 25mm		
1931 20,000,000		1.75
Peter II		
Y18 (nickel) 23mm		
1938 25,000,000		1.00
Federal Republic		
Y29 (aluminum-bronze) 21mm		
1955		.25

20 DINARA

	Mintage	Value
Alexander I		
Y8 (silver) 31mm		
1931 12,500,000		$4.00
Peter II		
Y19 27mm		
1938 25,000,000		1.50
Federal Republic		
Y30 (aluminum-bronze) 23mm		
1955		.50

50 DINARA

	Mintage	Value
Alexander I		
Y9 (silver) 36mm		
1932 11,000,000		10.00
Peter II		
Y20 32mm		
1938 16,000,000		2.50
Federal Republic		
Y31 (aluminum-bronze) 25.5mm		
1955		1.00

For World War II coinage see Croatia and Serbia.